Ralph Adams Brown

at Cornish Flat, N.H.
18 Sept, 1945

SELECTED SPEECHES AND STATEMENTS

OF

GENERAL OF THE ARMY GEORGE C. MARSHALL

Chief of Staff, United States Army

GENERAL OF THE ARMY GEORGE C. MARSHALL

Selected Speeches and Statements
of
General of the Army
George C. Marshall

Chief of Staff
United States Army

EDITED BY
MAJOR H. A. DeWEERD

WASHINGTON
THE INFANTRY JOURNAL
1945

FIRST EDITION

JULY 1945

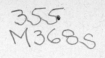

Contents

CONTENTS — *Continued*

CONTENTS — *Continued*

Part Two: The Nation at War

CONTENTS — *Continued*

FOREWORD

The Chief of Staff of the United States Army occupies a position of unique importance in our government. He is the principal military adviser of the Secretary of War and the professional head of the Army. Responsible for the military security of the country in peace and for the leadership and operation of the Army in war, he carries a tremendous burden of authority and accountability. By Executive Order of the President, he is directly responsible to the Commander-in-Chief in matters of strategy, tactics, and operations. With the approval of the Secretary of War he shapes the military program of the War Department. After legal authorizations and appropriations by Congress, he carries out that program. He is responsible for the expenditure of the large sums of money required to maintain the Army in peace and the gigantic sums required to carry out the nation's objectives in time of war. He explains the needs of the armed forces to Congressional committees and must show both the people and their representatives the necessity for the military steps he recommends.

General Marshall is the first Chief of Staff in our history to have prepared the Army in peace which he directed in war. His association with the office of Chief of Staff covers a period of years. From July 6, 1938, to September 1, 1939, he was successively Assistant Chief of Staff, Deputy Chief of Staff, and Acting Chief of Staff. On the day that saw the German armies invade Poland he became Chief of Staff. He has carried out the modernization and expansion of the Army made necessary by the rearmament of Germany and the military aggressions of the Axis Powers.

As one nation after another became engulfed in war, General Marshall's position became one of increased responsibility and difficulty. He had to shape an Army program that could meet all eventualities, yet a program that could not, before the outbreak of hostilities, be considered as actively directed at any particular future adversary. The skill, foresight, patience, and political acumen required to surmount these difficulties and to work effectively within the other legal restrictions imposed on the Chief of Staff, are rarely found in a single individual.

Our isolation between two great oceans and our faith in the capacity of American industry to equip and supply vast armies after a crisis arrived accounts in part for our false sense of security in the years 1931-1941. Having no aggressive intentions ourselves, we were reluctant to believe that any other power directly threatened us. At a time when great sections of our population were unaware of how directly the German triumphs of 1939-1940 affected our security, General Marshall warned that the United States was facing the gravest crisis in its history. While certain editors and legislators were insisting that he was unduly alarmed over the German menace and that he was requesting greater military expenditures than were required, his only fear was that he was recommending too little. He felt that the security of the nation could not be hazarded simply because the Chief of Staff might be misunderstood when he spoke his mind and gave his responsible estimate of the situation.

It is our traditional policy to rely on a small Regular Army, the National Guard, and Organized Reserves to meet the first dangers of war. When the crisis in Europe became threatening, General Marshall did not think we should abandon the policies and plans worked out by the War Department. One of his chief preoccupations during the critical months prior to December 7, 1941, was to see that our defense program developed in a step-by-step, balanced manner. We had fought all our other wars by hasty and wasteful acts of improvisation. General Marshall's experiences with the AEF in France from 1917-1918 showed him the price we had to pay then for such lack of foresight and preparation. He was determined that this time we should meet the rapidly intensifying world crisis with a practical and systematic program. But he would not in any way use this crisis to "aggrandize the Army."

While machine-warfare enthusiasts, having read only part of the lessons of the Polish and French campaigns, were clamoring for an army mainly composed of tanks and planes, General Marshall maintained a balanced development of our forces. He fully appreciated the developing rôle of air power, but saw the weakness in the popular urge to build fleets of planes and great units of tanks before effective types were standardized and the necessary crews were trained and available. He also understood from the beginning that machines, though necessary to modern warfare, could not replace the hardened, disciplined, well trained and well equipped fighting man as the final arbiter of battles. A balanced team of all arms was his objective, and as he guided the Army toward it, he constantly stressed the time it would take to prepare for war on a modern scale.

Few government officials were busier or carried greater responsibilities than General Marshall during the years 1939-1941. He is a professional soldier, not an orator. Yet he did not turn over speaking engagements to assistants if it was humanly possible to meet the engagement himself. On some occasions it was necessary for him to speak with limited preparation or with no preparation at all. At these times he simply told his audience of the circumstances and spoke from brief notes or from a rough draft of the speech he had intended to write.

Many excerpts from the hearings of Congressional committees are included in this book because they show General Marshall and the elected representatives of the people working out the military program of the government by the give-and-take methods of democratic procedure. If there is some repetition in certain of these statements it is because prob-

lems of national defense are not simple matters to be explained in all
their ramifications by a single statement. On some issues involving matters of grave responsibility, repeated and emphatic statements were required to make the military situation so clear that appropriate action by
Congress followed.

This selection includes most of General Marshall's important public
statements during the years of crisis.

H. A. DeWeerd,

Major, Infantry,

Associate Editor, *Infantry Journal.*

Washington,
June, 1945.

PART ONE

The Nation Prepares For War

1
The Air Corps and the Army Team

An Address at the Opening of the Air Corps Tactical
School, Maxwell Field, Alabama, October 1, 1938

The War Department needs air experts who understand
the Army, for we must have a team.

YESTERDAY afternoon the senior members of your faculty gave
me an outline of your course. I was much impressed by what they
are doing to carry out the principal purpose of the school—the education of Air officers in a knowledge of the combined arms.

Young Air officers probably consider their future as irrevocably tied to
air activities, and do not visualize service not intimately connected with
Air Corps. These are quite logical reasons why their approach to the national military problem may sometimes lack consideration of the multitude of other factors involved. Military victories are not gained by a
single arm—though the failures of an arm or service might well be disastrous—but are achieved through the efforts of all arms and services
welded into an Army team.

There is still another point of view for the younger officers. Many
will be called upon to fill positions as principal staff officers or as high
commanders with mixed forces; positions which require an intimate
knowledge of the combined arms, and a breadth of vision impossible to
the man who devotes his entire interest to a single arm. General Pratt
[Major General Henry C. Pratt, the former Commandant of the Air
Corps Tactical School], is an example of an officer trained and experienced in the Air Corps, who is on his way to high command. Now en
route to the Philippine Islands, he will serve there with the ground
forces.

The most difficult problem for the War Department is the determination of the best organization for the Army, within the limits of the
funds available. Fortunately, in some respects, we are not like European
nations who clearly recognize potential enemies and therefore can plan
for national defense along definite lines. The size and character of the
military organizations that will best meet their special situations can be
accurately determined.

With us, geographical location and the international situation make it
literally impossible to find definite answers for such questions as: who
will be our enemy in the next war; in what theater of operations will

that war be fought; and what will be our national objective at the time? These uncertainties lead inevitably to the conclusion that the only sensible policy for us to follow is to maintain a conservatively balanced force for the protection of our own territory against any probable threat during the period the vast but latent resources of the United States, in men and matériel, are being mobilized.

Now it is a very simple matter to say that we need a balanced force, but the headache develops when we work out the detailed composition of such a force that is within the financial means available. There are no series of facts that will lead to the one perfect solution, and short of war, there is no method for testing a solution. The decision must be based largely on opinions, and opinions will necessarily vary.

It is no exaggeration to state that the War Department is devoting more study to the size and composition of the Air Corps component of the Army team than to any other single subject, because aviation is a new arm and there is only a meager background of major war experience to guide us in its use. Also, in its rapid development, the theories of to-day are often in the discard of tomorrow, and the question of dollars and cents absolutely dominates the field. That there is no neglect of aviation is evidenced by the fact that almost one-third of the total funds appropriated for the Army are expended on the Air Corps.

Sit down sometime and try to balance all the factors concerned with the national defense—including limited appropriations—and then attempt to outline the organization for a balanced army. Divorce yourself for the moment from the Air Corps and assume that the responsibility for the decisions regarding National Defense rests solely on your shoulders. Conscientiously consider the limitations imposed by annual appropriations—and weigh carefully the necessity and requirements for each arm, including the present problem of archaic equipment for which there are no replacement funds. Having reached a general conclusion, which checks with probable appropriations and the basic law, then set up, within those limits, the air force that you feel will best meet our requirements. Be conservative as to the powers of aviation and honest as to its limitations.

Your first decision will probably be to equip your air organizations with modern matériel. That is a sound decision, but how are you going to carry it out? Aviation matériel is extremely costly; it takes a long time to produce; and—remember this—is rapidly outmoded. Can you afford to discard the expensive matériel you have on hand for yet more modern types? Another consideration: the more costly the plane, the fewer of them you can have, and for each plane, guns, instruments, bombs, ammunition and maintenance must be provided. Study the emergency situations you think we may be required to meet, and then decide on the proportion of plane types to meet those situations. Is it more desirable to have a large number of small planes or a small number of large planes? Consider the major emergency problem of training of pilots rapidly, or rather, the use of rapidly trained pilots; and that your air force may be required to operate in theaters where airdromes are limited in number and size. In view of these factors, are combat planes, simple to operate and rugged in construction, indicated? Is it wise to sacrifice desirable technical features in order to obtain planes with special characteristics? There are almost unlimited permutations and combinations to resolve into an acceptable solution.

You must set aside funds for research and development, and for the maintenance and training of personnel, year in and year out. We have a very fine commercial air system and splendid naval aviation. What effect will these have on the solution of your problem? The questions I have outlined are not academic—far from it, they are before the War Department for consideration every day.

Saturday morning, before leaving for Maxwell Field, it was necessary for me to pass on the proposition of an allocation of more funds for bombs. A great bombing plane without bombs—and it now requires a year to make a bomb—would be an expensive futility in the scheme of national defense. The project concerned the increase in the number of missions of bombs to be procured. It was favorably acted upon. But—and this is the point I wish to make—at the same time that I was considering the millions involved in aviation munitions, I had in mind the fact that the rifle for the troops of our first war Army is of a type 34 years old, and we have developed a semiautomatic shoulder rifle which is at least the equal of any similar weapon in the world. You gentlemen in the Air Corps would have no hesitation about the matter of bombs. But what about the 34-year old rifle?

I leave this problem with you. Please give it serious thought and contribute toward its solution, for it is my firm conviction that aerial supremacy in the next war will not be merely a matter of technical excellence and tactical skill, but will depend fundamentally on the soundness of our peacetime planning and preparations.

We have the finest pilots in the world and planes that are at least equal in efficiency to those of any other nation. You can be justly proud of your contribution to these achievements. But you are now about to enter into a broader field of study where consideration is given to the rôle the Air Corps plays as a component part of the Army. Seek to obtain a clear picture of every aspect of National Defense, so that you may think straight and advise wisely. The more outstanding you become as an officer of the Air Corps, the more important it is that you thoroughly understand the requirements and operation of the combined arms. The War Department needs air experts who understand the Army, for we must have a team.

2
National Defense: The Business of Every Citizen

An Address at Brunswick, Maryland, November 6, 1938

≈≈≈≈≈≈≈≈≈≈≈≈≈≈≈≈≈≈≈≈≈≈≈≈

National Defense under modern conditions has become a tremendously expensive business, so much so that I think it is the business of every mature citizen to acquaint himself with the principal facts. . . .

AS I understand it, this gathering today is to celebrate the Armistice of twenty years ago, which brought to a close the active fighting of the World War. The anniversary of so momentous an occasion should be observed, not to celebrate a victory, but in consecration of the sacrifice of the young Americans in France, and to bring to mind the conditions of that frightful conflict, in an effort to provide for the avoidance of such a catastrophe in the future.

Unfortunately these present days, particularly these past few months, have involved a series of events frightening to every citizen, in their threats or implications.

No one of us wants war. I believe that is axiomatic in this country—certainly on the part of any veteran of the World War. There is nothing romantic, dramatic, or satisfying in modern conflict. It is all horrible, profoundly depressing; and now it carries with it a dreadful threat to civil populations. I think we are in general agreement regarding the statements I have just made, but the trouble, the difficulty of the problem, is what is to be done about it.

We honor our dead of past wars; we encourage the ideal of patriotic self-sacrifice of the individual; but, we must be far-sighted and sound in our attitude as to just what is the proper thing for this Government to do in the way of national defense.

You know, a photograph in a weekly magazine depicting some horror —like the bombing of a city in China or in Spain—not only creates a profound impression upon every civilian who examines it, but it more or less fixes in his mind a specific remedy—practical or impractical. But there is far more to this business than the bombing of cities—far, far more—and my desire today is to find the words to make clear the real issue, from a Governmental point of view, of a matter of vast importance to every citizen. Possibly by utilizing some homely examples, I might

[5]

better be able to make.clear the complications of the problem and the difficulties which are inherent in its solution.

In the first place, national defense under modern conditions has become a tremendously expensive business, so much so that I think it is the business of every mature citizen to acquaint himself with the principal facts, and form a general idea as to what he or she thinks is the wise course for this country to follow.

I am not discussing the evil of war, or what brings about war, or whether or not I think there is any possibility of our being involved in a war in the near future. I want merely to present the problems involved from the viewpoint of the professional soldier on duty in the War Department.

Allow me to give you a few examples of this so-called unpreparedness:

The most of our military strength developed during the Revolutionary War had been disbanded at the time of the outbreak of the War of 1812. I think we had then some six thousand soldiers, and it therefore became necessary to create an army out of whole cloth. Public opinion, and mark that well—public opinion forced us immediately to an invasion of Canada, and we enjoyed a series of the most humiliating military episodes on record. Fortunately, or maybe unfortunately, our schoolboys have had their attention diverted from these tragedies by the splendid but local victories of American privateers on the high seas in conflict with isolated English naval vessels, and by the magnificent performance of General Jackson at New Orleans.

The Mexican War had a slow approach, giving us time for preparation of an army in the field in Texas. We were dealing with a weak country and had every advantage in means and men. But even here we find some remarkable examples of American military policy. For instance, we find General Scott's army hurrying up from the coast at Vera Cruz to cross the fever district of the plains before the hot season developed, forcing its way into the mountains at Cerro Gordo in order to secure the passage of this high mountain range before the time of service of a large portion of his men expired, to leave him in Mexico, in the enemy's country, with the mere remnant of an army. He had to wait there until the new men arrived. Fortunately, the enemy was not capable of taking advantage of what might well have been a fatal dilemma.

The Civil War was so full of illustrations of our lack of preparation that it is useless to recite them.

However, when we come to the Spanish-American War, which is within the day of many of us here, we find most surprising situations. Out in San Francisco an expedition was embarking to sail to the Philippines, to back up Admiral Dewey. They lacked all knowledge of the country, of the people, of the general necessities; they lacked training and organization; and yet they sailed off across the broad Pacific to fight, seven thousand miles from their base, with only one hundred and fifty rounds of ammunition available per man, just about one day of rifle fire on a battlefield. What was to happen the morning following the first encounter, had to be completely ignored.

In those days we had nothing, literally, but small garrisons at old frontier posts, and little units along the coast to man ancient guns. There were no reserves of war supplies, and practically no modern equipment. Our losses, due to ignorance of leadership on the part of troop commanders, and poor sanitation on the part of an untrained medical personnel, were greater in the camp and hospital than they were on the battlefield.

Following this disgraceful display, in which the question of personal courage and patriotic energy were never questioned, a deliberate effort was made for the first time to remedy conditions. Mr. Elihu Root stepped into the picture as Secretary of War, and out of his great mind came a revolutionary step in the modernization of the American Army—the introduction of the military school system which culminated in the War College at Washington, the creation of a General Staff which consists of a group of highly trained officers to coördinate all military effort toward the best preparation of the Army for its ultimate purpose. These growing pains brought about many difficulties, as was natural, and we reached the World War in the midst of the transition of the National Guard—our principal immediate available forces—and before we had had time to develop organizational methods for handling large bodies of troops. Our part in the World War is well known to all of you, but many of our blundering steps are unknown to the general public.

Allow me to give you a few examples within my own experience. I sailed from New York on the first ship of the first convoy, in June 1917. This was the 1st Division, a unit which eventually had 27,000 men in its ranks and suffered nearly 25,000 casualties in France.[1] It went over with the first convoy and it returned with the last in September 1919. We embarked hurriedly in Hoboken, put out from the dock in the several boats, and anchored awaiting the completion of the installation of naval guns, and the preparation of convoy arrangements for crossing the Atlantic. The staff of that division, of which I was a member, immediately got together—having assembled for the first time on the boat—to study

---

[1] Divisional organization in effect November 11, 1918, called for a strength of 28,105. At the highest point of its strength the 1st Division had (August 31, 1918) 26,734 officers and men. Total casualties are listed as 22,011. See *1st Division: Summary of Operations in the World War*, prepared by the American Battle Monuments Commission. Washington: Government Printing Office, 1944. Pages 97-98.

our situation. We found, while anchored in the Hudson River, that the organization of the troops was entirely new to us, that there were four regiments of infantry in the division instead of the nine of our previous experience; that there were units of which we had never before heard, armed with weapons of which we knew nothing. And like that expedition from San Francisco to the Philippines in 1898, with only 150 rounds per man, we were sailing three thousand miles from home to fight on foreign soil, and not until we arrived in France did the division commander and the members of the division staff learn that these new weapons were non-existent, and that the troops which on paper were charged with operating these weapons had never seen even a model of one. We found that eighty per cent of the men in ranks were recruits, to many of whom rifles had been issued on the trains between the Mexican border and Hoboken. They were all good men, they were all splendid Americans—but they were not soldiers.

The day we landed in France I saw the French general in command of that region, in full dress uniform, with his medals on his chest, arrive at our headquarters, which had been hastily established in a stubble field. He was calling on our commanding general to extend the welcome of France to the first unit of American soldiers to arrive on the soil of France, to repay our debt to Lafayette. He was calling on an organization of the Regular Army, as he thought. The sentinel at the gate was a tall, rangy, Tennessee mountain type. As the general approached, the Tennessean did his best with a salute—and I was concerned to see that not only was his blouse partly unbuttoned, but he had a watch chain stretched from one pocket to the other. The French general made an evident comment regarding the rifle, and our sentry handed his gun over to the Frenchman and seated himself on a near-by post to roll a cigarette.

I am not deprecating the quality of these men. I saw them on a series of terrible battlefields where they established an outstanding reputation in the AEF, and a world-wide reputation in Europe. Finer soldiers you could not have found, but the point is, at this moment, they were not soldiers; but our peculiar fortune in that war was, that our Allies protected us on the field of battle for a long year while we slowly got ready—for we landed in France on June 26, 1917, and it was not until September 12, 1918, that an American army deployed in a battle. Prior to that time there were engagements in which smaller detachments of American troops were engaged. The 1st Division made the first American attack at Cantigny on May 28, 1918, and participated in the famous counterattack at Soissons, the turning point of the war, on July 18, 1918. Other divisions operated in the Marne salient that summer. But, more than a year elapsed after our declaration of war before our first divisional unit engaged in battle, and seventeen months before an American army appeared on the field.

I emphasize these time elements because the implications of the past few weeks have indicated that war is a sudden and terrible business, with the accent on the sudden. Nothing that has recently been said or printed seemed to indicate that we would have a year in which to get ready. Now, what we are interested in, as our simple duty in the War Department, is the development of logical plans suitable to our national characteristics and adequate for our protection.

There are a few thoughts I would ask you to keep in mind. Remember that almost every weapon of war, certainly every gun—big or little—and every device for aiming and firing that gun, like the elaborate instruments necessary for antiaircraft artillery, require a year to a year and a half to manufacture. So, no matter how many billions of dollars Congress places at our disposal on the day war is declared, they will not buy ten cents' worth of war matériel for delivery under twelve months, and a great deal of it will require a year and a half to manufacture. In other words, whatever your son and my son is to use to defend himself and to defend us and the country, has to be manufactured in time of peace.

We have models of the best weapons and mechanical devices, we think, in the world, and we have the finest aircraft in design and performance; but what we must have is the accumulation of an adequate reserve of this matériel, not just some popular item, but a balanced program suitable for the instant arming of our first modest war army, in the event of trouble.

Our primary need is matériel, everything else is of secondary importance.

Our policy is, I think, thoroughly in keeping with American thought and characteristics—only the means necessary to defend ourselves until the vast resources of this country, in men and industry, can be mobilized. We want nothing today for armed invasion, we want no huge forces on foot or wing; but we do want the matériel and the nucleus for the rapid equipping and expansion of the Regular Army and the National Guard to a strength adequate to protect us; that is, the United States, Panama, and Hawaii, while our great industrial plants are set going toward the production of war matériel, and our vast resources in men can be organized and trained.

3
Infantry in Modern War

A Talk Before the National Rifle Association,
Washington, D. C., February 3, 1939

*He [the infantry soldier] will never be the subject
of much acclaim, but he will continue to be the
solid rock on which wars are finally settled. . . .*

GENERAL RECKORD[2] has asked me to talk to you on any subject that I might select, but he mentioned his interest, and the purpose of this organization, in keeping alive a realization of the importance of the rifleman in the settlement of any war—especially in these days of myriads of planes, of mechanized cavalry, and of submarines and mysterious gases.

And I am glad to take that as the text for some informal remarks this evening, though I admit to embarrassment in holding forth on any military subject in the presence of the Assistant Secretary of War and the Chief of Staff of the Army.[3] When my invitation for this evening was delivered, no mention was made of the fact that I would be called upon to talk under these circumstances, so while complimented and honored by the invitation, it seems inappropriate, as it certainly is embarrassing, for me to be advising on military matters in the presence of these two high officials of the Army.

The world is air-minded today, all thoughts turn to attack from the air. A glance through military history shows a monotonous repetition of such special interests. Chariots were once heralded as the dominators of the battlefield, then elephants; the mechanized force of the Macedonian phalanx played a brief determining part, but the short sword of the Roman infantryman brought back to the battlefield its basic factor. Hordes of horsemen, comparable to the threatened hordes of airplanes, carried Genghis Khan and his leaders across Asia to the gates of Vienna; and through a series of changes we reach the period of the armored knight. Then came the crossbowman to dominate the field; and artillery appeared, to reach a peak in employment under Napoleon. This special arm again reached dominating importance in the World War, when the

---

[2]Major General Milton A. Reckord, President of the National Rifle Association and Commanding General of the Maryland National Guard and 29th Infantry Division; later Provost Marshal General, European Theater of Operations.

[3]Mr. Louis Johnson and General Malin Craig.

infantry casualties became prohibitive in prolonged attacks. For the same reason the tank put in an appearance and played a leading part in the last phase of the World War. But meanwhile, the airplane, starting with shotgun and revolver armament, rapidly developed into a carrier of synchronized machine guns and a dropper of bombs, though remaining of value largely as a reconnaissance weapon. The air fights in France were almost entirely concerned with the gathering of information.

But in all these struggles, as the smoke cleared away, it was the man with the sword, or the crossbow, or the rifle, who settled the final issue on the field. Probably the most impressive exception could be made to this statement in connection with the completely horsed armies of Genghis Khan—this was one of those exceptions that prove the rule.

To return to the airplane. Since the World War its development has gone ahead by leaps and bounds, due to its suitability for commercial usage, and its adaptability to offset sea power, on a quick-production basis. Antiaircraft measures have lagged for the opposite reason, being entirely of a non-commercial character and dependent upon military appropriations.

We now come to a most unusual development in world armaments. A nation which has been disarmed, and deprived of practically all of its military matériel, a nation which had been barred from the development of aviation and of tanks, suddenly throws off the yoke and launches a huge program of military preparation.

People generally do not comprehend the far-reaching effect of this unusual base of departure for the rearmament of Germany. Had that country possessed an accumulation of World War weapons, it would probably have suffered the necessity of compromising the desire to procure more modern equipment, with the more economical possibility of modernizing some of the existing matériel, and of utilizing the remainder unaltered—a procedure in which the other nations of the world were and are engaged, and which never produces even an approximation of a complete modernization of munitions.

But Germany had nothing with which to start, except the little force of one hundred thousand men permitted to her by treaty; her cannons decorate the public parks of the Allies, her wartime machine guns had largely been destroyed, she was prohibited planes and tanks. But, she was spared the expensive procedure of the development and outmoding of airplanes or tanks or mechanized cavalry. When the yoke of the Versailles Treaty was discarded, Germany started from scratch, as it were, without necessity for compromise, and initiated the development of a complete armament program, closely integrated with civil industry. She had the full benefit of the experimentation of the world in planes and tanks; in artillery, mechanized vehicles, and in the production of ammunition. Evidently, during her period of restricted military activities following the World War, she had concentrated on experimental research along military lines. Her sudden departure on a program of rearmament was not so revolutionary as might appear, because it is apparent that she had carefully laid a sound basis for the initiation of the program. It was no hastily improvised affair.

Had the great nations grown old together, in the gradual elimination of outmoded weapons, planes and equipment, no single country could have gained such a long lead in the matter as attained by Germany. Contradictory as it may seem, she actually profited by the forcible wiping out of her World War armament. She also profited by the forced reduction of her army, because in the rapid swelling of numbers to her present standing army, she was free of the normal resistance to changes in organization, and has therefore approached her ideal of military power.

There is a world of controversial phases of this matter that might be discussed, but which time and restraint cause me to avoid, but I will say that it is most important in judging these matters to gain a proper perspective, and not permit the trees to obscure the woods.

For example, there is nothing dramatic about industrial preparedness, except in its appeal to the manufacturer; but it is evident that unless we set up a practical program in this respect we will be impotent, even if we have a collection of Galahads in the ranks. The same thought applies to the equally undramatic business of reserve stocks of critical materials.

In all this present welter of conflicting information as to what is happening in Europe, the dramatic features have been widely publicized while other equally important measures have been ignored. I might illustrate this phase of the matter by a single example. We have all heard how many planes Germany has and what vast numbers she can produce, but I doubt if very many have learned that for more than two years she has turned out a million rounds of artillery ammunition a week![4] Now, you, of the National Rifle Association, would be primarily interested in what she had done in terms of the rifle and the man. Whatever that is will be of no public interest, lacking all dramatic quality, until we find a Horatius at the bridge.

Those of you who fought in France will remember that the daily communiqués of all the Allies—and of the Central Powers—usually cited

---

[4]By comparison the U. S. Army had on hand on May 1, 1940, a total of 1,067,000 rounds of high explosive shell for 75mm. and 155mm. howitzers. See *Hearings Before the Sub-Committee of the Committee on Appropriations, United States Senate, 76th Congress, 3d Session, on HR 9209: A Bill Making Appropriations for the Military Establishment for the Fiscal Year Ending June 30, and For Other Purposes.* Washington: Government Printing Office, 1940. Page 241.

by name some gallant knight of the air who had driven down an opponent in flames or to a crash. Practically never did you read a similar public reference to the poor devil with the infantry platoon, who labored in the cold and mud, under shell and machine-gun fire, was bombed and gassed, and who carried the battle to the enemy, and actually conquered the disputed ground. Yet it was this soldier who forced the issue to the Armistice. I only recall one exception to these comments, and that was in the case of an infantry lieutenant of the German Army who was cited by name in the radio communiqué in April 1918, for having forced a river-crossing ahead of schedule and permitted the German advance down the Valley of the Lys to proceed so rapidly that it resulted in a near catastrophe for a portion of the British Army.

I have at last arrived in this talk at the point of discussing the activities of the National Rifle Association in the promotion of National Defense.

Without giving much thought to the matter, we all know that the old days of the squirrel hunter and the pioneer have departed, and with their departure has been lost that intimate knowledge of the rifle common to early American history. Your association undertakes to keep alive this knowledge, and to develop better technique, better weapons, and better powders for the rifle.

Almost thirty years ago I got myself ordered to Camp Perry, Ohio, for duty as an official of the National Rifle Matches, in order that I might see for myself just what was accomplished there. At the time I was an instructor at Leavenworth, and so supercharged with theoretical conceptions of making war that I thought it would be an excellent thing to get a more practical slant on certain aspects of the battlefield. I was much impressed by that experience. While not a high-powered rifleman, I had on at least one occasion been high gun of the post, but my duties had carried me away from the target range, and I never found opportunity to develop myself into anything of a rifle shot; that is, according to the standards necessary for an Army officer who enters the lists at Camp Perry. Before I found the time and opportunity, my eyes had settled the question with finality.

Every hour of my experience in France impressed me more and more with the importance and potential power of the infantryman on the battlefield, *if* and *provided* the man was hardened and disciplined, and *if* he was trained to use his weapon with efficiency under the conditions of combat. It was clear to all present in France that the burden of the war fell on the shoulders of the members of the infantry platoon. No other group competed with them in hardships and casualties. But they received little public recognition for their work and sacrifices.

There is another aspect to this matter which, I think, is not fully understood, and possibly, I can illustrate my particular view of this phase by a comparison with the present development of the National Guard. I must ask you to treat the following statement as somewhat confidential, because it is purely my personal opinion, gained from intimate contact with these troops.

Under the conditions controlling the development of the National Guard as to limited time, restricted training facilities, etc., it has seemed to me that the units most readily developed to a high point of efficiency have been, strange to say, the observation squadrons of the Guard air force; next, the Engineer regiments; and then the Field Artillery. I won't go further down the list, but will merely mention my opinion that the most difficult unit to develop satisfactorily in the National Guard is the infantry regiment. And there is a very simple reason for this situation.

The infantryman on the battlefield is distinctly on his own, without a horse or a motor to turn to, and lacking the anchor of a field gun or tank, or other heavy equipment. Once the field of action has been reached and the deployment completed, the infantry soldier becomes an isolated individualist, with all the frailties of the individual magnified a thousand-fold. Only a corporal remains near by to back him up, upon whom he can depend for reassurance. He lacks a physical rallying point—no ship, no heavy gun, no fortification, nothing but a few scattered buddies. He is a young fellow, depressed by a heavy physical burden on his back, exhausted by long marches of concentration and deployment, and lack of food, and he is virtually alone under the terrific pounding of hostile fires of every character. Of himself, by himself, he can apparently do very little, though collectively he can win the war.

He must be supported by artillery, which means in turn that his platoon commander must have a skilled knowledge of topography and be able to report exactly where his line is established—on ground never seen before and of which he probably has no map. This information, coupled with accurate observations of the enemy's opposing installations—which usually are at a distance and on a decided angle from the front of the platoon—must be communicated through an elaborate but hastily established communications system, by runner, telephone, radio, through company, battalion, and regimental headquarters, to some distant battery of artillery, probably a mile to the rear, and which the platoon commander has never seen and possibly never will see. It may be necessary to coördinate his isolated activities with an infantry cannon or Stokes mortar, and certainly with distant machine guns. He may even have to initiate procedure to secure the support of tanks still miles to the rear. All of this he does, lying on his stomach, under a hostile fusillade—with a diet of gas thrown in for good measure. And what he proposes must be coördinated with the scattered units along a regimental, a brigade, a divisional front, and through its depth of supports and reserves. Altogether, it is *the* most complicated problem of troop leadership, and requires a higher degree of training and discipline, I believe, than for any other military preparation —except for the actual flying of the airplane. There are no convenient electrical buttons as on a battleship to launch a broadside; no hot meals, no rest, seemingly no end to a long drawn out battle of endurance.

Yet with all this, we seldom hear this phase of the matter referred to. As a matter of fact, I think the common belief is that the most quickly created instrument of war is the infantry regiment. Yet, I would say that we have lost more lives and been delayed more in battle by the acceptance of this doctrine than for any other purely military reason.

There is another aspect of this same matter. In ordinary training little that the infantryman does closely simulates what actually happens on the battlefield, and what is more important, the most serious errors or lacks of the peacetime training can seldom be made apparent in that training, or even in maneuvers; because until the leader or individual has once been submerged with hostile fire—bullet, shell, and bomb—and left apparently unsupported in an exposed position, and has found himself utterly unable to secure any artillery fire or machine-gun fire, or other supporting action, he will never appreciate the special importance to infantry—above all other arms or services—of discipline and leadership, and of communications; and their absolute determining effect on the battlefields.

Today, when people think of bombs dropping like hail, certainly not like the gentle dew from heaven, they probably dispose of the infantryman's problem with the thought that, "Certainly he has no defense against such war-making methods." Well, one infantry sergeant in the old 69th Regiment of New York, infuriated by the return a second time of a German low-flying strafing plane, fired at the plane with his machine gun, killed the pilot and crashed the ship, which fell on another German plane flying under it, bringing down two planes. He was not mentioned, like the successful aviator, in the day's communiqué, but he did receive the Distinguished Service Cross.[5]

I am not implying that we expect to shoot down many planes with small-arms bullets. But recently the infantry has forced the rather low-

---

[5] The Infantryman referred to by General Marshall was Sergeant Frank J. Gardella, Jr., of New York City, a member of Machine Gun Company, 165th Infantry (69th Infantry, New York National Guard), 42d Division, whose citation is given in *Decorations, United States Army, 1862-1926*. Washington: Government Printing Office, 1927. Page 298.

flying tactics of the air people into higher altitudes because of the recorded effectiveness of fire from trained infantry riflemen.

I do mean, by implication, that the foundation on which a successful war is carried to conclusion, aside from the character and resolution of the people, eventually rests with the infantry soldier, no matter what the scientific developments and clever gadgets developed for making war. Of course, without air support he is doomed, just as he cannot live on the battlefield without the fire of his own artillery; and frequently could never advance without the support of tanks; and usually would be completely in the dark without the reconnaissance of plane or car, or cavalry, or humble foot patrollers. He will never be the subject of wide acclaim, but he will continue to be the solid rock on which wars are finally settled; and everything we can do to give him prestige, to develop his weapons, to afford a general knowledge of the use of those weapons, are just so many steps exactly in the right direction. Therefore, the justification for the National Rifle Association.

4

Industrial Mobilization for War

Remarks at the Opening of the Army Industrial College,
Washington, D. C., September 9, 1939

*Our standard of living in peace is in reality the criterion
of our ability to kill and destroy in war.*

WHEN Colonel Miles[6] invited me to speak at this year's opening of the Army Industrial College, I felt it to be my duty to accept, for I am convinced the College is doing work of vital importance to National Defense and is deserving of serious support by the Army.

I am going to outline to you my reasons for such a conviction, but in doing so I make no claim to new thoughts. They have undoubtedly occurred to you, but I hope a review of them will help us all.

The real truth about war is that by its very nature it requires the use of force to kill and demoralize peoples and to destroy property in order to subdue the enemy. This has always been true through the ages and will continue through the generations to come. The one thing that is changing about war is the force available for the killing and the destruction. This keeps pace with the progress of civilization. We just convert to war uses all advances in scientific and engineering lines and in production capacity. Our standard of living in peace is in reality the criterion of our ability to kill and destroy in war. In other words, present-day warfare is simply mass killing and mass destruction by means of machines resulting from mass production.

Today, we must be prepared to go to war with the most efficient killing and destroying machines mankind has ever devised and in quantities corresponding to the production capacity of the present age. The true philosophy of the maximum war effort of any nation is for it to devote to this purpose as much man power in the form of soldiers and sailors, and as much supply power in the form of weapons and ammunition as the country can support.

If we have any doubt about the logic of this statement, we only have to summarize in our minds what is happening in Europe. I suspect that Germany is pursuing the very philosophy I have just outlined. The information which reaches me is to the general effect that she, for some years now, has been devoting approximately fifty per cent of the pro-

---

[6] Colonel Francis H. Miles, Jr., Commandant, Army Industrial College, 1939.

ductive effort of her country, including men, plants and materials, to preparation for war and now to actual war. I am also told that during the World War she was able to devote as a maximum some sixty-five per cent of her effort to the war load, so it follows she is now geared up to practically the maximum effort. It is important to note, however, that Germany was not able to reach this status overnight. It has taken her some four or five years of intensive effort under complete regimentation to produce the war stocks she believed to be necessary and to develop the industrial and raw material capacity required to support her maximum effort. Her pact with Russia was undoubtedly made in order to assure her the new materials which her industrial mobilization activities disclosed and which could apparently best be obtained from that source.

We know that because of the tremendous resources of America in men, materials, plants and knowledge, the potential war power of our country is greater than that of any other nation in the world. We also know that it is the well established policy of America, because of its favorable geographical position and its strong navy, to maintain only a relatively small peace army, both as to man power and supply power. In round numbers, we plan for an M-day force of some four hundred thousand men, made of the Regular Army and the National Guard, to be augmented within some three months to one million men and thereafter in accordance with military needs to the final maximum effort.

We know that, even with maximum efficiency, the time factor involved in expanding our peacetime man power and supply power to the war effort would be long—too long. Perhaps the most important task of the Army is to plan and scheme and work to the end that this time factor will be kept to the minimum.

It is now generally accepted as a fact that it requires more time to mobilize the industrial effort of the nation to the war load than it does to convert the civilian manpower into soldiers. It follows that every reasonable effort must be made to speed up industrial mobilization. This is the real objective of the Army Industrial College and it is, therefore, obvious that it is our duty to give it every reasonable assistance.

In conclusion, I would like to add that for years we have been striving for an M-day force to be augmented in accordance with a definite program. We are making progress on that plan. But I will not be satisfied until we are actually prepared for that M-day force and its augmentation. We should not be satisfied to be ready for M-day ten years, five years or even two years from today. It is our duty to be ready instantly. Of course, I know we cannot do so, for in the field of supply alone our stocks plus production are not in all cases equal to requirements and even with unlimited appropriations we cannot eliminate the time factor.

5
The Lessons of 1917-1918

An Address at the Army Ordnance Association Meeting,
Washington, D. C., October 11, 1939

~~~~~~

Whenever changes are proposed, modern theories advanced, or surprising developments are brought to my attention, I automatically search for the fundamental principle involved in the particular matter at hand.

GENERAL CROWELL, Admiral Stark, General Wesson,[7] Gentlemen: I am a little embarrassed tonight. First, in following the distinguished gentlemen who have already talked to you, but more particularly because of the recent decision of the War Department to discourage officers from engaging in public discussions of military matters, which to be interesting would immediately involve questions that still must be regarded as somewhat confidential. I will, however, do my best to talk frankly as to what our thought is today in regard to the Army generally; in regard to what is taking place in a military way and, especially, in relation to industrial preparedness.

As a beginning, I think it might be well to submit a few comments regarding the present discussions as to the great changes that have taken place in the manner of making war, judging, for example, from what has happened recently in Poland. I will preface that thought with a personal experience, if I may be permitted, which was to me a lesson in the matter of getting down to fundamentals, believing, as I do, that they are usually unchanging.

As the toastmaster remarked, I sailed to France with the 1st Division in June 1917. Filled with recruits and newly organized, the division went into the line that fall, as a complete division, entered the sector north of Toul on the St. Mihiel front in January 1918. We occupied a locality in which there had been no active fighting for almost three years. It had been maintained on the same basis until, in some respects, it was almost like a hotel—with divisions coming and going as the guests of the permanent sector organization. The troops were largely disposed in the forward zone of the sector, and I recall that the principal dugouts were under the parapets of the front trench.

---

[7]Brigadier General Benedict Crowell, President of the Army Ordnance Association; Admiral Harold R. Stark, Chief of Naval Operations; Major General Charles M. Wesson, Chief of Ordnance, 1938-1942.

We had been there but two or three weeks when there was received from the Intelligence Bureau of the French Army a description of an expected assault to be made by German forces, which had been heavily reinforced with divisions drawn from the collapsed Russian front. The reported nature of this new attack, termed a "maneuver of rupture," was such that it caused the French High Command to direct a complete reorganization of the defenses—from that of a shallow nature to one of considerable depth. This meant the complete change of a system which had existed for nearly three years. It meant, in brief, that a regiment which had occupied a deployed depth of about five or six hundred yards, would be disposed over a depth of a mile or more, and that the regiments, the companies, the individuals, could be much more widely dispersed; that a great many machine-gun emplacements which had previously been located along the lines of trenches, would have to be relocated in staggered formation of great depth.

To the 1st Division it meant a tremendous planning problem, and for the troops hard manual labor and much exposure to the weather of that bitter winter of 1917-1918. Snow was deep on the ground. Every move we made could be readily traced by the tracks of vehicles and of men on foot, as well as by the signs of extensive excavations. Construction was started and the men worked very, very hard. They suffered extreme hardships because of the inadequacy of the arrangements we could make for their shelter in the newly deployed positions in depth, but they did their work uncomplainingly. Then, when we were about half through with this program, the great German offensive of March 21, 1918, broke against the right of the British Army.

The 1st Division was hurriedly withdrawn from that sector and sent to Picardy. As its trains were arriving northwest of Paris, I personally reported to the headquarters of the group of French armies in which we were to serve. There I was informed that the system of organization in depth which we had just been carrying out on the St. Mihiel front, had since been greatly modified as a result of the experience of the recent heavy fighting. I was given the new method for taking up dispositions in depth which we were to follow as we went into the new sector, on ground but recently occupied and without trenches. We started work on the defenses under this new arrangement. Again the men worked in the cold and mud of early spring in northern France, but just as they had gotten well into it, another German offensive broke, this time down the Valley of the Lys. Two weeks later new instructions were received for a further modifying of the method of deployment in depth. Once more we were forced to abandon the results of work that had been laboriously accomplished.

The troops were very tired. They had had no relief since early January. They had endured the cold, the mud, and the snow or rain of that bitter winter. It is true that they had not been engaged in an active operation, but they had been under such heavy fire that about three or four thousand men were casualties. Nevertheless, every man set about this newest task of reorganization in a fine, soldierly spirit. And then we entered into the Cantigny operation, where we suffered heavy losses due to a series of desperate German counterattacks and violent artillery reactions. Simultaneously with that fight came the German attack on the Chemin des Dames, which thundered down to Château-Thierry—to make of it historic ground for our Army. And then once more, two weeks later, we received a new set of instructions completely modifying the organization in depth that we were then in the process of completing.

I recall that in our reply to these new instructions we notified the French headquarters that we could do one of two things; we could fight or we could dig, but it was no longer possible for us to do both.

We now come to the point of this series of events. That last modification (which was a modification of previous modifications—the first being a change in a system that had stood for almost three years), though written in French, was expressed literally in the language of the *Field Service Regulations* of the United States Army in 1914. In other words, there had been no change in fundamentals, but during three years of trench warfare those fundamentals had been lost sight of, and now in that critical summer of 1918, we were back again to first essentials of warfare.

To me that was an impressive lesson, and since then whenever changes are proposed, modern theories advanced, or surprising developments are brought to my attention, I automatically search for the fundamental principle involved in the particular matter at hand.

Many of the discussions at the present time, in relation to what we have learned of the occurrences in Poland, seemingly proposes new fundamentals as a basis for warfare. I might comment here on the fact that the American public is remarkably well informed on events in Europe as indicated by our confidential reports. But our knowledge at the present time, official and public, is superficial. However, it does appear that much of the procedure in Poland was merely a modification or a speeding up of the time-honored methods of making war, especially adapted to the terrain, the season of the year, the character of the people and the geographical set-up.

You have undoubtedly read in the papers of the concentrations we are inaugurating for the mobile troops of the Regular Army. Some four infantry divisions and one cavalry division, together with the necessary corps troops, a few of which now exist and others which are being organized, are being collected for special training. As soon as those divisional concentrations have permitted officers and men to gain familiarity with the new organizations, corps formations of three or four divisions, with the special troops concerned, will be carried out in large maneuvers to give the higher command experience with operations of large formations under modern conditions. This will be the most extensive maneuver ever attempted by our Army in time of peace. It will be, in effect, a great college of leadership for the higher officers, not only of the Regular Army, but of the National Guard and the Reserve Corps. It will provide a wonderful practical schooling for the young products of the ROTC in the Reserve Corps, and I hope it will lead to a policy for an annual concentration of a force of this general character of regular troops, so that we may keep abreast of the technique necessary for the handling of large bodies of troops, and keep before the public the evident necessity for maintaining a balanced force sufficiently complete for immediate employment.

In this connection, I would like to make some comments which I think are rather pertinent. It has seemed to me, from a study of the hearings before Congress, that the Army has suffered continuously from lack of understanding by the public, and to a certain extent, by the Congress. The responsibility for this, in my opinion, rests largely with the Army because of the manner of our presentations and our use of military-technical terminology. At present, an army involves so many complex and varied activities and technical requirements that it is difficult even for a professional soldier to keep in close touch with the entire problem. I must confess that, in going into these matters in the War Department, I frequently have difficulty in understanding just what a particular staff officer is discussing, so far as all the related factors are concerned. If that is so in my case, it is probably much more the case with members of Congress, and must involve still more of misunderstanding by the general public.

We suffer from another disadvantage. The Army, I might say, is not photogenic. The more efficient, the better its organization, technique, and deployment, the more nearly it is invisible, except for the Air Force and the Mechanized Force. For that reason, these last two forces have less difficulty in convincing Congress of the necessity for appropriations; and for exactly the same reason, if we could offer for the mobile army something approximating the beautiful photographs of columns of battleships or destroyers bucking a heavy sea, I think we would have less trouble in developing our military program for the National Defense.

We recently had an excellent example of the force of such publicity.

Several years ago publications were filled with photographs of the horrors of bombing women and children in China and in Spain. Promptly public pressure developed and Congress responded, and we finally received long overdue appropriations for antiaircraft matériel and airplanes. But until the war photographs had reached the public, there had been indifference or great reluctance to respond to our urgings for such equipment.

There is another factor—a most important factor, which pertains to our geographic location. The American people are naturally loath to see large appropriations made for war purposes, believing extensive defensive measures to be unnecessary due to our geographical location between two great oceans. The Atlantic and Pacific oceans are of tremendous value to our defensive situation but they are not unpassable.

In reviewing various hearings before committees of Congress, and the published articles stressing this, that, and the other military development, I have come to the conclusion that if we can find simpler terms for expressing our problem, if, for example, we can settle on a single unit, the army corps, for example, of two or three or four divisions, with the necessary corps troops—heavy artillery and antiaircraft, observation squadrons, engineers, truck-trains, medical troops, signal battalions, and all the supporting elements that are essential in battle—if we can focus on an army corps as our unit of measurement, as our basis of calculation, then I believe we will have much less difficulty in making our problem understandable. Such a policy, so far as concerns the matériel consideration that is foremost in the minds of you gentlemen, should offer a simple basis of calculation, and the fundamental consideration of your great problem is the basis for calculating actual requirements. So, if we take the army corps, in so far as the ground army is concerned, together with the proper percentages for other related forces, as a medium of measure—a yardstick, as it were—we will have a simple problem of arithmetic for the determination of the requirements in personnel, in matériel, and of reserves for any multiple of that force.

Incidental to the concentration we are now bringing about in the South, we have made a step forward in the reorganization of our infantry divisions. At present we will only reorganize divisions of the Regular establishment, leaving the question of reorganizing the National Guard divisions to a later date. When it comes to corps troops, however, we will have to create a number of new units. This can be done only if we are permitted to expand to the authorized peace strength of both the Regular Army and the National Guard. When and if we reach such strength, we can provide four more divisions in the Regular Army, another group of corps troops, and some important special troops for the General Headquarters Reserve, as well as reinforcements for foreign garrisons; and in addition, create the necessary corps troops that logically should exist in the National Guard.

I believe that our military personnel problem in this country is often misunderstood by reason of the fact that we have such a large portion of the Regular Army on foreign service. We might characterize these last posts of duty as naval garrisons, since they guard vital naval installations, such as the Panama Canal, or Pearl Harbor in Hawaii, and naval defenses we are developing in Puerto Rico as a rear guard of the Panama Canal. There is thus left within the continental United States only a small combatant force of the Regular Army, for which we have found it difficult to arrange adequate training—training for our own education in the regular establishment as well as for the education of the senior officers of the National Guard and of the Reserve Corps, who constitute the major portion of our war army. As a matter of fact, the National Guard must be considered as the first line of the Army, since it will form about seventy-five per cent of our first army.

I have been talking about rather small forces, compared to the tremendous program with which you gentlemen are concerned in industrial preparedness. But the problem today is one of immediacy with regard to the existing troops that must be brought to a full state of efficiency as quickly as possible. I might remark, that we are most fortunate in the character and degree of military planning which has been accomplished. We are also exceedingly fortunate, and it is gratifying and reassuring to report, that we have at the present time a War Department staff composed of a highly educated group of officers who coöperate as a team in a remarkably efficient manner. This is one of the most reassuring and helpful features of the present situation. And along with that comment, it is appropriate for me, I think, to mention, in relation to questions of matériel or munitions, the large proportion of which are critical items of ordnance, that we have in the Ordnance Department one of the most efficient, one of the finest group of officers in the Army. That is the common opinion of the Army, of everyone who has come in contact with the Ordnance Department, and I am certain that it is the opinion of you gentlemen assembled here tonight.

I will not attempt to discuss the problem of industrial preparedness. General Wesson has already commented in some detail on the various factors involved. You have had your meetings since you came here, and you have known, most of you, for years what the great problem has been. You are familiar with the time factor, so it is unnecessary for me to go into that phase of the problem, except to say that you know, I know, all of us know that the time factor is the vital consideration—and vital in the correct meaning of the term—of our National Defense program; that we must never be caught in the same situation we found ourselves in in 1917.

General Harbord [Major General James G. Harbord] went to France as Chief of Staff of the American Expeditionary Forces—a force devoid of matériel. I sailed with the 1st Division, on the first boat of the first convoy, and I cannot recall a better picture of the vast and terrible problem that General Pershing and his staff had to undertake, than a description of the conditions under which that expedition embarked for France. We embarked with a part of an entirely new division, of which I had never even seen a photostat of the organization until we were aboard ship. I then discovered—and I was a member of the General Staff of that division—that we had units in the division of which I had never heard. They were on other boats, and because the use of the wireless was forbidden, we could not communicate with them to find out what they were and what they knew about themselves. We studied all the available charts. We sought to familiarize ourselves with the new organization, but there was very little literature on the war as it was then being conducted. We had one small English pamphlet, a single copy, which we studied conscientiously. But our thoughts would always go back to these new units and how they should be employed.

Landing at St. Nazaire, I was immediately sent on a circuit of the division as the troops came ashore, to find out what they had, what manner of men they were, and what they knew about this new organization. I discovered that of two hundred men to a company, approximately one hundred and eighty were recruits. I found that some of these new units—howitzer companies, the people with the Stokes mortars and 37mm. cannon—not only did not have the weapons, but the men themselves had never even heard of them. And we were landing on a foreign shore three thousand miles from home, to enter the greatest war in history!

I recall the first time the American troops were put into line. They went in by battalions, and it fell to me to make the arrangements. We literally borrowed everything that was loose in France. Some items we didn't even borrow. We had no rolling kitchens; we didn't have this, and we didn't have that. I remember that some of the staff from the great GHQ, to which we looked in reverence rather as the rising sun and all the powers inherent in it, came down to inspect our departure, and were horrified because some of the soldiers had cut the brims off their campaign hats and were wearing the remaining crowns; others wore headgear made from bath towels, for with the steel helmet they had to have something that could be folded. Some of them had the Belgian *képi*, probably because it had a gold tassel dangling in front. But we went into line in that shape for our first experience—everything begged, borrowed, or stolen—certainly not manufactured in America. That was a trying experience, a complicated affair to manage. Later I became involved in movements of troops up into the hundreds of thousands, but the problem didn't approximate the difficulties of managing that small first group of the 1st Division, of which nothing was normal except that fact that the men were Americans and they were willing to fight.

It has been an inspiration tonight to see a group of gentlemen of your patriotism, especially of the continued service you have rendered through the years in the very serious, the difficult, and really stupendous problem of the industrial program for the support of whatever military and naval effort we may have to make. I feel that it is a reassuring indication of the temper of the businessmen of America. Speaking for the Army I wish to express our appreciation of your patriotism, especially of the continued service you have rendered through the past twenty years.

6
Training by Maneuvers

Statements on the Purpose and Advantages of Army Maneuvers before the House of Representatives Subcommittee, Committee on Appropriations, 76th Congress, 3d Session, November 30, 1939

∿∿∿∿∿∿∿∿∿∿∿∿∿∿∿∿∿∿∿∿∿∿∿∿

Fortunately the AEF had Allies to protect it for more than a year, while it found itself. The future problems of our Army visualize no such protected period for overcoming peacetime military deficiencies. We must be prepared to stand on our own feet.

Mr. Clifton A. Woodrum of Virginia: General, Mr. Taber has some questions he wants to ask you.

Mr. John Taber of New York: The thing I want to ask you about is this, and it ought not to take very long, but I regard it as of considerable importance: The maneuvers that have been set up here involve something like eight months, of one type or another, and at one place or another. Why should they last that long?

General Marshall: That is a pretty large question, Mr. Taber, and it covers a broad field. In the first place, the duration of the maneuvers, or rather the concentrations, has little to do with the cost. Pay, rations, and other fixed charges continue unchanged whether in the field or in garrison. The largest item of cost pertains to the matter of transportation to and from the concentration points. The shorter the duration of the maneuver or concentration ordered, the greater the cost per soldier, due to transportation charges. Therefore, once we concentrate troops, once we have expended the money to transport them to the maneuver areas, it is usually better business to make the most of the opportunity, unless demands for their employment in connection with summer training of the civilian components requires their return to home stations, and that is not the case in the winter season, as at present.

We have never had any real maneuvers of large bodies of troops in our Army in time of peace, and there are several reasons for this. The few tactical divisions of the Regular establishment that we have maintained have not been complete, have been distant from each other, and so scattered about among themselves that lack of funds has usually made it impossible to assemble more than one division. We have eighteen divisions in the National Guard, but they could only be assembled for two weeks' training, and as the men were fresh from civil pursuits with soft muscles and tendons, and had had no field training since the previous summer, it was necessary to devote at least a week to company, battalion, and regimental training. This left but three or four days for training or maneuvers of larger units; and even so, it was only possible once in four years to concentrate a particular National Guard division for the so-called army maneuvers.

Another deficiency has made it impracticable to conduct genuine army maneuvers, and that has been the almost complete lack of corps troops, and the fact that we had no corps commanders and no corps staffs and headquarters. In the elementary efforts we have made to conduct large maneuvers, under the limitations I have referred to, the corps commanders, staffs, and headquarters have had to be improvised from officers brought in from other assignments and from men taken from other duties. But even so, with the limitations on the employment of the National Guard in the strenuous service necessary in large field maneuvers, it has been impossible even to approximate the real thing.

As a result, we have been forced to build up our technique of command and control and even our development of leadership, largely on a theoretical basis. We have, I believe, the best military school system for the training of officers in the world, but of necessity the instruction has had to be based largely on theoretical conceptions in relation to units larger than a brigade. This is a source of weakness, just as it would be a source of weakness for a football team never even to have had team practice until the day of the game. What appears satisfactory on paper too frequently we find quite impracticable in actual operations. Organization and planning, based too largely on theoretical grounds, result in cumbersome organizations, too large staffs and too lengthy and complicated orders.

Training the ground forces of an army for actual campaign in battle is a difficult business at best, as there is little that can be done in time of peace to simulate closely the conditions under which troops operate in war. Therefore, it is all the more important that we make every effort to learn the practical business of troop leadership and teamwork, utilizing field maneuvers for this purpose, and especially to wash out the overtheoretical or academic conceptions.

We must have more simplicity of procedure, and that requires teamwork, and teamwork is possible only if we have an opportunity to practice as a team.

It is probable that you, gentlemen, may have been somewhat confused by our military terminology, which I confess is too frequently misleading. We have nine corps areas. Those are territorial affairs, and would have a tremendous amount to do with the mobilization and other territorial problems in preparation for war. But they are in no sense army corps. An army corps is a tactical command of two or more divisions, backed up by a group of special corps troops—heavy artillery, antiaircraft artillery, antitank guns, observation squadrons of airplanes, truck trains, a medical regiment, a signal or communication battalion, and so forth. The whole is directed and led by a corps commander with a corps staff. This is the real battle unit of the ground army, and I might add that it is the fundamental war-making unit upon which everything else depends, extending to the harbors or sea bases for the Navy, and the air bases for the Air Corps.

You, gentlemen, have probably seen in the papers frequent references to the new "streamlined" division. In the War Department we call this a triangular division, because it has three regiments of infantry instead of the four of the division used in the World War and as somewhat modified in 1920. The popular impression seems to be that this is a motorized division, apparently meaning that everybody will ride in a motor vehicle. This is not the case, as the infantry riflemen and the other foot soldiers will still have to walk, the motors having merely replaced the horses and mules of the artillery, machine guns, and trains of the old division.

The peace strength of the old square division was twelve thousand men. The peace strength of the new triangular division is a little short of nine thousand men, and an important consideration in this reduction in strength is that we have economized in artillery and other special troops by pooling them in a group of army corps troops. In other words, we give the division less of these special troops and hold them in the army corps to be used whenever their services are required in a specific situation. This is much more economical of men and organizations, as it would require a great many more if each division was given a fuller complement of special troops. But, if we have no corps troops then the triangular division is doomed to failure on the field of battle, because it will lack the necessary support of the heavy artillery, antiaircraft guns, and similar weapons, as well as the truck trains, medical service, and communication material and personnel required.

Since none of our Regular Army divisions were complete, and all were much scattered, and since an experiment of over one and one half years had been carried on to determine the better organization for the smaller division, it seemed necessary in the present state of the world to reorganize the Regular Army divisions immediately, and this was done. The organization of the National Guard was not touched at this time, it having been thought better to wait until we had had a full test in the field of a number of divisions of the Regular establishment with the new organization.

Now, returning directly to the question of these maneuvers, regarding which Mr. Taber has questioned me, I would like to outline the various phases of the matter, which involve the necessity for training.

We now have a new strength for the infantry rifle company, we have a new heavy-weapons company. We have, therefore, a new infantry battalion organization and a new regimental organization. This same divisional change applies to the artillery, and more or less to the other troops, and it has a very special application to the complete reorganization of the higher control of the division. Brigades have been abolished, and the division headquarters has been set up on a different basis. It is therefore necessary for the company, battalion and regimental commanders to learn, successively, how to handle these new units. That could not be well managed in limited areas and in the cold and snow of a northern winter. Furthermore, many of the regiments were not together as units. In this connection an army commander commenting yesterday on the enthusiasm with which this concentration was being received, referred to the remark of a young captain who had said: "This is the first time I have ever seen my regiment together."

After the regimental units have gotten their training, and that takes a considerable period of time—and they will have the terrain in which to manage that special training—then the brigadiers and the major generals must learn how to handle the new groupings or units, and this especially requires considerable terrain and other troops to provide the hostile resistance—or the scrimmage, to use a football term which will be understood by all of you. As soon as this phase of the training has been completed, then we are ready to concentrate these divisions into an army corps, with the corps troops that it has been possible to organize under the increased strength of seventeen thousand given the Army by the Presidential Executive Order of last September. Here will be the first occasion in time of peace in our Army that the officers will have had an opportunity to learn how to coördinate, maneuver, and lead a corps unit.

Mr. Clarence Cannon of Missouri: Where will these maneuvers be held?

General Marshall: I cannot answer that question at the present time. The army commander responsible for the conduct of the maneuvers arrived in Washington this morning and I have not yet had an opportunity to discuss the matter with him. We have concentrated four of the divisions in the Southeast, where we had facilities for camping them at a minimum expense. We have borrowed the use of National Guard camp installations near Columbia, South Carolina, and near Anniston, in Alabama; we have utilized such facilities as existed on the large reservation at Fort Benning, Georgia. Fortunately, each of these three localities provides terrain suitable for field training, and they are so related in point of distance that the concentration of the divisions is a relatively simple matter. Also, Fort Bragg in North Carolina and Fort Knox in Kentucky are not far distant; therefore the corps troops and the mechanized forces can be economically and conveniently brought into the maneuvers from those posts. We are looking for terrain which is conveniently and economically accessible, and which is of such a character that it affords the necessary diversity for advantageous training, and which is in thinly populated country and will be economical from the viewpoint of possible minor damages.

MR. TABER: How long will you keep them together after you get them together?

GENERAL MARSHALL: The army corps maneuvers will probably only last from three to four weeks. I might say at this moment in relation to the duration of the maneuvers, that the limiting factor is the time of delivery of the motor transportation required for these division and corps troops. As I testified the other day, the orders for the motor transportation were placed the latter part of October, and the first deliveries will not occur until some time in January and the order will not be entirely filled until the first of May, and probably even later. Until most of the motors are in the hands of the troops we will not have the necessary transportation to carry the guns, the kitchens, the supplies, and so forth. We are limited in what we can do for the large groupings. This is not exactly the case with the regiments, as they can manage a great deal of training, based on their concentration camps.

MR. TABER: You must be familiar with the operations of other countries along the line of their troop concentrations for maneuvers.

GENERAL MARSHALL: Yes, sir.

MR. TABER: They are not accustomed to have more than two months of maneuvers.

GENERAL MARSHALL: The situation with them is quite different from the status and conditions in our Army. They have, referring to the French Army, for example, divisions and corps and army units in time of peace; and the divisions are together as a unit. Their war missions are similar so far as advance knowledge of where they are to go is concerned. As a rule the maneuvers are conducted in those regions, or at least under conditions simulating the situation in those regions. The distances are short and the concentrations are, therefore, simple to effect; there is little to improvise. Furthermore, under the law, at least in France, they have arrangements whereby areas can be utilized not only for maneuvers, but for actual artillery firing—areas which involve farmland, facilities, and so forth. The procedure is well settled, the basis for damages clearly defined, and all the people are conscious of the necessities of the situation. Practically every physically able man has served in the army and probably trained in the region of his home, so there is nothing novel or uncertain about the business to him. Training under those conditions is quite a different matter from the problem that confronts us, with divisions widely separated, and in themselves widely scattered; the corps units and corps commanders virtually non-existent.

MR. WILLIAM P. LAMBERTSON OF KANSAS: I wonder as to the value of these big maneuvers, in view of the fact of the imminent danger of sending men to Europe.

GENERAL MARSHALL: That, the question of sending men to Europe, has nothing to do with these maneuvers.

MR. LAMBERTSON: There they would not be in any great groups or divisions.

GENERAL MARSHALL: I would prefer not to discuss that.

MR. LAMBERTSON: In the World War, were they not swapped around?

GENERAL MARSHALL: To a certain extent, but that was in time of battle. We finally got twenty-nine divisions organized in our Army in France. I would like to quote from a statement by General Pershing regarding this training question, and he had considerable experience in handling the National Guard divisions as well as the so-called Regular divisions.

MR. J. BUELL SNYDER OF PENNSYLVANIA: Before you do that, was it not true that General Pershing would not move until he got a certain number of American troops together to move as one organization?

GENERAL MARSHALL: Yes, sir; but there was an exception even to that, when his hand was forced at the time of the great German offensive in March 1918 and he felt it necessary to offer Marshal Foch everything that we had in France at that time. Later on in the summer of 1918 General Pershing found it very difficult to get the organizations together again. General Pershing made this comment in his book on his experiences in the World War:

Although the 34 National Guard and National Army Divisions that eventually came to France were, with two exceptions, organized in August and September, 1917, they did not receive training as complete units from that time on. They were filled gradually and by piecemeal, weeks and even months elapsing before they reached full strength, and, as we have seen, the personnel was constantly changing.

Therefore, when the time came for service abroad, a very large proportion of the men in these divisions had little or no experience, and the training of the unit as a whole had been seriously delayed. All this was discouraging to their officers, disastrous to morale, threw upon the American Expeditionary Forces an extra burden of training, and resulted in our having a number of divisions only partially trained when the time came to use them.

This condition of things signalized the failure on the part of the General Staff at home to realize that their most important function was to supervise the organization and training of complete divisions for combat and provide them with equipment and supplies. Their obligations to the armies in the field were not fulfilled by merely sending units carelessly prepared and with an undue proportion of green officers and men to fight against trained veterans.

Fortunately the AEF had allies to protect it for more than a year, while it found itself. The future problems of our Army visualize no such protected period for overcoming peacetime military deficiencies. We must be prepared to stand on our own feet.

To summarize: With a view to providing for the training of large units we are now concentrating in southern camps and on the Pacific coast five infantry divisions, corps troops, two cavalry divisions, and the mechanized cavalry brigade. Before the end of this fiscal year it is proposed to complete the divisional training of the divisions, assemble them with corps units as two corps for additional field maneuvers, and to assemble the two corps for one extensive maneuver involving all units up to and including an army. Intensive field training is to be given to all other units in the United States not part of larger organizations.

In conjunction with the concentrations and the field training of large units, it is proposed to give added training to as many Regular, National Guard, and Reserve officers as practicable, in addition to officers regularly assigned, by bringing them into the organizations for varying periods to perform duties appropriate to their grades in command and operative staff positions. Steps have also been taken to increase National Guard armory drills from forty-eight to sixty and to give the Guard an additional seven days of local field training in this fiscal year. We cannot afford, in the present situation, to allow the new recruits of the National Guard to wait until next July for their first field training and rifle practice.

In addition to this training in the United States, it is proposed to conduct extensive field training of our overseas garrisons to insure their fitness to perform their defense missions. Funds to carry out this year's program are requested in supplemental estimates. Such a program will cost a great deal of money, and necessitates a new yardstick for funds for training to be established.

MR. TABER: Your idea, General, is that you should profit by the experience that the officers will get out of the maneuvers?

GENERAL MARSHALL: Not only the officers, but particularly the non-commissoned officers.

MR. TABER: As to the troops themselves, it does not matter so much about this intensive training?

GENERAL MARSHALL: It matters tremendously, sir; particularly as to morale. Soldiers get very tired of never being in the picture except in a little primary way. They all want to be in the big league, and to see how the game is played.

The maneuvers will be of vast importance to the corps commanders and their staffs and the corps troops, and to the division and brigade commanders and their staffs. But the exercises will be of great benefit to every individual involved; the experience of new terrain, the uncertainty as to enemy strength, the operations with all the new types of combat units; the try-out of horse-cavalry divisions and so-called mechanized-cavalry divisions in connection with large bodies of troops, and possibly in opposition at times to each other—all these phases will make the maneuvers of tremendous benefits to all concerned.

*   *   *

. . . We have not had a basis for real corps and army maneuvers, and the present concentration will be the first opportunity for full training in this respect. I feel it will be productive of tremendous good for the military efficiency of the Army, and, therefore, for the National Defense.

*   *   *

It is hoped that we will be permitted to carry out each winter a phase of such maneuvers and every so often a large concentration of the same nature. By no other system can the Army be maintained at the efficiency required, at the efficiency which will justify the heavy expense of maintaining a military establishment in this country according to American standards of living.

*   *   *

7
National Organization for War

An Address before the Joint Meeting of the American
Military Institute and the American Historical Association, Washington, D. C., December 28, 1939

*In our democracy where the government is truly an
agent of the popular will, military policy is dependent
on public opinion, and our organization for war will
be good or bad as the public is well or poorly informed
regarding the factors which bear on the subject.*

THE character of the organization of nations for war appears to be
determined largely by their state of civilization, their geography,
and their politics. From a military point of view, the state of
civilization of the dominant nations approximates the same level; all use
similar weapons, organize their forces in corresponding units, and man
and equip their armies in much the same manner. Their military set-up
differs principally in the extent of organization and in the degree of
readiness of the major forces, and these differences appear to be dictated
principally by geographical and political considerations.

The influences of geography are numerous and usually obvious. In-
vading forces, for example, prefer open frontiers and avoid ocean barriers. The possibility of conflicting interests between nations diminishes
as the distance between them increases. This country is fortunate in its
geographical position, and if the Atlantic Ocean has not guaranteed complete immunity from wars with European powers, it has made such wars
so difficult of management as to be approached with caution and reluctance, and it does make sudden attack on us seem unlikely. The influence
of distance has been modified by the airplane, along with increased speeds
on land and water, but these changes have not as yet materially affected
our unusually favorable situation.

If these views regarding the effect of civilization and geography on
the organization of this country for war are accepted, then we must turn
to political considerations to find the dominating influence in this vital
matter. In our democracy where the government is truly an agent of the
popular will, military policy is dependent on public opinion, and our
organization for war will be good or bad as the public is well informed
or poorly informed regarding the factors that bear on the subject.

Public appreciation of international affairs is of course important to a sound view regarding military policy, and the radio and press are doing a remarkable job of keeping the public informed. School children today are probably more fully informed on current international developments than were many high government officials of thirty years ago. But even more important are the lessons of history. Therefore, it is to the historian, to you gentlemen, that we must turn for the most essential service in determining the public policy relating to National Defense.

Popular knowledge of history, I believe, is largely based on information derived from school textbooks, and unfortunately these sources often tell only a portion of the truth with regard to our war experiences. Historians have been inclined to record the victories and gloss over the mistakes and wasteful sacrifices. Cause and effect have been, to an important extent, ignored. Few Americans learn that we enrolled nearly four hundred thousand men in the Revolutionary War to defeat an enemy that numbered less than forty-five thousand, or that we employed half a million in 1812 against an opponent whose strength never exceeded sixteen thousand at any one place, and fewer still have learned why these overwhelming numbers were so ineffective. The War between the States pointed numerous lessons for our future protection, yet seldom has a nation entered a war so completely unprepared, and yet so boastfully, as did the United States in 1898. Veterans of the World War often seem to overlook the fact that almost a year and a half elapsed after the declaration of war before we could bring a field army into being and even then its weapons, ammunition and other matériel were provided by our Allies. And many of them seem unaware of the fact that the partially trained state of our troops proved a costly and tragic business despite the eventual success.

What the casual student does learn is that we have won all our wars and he is, therefore, justified in assuming that since we have defeated the enemies of the past we shall continue to defeat the enemies of the future. This comfortable belief in our invincibility has been reflected legislatively in the inadequate military organization of past years, resulting in stupendous expenditures in each emergency, invariably followed by a parsimonious attitude, if not the complete neglect of ordinary military necessities. In addition to the perils of war there is the issue of huge war debts with their aftermath of bitter years of heavy taxes. I think it apparent that much of the misfortune in the life of our democracy could have been avoided by the influence of a better informed public on the decisions of the Congress.

Personally I am convinced that the colossal wastefulness of our war organization in the past, and the near tragedies to which it has led us, have been due primarily to the character of our school textbooks and the ineffective manner in which history has been taught in the public schools of this country. In other words, I am saying that if we are to have a sound organization for war we must first have better school histories and a better technique for teaching history.

I have had no opportunity for research in preparation for this discussion but I have found in a brief survey of some of the present school textbooks on American history that there has been a great improvement since the days of my early schooling, and a material improvement since the period, a few years after the close of the World War, when I became officially interested in this question. I should confess that I was particularly impressed with Dr. Albert Bushnell Hart's volume, but I have no data as to the extent to which it is used in the schools of this country.

I might attempt a philosophical discussion this morning regarding the proper organization of this country for war, or, to put it more tactfully, for the National Defense; but however convincing this might be, the effect would be negligible—or at least but momentary. The members of a Congress, wise on the heels of a war, will legislate with serious purpose to avoid a repetition of the crises, the plights and frights of their recent experience; but what is done is usually undone, the military arrangements emasculated, the old story of unpreparedness continued on into the next chapter of repetitions, because of the pressure of public opinion.

To maintain a sound organization the public must understand the general requirements for the defense of this particular country—the requirements for the maintenance of peace as we soldiers believe, before Congress can be expected, year in and year out, to provide the necessary legislation with due regard both for the economics of the situation and for the essential requirements for an adequate army and navy, with the necessary industrial organization behind them. When the high-school student knows exactly what happened, and most important of all, why it happened, then our most serious military problem will be solved. Potentially the strongest nation on earth, we will become the strongest and at a much smaller cost than has been paid for our mistakes in the past. The historian, the school history and its teacher are the important factors in the solution of the problem I am discussing so superficially this morning.

History as a science has many specialties. The military historian is a specialist. Normally he is not concerned in the preparation of school textbooks. Furthermore, military history, since it deals with wars, is unpopular, and probably more so today than at any other time. Yet I believe it is very important that the true facts, the causes and consequences that make our military history, should be matters of common knowledge. War is a deadly disease, which today afflicts hundreds of millions of people. It exists; therefore, there must be a reason for its existence. We should do everything in our power to isolate the disease, protect ourselves against it, and to discover the specific which will destroy it. A complete knowledge of the disease is essential before we can hope to find a cure. Daily we see attacks on war and tabulations regarding its cost, but rarely do we find a careful effort being made to analyze the various factors in order to determine the nature of war; to audit the accounts as it were, and to see to whom or to what each item of the staggering total is really chargeable.

As to the character of the organization for war suitable and acceptable to this country, I might say that certain definite policies have been developed through the years, and given a degree of permanence in the genral amendments to the National Defense Act of June 1920:

1st, a small Regular Army as the keystone of our land defense program. It should provide the small force that might be immediately required for the security of the interests of this country, and supply the training standards and the training staff for the development of a citizen army.

2nd, a territorial force, the National Guard, voluntarily maintained by the State governments in coöperation with the Federal Government, to supplement the small standing Army for the first phase of the defense of the country in the event of war.

3rd, a democratic system for developing a Reserve of trained officer material—the ROTC and the CMTC, and a practical plan for the prompt procurement of manpower to fill up the ranks of the Regular Establishment and the National Guard, and later to provide the necessary replacements and the men for the new units which will be required.

4th, a reserve of noncommercial munitions.

5th, a practical set-up for the prompt mobilization of the industrial resources of the nation, to provide, with the least practicable delay, the munitions that are required.

And lastly, an adequate reserve of the raw materials essential for war purposes, which are not available in this country.

The foregoing policies have been generally accepted by the public and are a part of the organic law. Properly administered and developed, they provide a democratic basis for the National Defense suitable to our form of government and to our particular international situation.

In the development of these policies two factors dominate the thought of the War Department. The first pertains to economic considerations. Everything in this country is expensive, in keeping with the high standards of living demanded by our people. Therefore, the military establishment is very expensive, and its maintenance on a sound basis is always endangered by the natural demand of the people for economy in government. This demand concentrates first on the Army and Navy immediately following a period of war, gradually grows more insistent in time of peace, and finally becomes politically compulsory with a depression in business. The War Department, therefore, concentrates earnestly on the problem of how best to maintain an adequate standard of national defense for a minimum of expenditure.

The time factor is the other dominant consideration which influences the planning of the Department. It is related to all our preparations— the production of matériel, the training of troops, of pilots and of mechanics, the organization of new units, and the mobilization of a war army. The Navy in peace is seventy-five per cent fully prepared. The Army machine is probably less than twenty-five per cent ready for immediate action. Our problem, therefore, involves the development of a war force after the emergency has arrived. The time factor dominates the situation to a degree not approximated in any other great country. For this reason in particular the problem of a suitable war organization for the United States is one of many complications, and the influence of a well informed public is of profound importance.

8

Our Military Policy

A Radio Broadcast to the Reserve Officers' Association of the
United States, from Washington, D. C., February 16, 1940

*Two oceans guard us against sudden attack; they afford us
time to train additional manpower for defense, but not enough
time to manufacture the necessary munitions to capitalize our
tremendous manpower. That is why we can entrust our national defense to a small permanent military force which is in
keeping with our national traditions, with an organized and
partially trained National Guard in close support, provided
we have on hand a reserve of arms, ammunition, and equipment sufficient to equip the larger force we might have need of.*

I WELCOME the invitation to speak as the guest of the Reserve Officers' Association on the subject of National Defense. The present
tragic situation in the world has focused the attention of our people
on National Defense. Certainly the citizens of this country are entitled
to know what measures are being taken by the Army of the United
States to meet these responsibilities, and I am glad of this opportunity to
make an informal report.

Today we are engaged in vitalizing every department of the Army in
a practical, common sense manner. In spite of the severity of the winter,
we find today most of the troops of the Regular Army actually in the
field, under canvas, maneuvering, training, preparing in every way
within their power, to develop efficiency, teamwork, and the technique
of campaign. The National Guard undertook similar field training for
an additional week last fall. The Air Corps fortunately is well under
way to more than double its effective strength.

But more than training is required as a military precaution to guarantee
the security of our form of government. We must have an adequate
supply of munitions, meaning arms, ammunition, and equipment.

The Army has two general missions. It must be prepared to protect the
United States and our overseas possessions against *any* external attack or
raid, and it must prevent the domination of territory in the Western
Hemisphere by an overseas power. Our geographical position simplifies
this task. Two oceans guard us against sudden attack; they afford us

time to train additional manpower for defense, but not enough time to manufacture the necessary munitions to capitalize our tremendous manpower. This is why we can entrust the national defense to a small permanent military force which is in keeping with our national traditions, with an organized and partially trained National Guard in close support, *provided* we have on hand a reserve of arms, ammunition and equipment sufficient to equip the larger force we might have need of.

National policy is unalterably opposed to a large standing army, and we keep our Regular establishment at the smallest strength possible which will still permit it to perform its missions. It is the keystone of our land defense and it must supply the training standards, as well as the key personnel for the development of a citizen army in the event of a national emergency. It must also provide a small mobile land and air force sufficient to meet any unexpected threat against the security of our national interests, especially those concerned with the Panama Canal and the naval base in Hawaii.

The Regular Army does not need to be large, but it does need to be perfect in organization, training, and equipment. Until this fall, the Regular Army, although highly developed in the efficiency of its small units, has been largely an army of battalions. Seldom were regiments complete or united. Brigades were a rarity. We possessed no complete divisions and the battalions of the incomplete divisions were widely scattered. The army corps, the great battle team, existed solely on paper. Our reserves of arms and munitions were largely left over from the last war, and they had steadily, year by year, for twenty years, become antiquated. This winter, for the first time in peace, we were permitted to assemble five complete infantry divisions and one cavalry division for extended field training, to culminate in a general maneuver next May of some sixty-five thousand troops.

I have recently visited all of these divisions. They are living in the field, under tentage, and at times sleeping on the ground. The bitter weather of this winter has not retarded their intensive field training; the hardships have not discouraged the Regular soldier. He is giving a fine demonstration of fortitude, soldierly spirit and discipline. Morale is high, and the sick rate, low. The troops are reaching an extremely high state of efficiency in tactical training.

The increase last September of seventeen thousand men in the authorized strength of the Regular Army has enabled us to organize the necessary supporting units to complete one army corps, and to assemble one mechanized brigade. This is but a midget force by European standards, but by the end of May it will be a model force compared to the highest standards of any army. Trained, disciplined and seasoned, properly equipped, and organized into balanced army corps, the American soldier, in our opinion, is the finest in the world.

The National Guard is an efficient, well organized citizen force, voluntarily maintained by the State governments in coöperation with the Federal government, prepared to reinforce the Regular Army for the first phase of the defense of the country. It was recently increased in strength to 235,000 men, but its divisions are still far below strength and, like the Regular Army, the Guard is still lacking in the special units of heavy artillery, antiaircraft, engineers, etc., necessary to weld its divisions into modern combat teams of army corps.

The Officers Reserve Corps, and its sources of supply, the Reserve Officers Training Corps at colleges and universities, supplemented by the Citizens Military Training Camps, provide the reservoir of trained officers which we require for a national effort. We are using about 1,400 Reserve officers this year as platoon and company commanders with Regular Army units in the field. Most of these lieutenants will spend periods of six months on extended active duty. The combat planes of the great GHQ Air Force are eighty per cent piloted by Reserve officers. This system enables us to train Reserve officers, particularly in the junior grades, in a supremely practical way, and incidental to the course of this training it provides the additional officers needed for the Regular Army units during important field exercises.

The country has reason to be proud of its Reserve officers. The development of our Officers Reserve Corps is unique. Its personnel does not have the long period of preparatory training required by nations with enormous armies. Its senior officers are veterans of the War and its junior officers the product of careful military schooling in the ROTC under Regular Army instructors. We depend on the patriotic enthusiasm of this organization, which prompts our Reserve officers to give of their own time to perfect themselves in their military duties.

Current appropriations are enabling us to do a great deal to provide much-needed modern arms and equipment for both the Regular Army and the National Guard. The quality of the military equipment being developed in this country should be a source of great satisfaction. The new semiautomatic shoulder rifle is one of the finest individual arms in the world, and there are no better antitank and antiaircraft guns in existence than those which have recently been designed and produced by our Ordnance. American-made airplanes are of a world acknowledged standard of excellence. Our difficulties lie in the matter of quantity rather than in the quality of the material which we are producing. There is a two-year time lag between the placing of orders and the delivery date of many of the more complex items of equipment. It is this time factor which demands that our reserve of these critical items should be sufficient to equip our first war force.

All that we have done has cost a great deal of money. Everything in this country is expensive, in keeping with the standard of living demanded by our people. It follows that the military establishment is also unavoidably expensive, especially as it is on a purely volunteer basis. The great concern of the War Department is to keep the cost within reasonable limits. Our people resent any military program which might impose an economic burden that was not justified by world conditions. But, we must regain much lost ground. National demands for economy always concentrate on the military establishment immediately following any period of war. They grow insistent during peace, and become irresistible with any period of business depression. The Army has passed through such a cycle. For almost twenty years our land defense forces have been living on their World War hump until barely a skeleton remained. This is particularly true regarding the home forces, considering the fact that nearly seventy thousand Regular soldiers are stationed outside continental United States guarding the Panama Canal, Pearl Harbor in Hawaii and the Philippines.

We are committed to a small army, but we must have the best army of its size in the world. The strength may vary from year to year; a strength appropriate to the present emergency might not be supported by the nation under conditions of evident world tranquility. But until the world is a much more peaceful place, with men's minds directed toward home and firesides, farms and factories, the military necessities for our security must be carefully weighed and then created in fact, and not in theory.

9
Leadership in War

Statement before the House of Representatives, Committee on Military Affairs, on Consideration of HR 9243, a Bill to Provide for the Promotion List of Officers of the Army After Specified Years of Service in Grade, and for Other Purposes, 76th Congress, 3d Session, April 9, 1940

〜〜〜〜〜〜〜〜〜〜〜〜〜〜〜〜〜〜〜〜〜〜〜〜〜〜〜〜

Leadership in the field depends to an important extent on one's legs, and stomach, and nervous system, and on one's ability to withstand hardships, and lack of sleep, and still be disposed energetically and aggressively to command men, to dominate men on the battlefield.

GENERAL MARSHALL: Mr. Chairman [Andrew J. May of Kentucky], I am for this bill. There are two factors in this matter from my point of view.

The first is the one which was largely discussed before I came on the stand, which has to do with the protection of the interests of the individual. That is essential for the maintenance of the morale of the Army. I am of the opinion that this bill is so written that it handles this aspect of the question about as well as can be managed. As the Secretary [of war] and General Shedd[8] have said, it does not discriminate against any individual. It treats all alike and protects their interests, I think, so far as it is legally possible to protect them, with due regard for the purpose of the Army.

The other factor which is of tremendous concern to me is the efficiency of the Army and the effect that such a measure as this will have on the state of efficiency—and I am talking primarily about leadership. As the Secretary has stated, if we do not do something of this sort in a few years, we will have a situation where officers in a position of comparative obscurity will be suddenly elevated to positions of great importance in command and control.

I listened to the questions that were asked General Shedd. One of them referred to the matter of age and experience. I think you should regard this in the Army from a little different point of view from similar considerations in other activities in life. One does acquire experience and

---

[8]Secretary of War Harry H. Woodring; Major General William E. Shedd, Assistant Chief of Staff, G-1, War Department General Staff.

judgment with the years, but also, unfortunately, we lose the resiliency of tendons and muscles, and leadership in the field depends to an important extent on one's legs, and stomach, and nervous system, and on one's ability to withstand hardships, and lack of sleep, and still be disposed energetically and aggressively to command men, to dominate men on the battlefield. We may have the wisdom of the years, but we lack, I know I do in many respects, the physical ruggedness of more youthful days. When I deal with my family in sports, I find I lack the agility that I once possessed, and they can wear me down. I may know more about the technique of the game, but nevertheless I come out at the short end of the horn.

Before the Senate committee yesterday I referred to the fact that I saw twenty-seven different divisions of ours engaged in battle—we employed twenty-nine—and there were more reliefs of field officers, those above the grade of captain, due to physical reasons than for any other cause. But by that I do not mean that they were definitely relieved because of a physical limitation, but because their spirit—their tenacity of purpose, their power of leadership over tired men—was broken through physical fatigue. They became pessimistic. They became nervous impossibilities in positions of leadership. A man must have a great deal of stamina to stand the racket of campaign. Many of our mistakes were due to physical deficiency; and, as I remarked, the majority of the reliefs, I think, were due specifically to physical exhaustion.

For these reasons this particular bill is very important to me. It is a means to correct the situation that now exists in the Army. I do not know of a better means that can be devised that will meet all the vicissitudes involved than the enactment of this bill. Therefore, I urgently recommend that it be favorably reported.

THE CHAIRMAN: General, we members of the House and Senate have the privilege of nominating for the Military Academy probably three-fourths of the cadets that go to that school, and, as I understand it, when they graduate and come from the Military Academy, the average age is about twenty-four years. Now, under the present system, how long would they have to serve before they got to the rank of captain?

GENERAL MARSHALL: By law they become captains in ten years, but the difficulty comes in passing into the grade of major. These men would be captains indefinitely. In the 1920s I have advised young men not to go to West Point, because the prospects at that time were so poor for promotion that they would face the certainty of spending much of the active period of their life in low grades with consequent limited opportunities. Now, for the present, young men coming into the service, while the law gives them certainty of rank up to the grade of captain, thereafter they will advance too rapidly, due to the retirement of the World War officers. This bill, however, would control that stiuation. It would not allow undue rapidity of promotion as has occurred in the past; otherwise we would have a repetition of the vicious circle of too rapid promotion for one group and too slow promotion for another.

THE CHAIRMAN: So that under present conditions it is not so desirable for a young man to get into the Military Academy, if he comes out of it and goes into the Army?

GENERAL MARSHALL: No, sir. Right now I would say it is a desirable time; but twenty years ago the prospects were poor, and the men I have been talking about are now suffering from that condition. These very men that are coming in now, and those to come in the next five or ten years will, if there is no control, get too rapid promotion.

THE CHAIRMAN: And this bill regulates all of those things and equalizes the opportunities, based on length of service?

GENERAL MARSHALL: Yes, sir; it endeavors to do that. And, incidentally, this is a very complicated business from a great many points of view. I might say that back in 1910 I was one of a group of four officers at Leavenworth who were nominated by the personnel there to go into the question of creating a single promotion list, the first time that ever was attempted; and I had charge of getting up the data. One of the other officers was General John Palmer,[9] who later had a great deal to do with the National Defense Act. We succeeded in developing a single list as an experiment, and, what was remarkable, we got the full acquiescence of the officers of the three arms concerned, with the exception of one individual. He had had so much of promotion he was unwilling to forego future advantages. It was sent on to the War Department and was buried there.

*   *   *

Later, in 1921 or 1922, I believe, I was the secretary of the Shanks board. My job for seven months was to present both sides of the case in the investigation of the promotion list, hearing hundreds of officers testify, both for and against the existing arrangement of the list. So I am somewhat familiar with the idiosyncrasies of the Officer Corps, with the injustices that have developed and apparent impossibility of remedying them without doing greater damage.

*   *   *

For example, consider the classes that have graduated from West Point from 1920 up to 1930, with a few other entries from civil life or

[9]Brigadier General John McAuley Palmer, Special Assistant to the Chief of Staff during World War II; author of *America in Arms: 1789-1943,* and other books and articles on National Defense, and life-long student of National Defense measures and legislation.

honor schools. These men have been held to low rank and small responsibility through a long period of years. They probably average forty-five years of age, the upper half of that group, and yet they are still in the grade of captain. They have spent the most active years of their lives in the grade of lieutenant, with a very limited opportunity for expressing their individuality and for the development of initiative and command responsibility. Under existing law, they will face more years of limited responsibility and of increasing embarrassment, as junior officers of advanced years, with contemporaries far beyond them in positions of dignity in the Army. That group from 1920 to 1930 represents a definite period of leadership in the Army. If we chain them to the company grades until the last moment and then suddenly advance them from obscurity to commanding positions, the result will be harmful in effect. This should be avoided, and this proposal is such a method and apparently the best method that can be devised for avoiding such a situation.

I am most deeply interested in this phase of the matter because it pertains to leadership and command.

*   *   *

The promotion situation has had an unfortunate effect on the morale of the Army for many years, and in certain periods a very serious effect. The difficulties never can be entirely remedied because of the manner of development of our Officer Corps, with its sudden accession of large groups of about the same age. I came in, for example, from civil life in 1901, and was commissioned immediately in the rear of appointees from the ranks of 1901. There was a large increase of the Army on February 2, 1901. I think there were thirty of us appointed from civil life in my arm of the service. Ahead of us were about 150 men appointed from the ranks, all of approximately the same age. Immediately ahead of the men from the ranks were the officers from the volunteers of the Philippine Insurrection and the Spanish-American War. All of us were injected into the Corps of Officers in one lump, at one time. So I found a place at the tail of a "hump"; not of the size of the World War "hump," but still of such a nature that by the process of ordinary retirements I would not have become a captain until I was about fifty-eight years of age; then I would have advanced rapidly through the field grades and reached my colonelcy at sixty-one, I think. As I recall it, I would have been a major eleven months, lieutenant colonel nine months, and colonel some three years. However, the increases of 1911, 1916 and 1920 permitted me to advance more rapidly. But this present "hump" is a tremendously greater obstacle than the one which resulted from the Philippine Insurrection and the Spanish-American War.

I think I was lieutenant colonel for about eleven years. During that period I was legally ineligible for promotion to brigadier general, and all the time I was growing older, until I came very nearly being barred by age from promotion to a generalcy with enough years to serve to be of any advantage to the Army. By sheer luck I reached the grade of colonel in time to get my opportunity. So I am deeply sympathetic with the officers caught in a similar plight, but along with that sympathy is a deeper concern over the question of leadership over the problem of national defense, which must outweigh the rights of the individual.

THE CHAIRMAN: The first thing you are interested in is National Defense, and in order to have that you must have efficiency in the Army?

GENERAL MARSHALL: Yes, sir.

THE CHAIRMAN: Now, we are spending several billion dollars in National Defense, and if we provide for mechanization of the Army and for 45,000-ton battleships, and leave the personnel stagnated, it would become a serious problem, would it not?

GENERAL MARSHALL: Yes, sir. Leadership is the most important consideration, if any one thing is more important than another. . .

*   *   *

10
We Are Not Trying to Aggrandize the Army

Statement before the Senate Committee on Appropriations, for Consideration of HR 9209, a Bill Making Appropriations for the Military Establishment for the Fiscal Year Ending June 30, 1941, 76th Congress, 3d Session, April 30 and May 1, 1940

There is not the slightest thought in any of our minds of trying to utilize this emergency to aggrandize the Army, or of making exorbitant demands, to put something over, as it were, under pressure of the situation.

GENERAL MARSHALL: In discussing War Department objectives before the House Appropriations Committee in February of this year, I stated in part:

As to the existing crisis abroad, we must face the facts. Any major developments there should be paralleled by added precautions in this country. If the situation grows more desperate, we should add to the numbers of seasoned troops in the Regular Army and to the strength of the National Guard. If Europe blazes in the late spring or summer, we must put our house in order before the sparks reach the Western Hemisphere. These should be but temporary measures, but they should be taken definitely, step by step, to prepare ourselves against the possibility of chaotic world conditions.

To put it in another way, I am opposed to plunging into a sudden expansion of personnel to the limit of present authorizations, and I am equally opposed to the policy of waiting until the last moment and then attempting the impossible, from the viewpoint of the dominating time factor. For the ground forces matériel presents the most serious problem, since from one or two years are required for its procurement. Therefore, it should be provided as early as practicable.

That statement was made two months ago. Since that time Europe has blazed. The war has spread into Denmark and Norway. Realizing the increasing gravity of the situation the President has submitted, for the consideration of the Senate, supplemental estimates for critical items of equipment totaling $18,000,000. This sum, together with the $14,-

250,000 added by the House and the amounts already in the President's Budget, will complete with some exceptions the initial equipment for existing units of the Regular Army and the National Guard, thus approaching closely to the immediate objective of the War Department. The world situation will not permit us to delay any longer in equipping our existing forces. It is imperative that the sums for critical items be provided. It is a matter of serious concern to realize that even after the money becomes available it will take from one to two years to obtain delivery on this critical equipment.

I hope you will agree with me when I say that further reductions in this bill will seriously endanger the National Defense and at a moment when the problem of National Defense seems of first importance to all neutral nations. However, the War Department appreciates the situation facing the Congress and is prepared to accept many of the reductions made by the House. Imperative requirements, however, make necesary the restoration to the bill of certain projects and certain related amounts.

I mention these things because, as I stated before the House Sub-Committee on Appropriations, that after the requirements for matériel, the next priority of the War Department is a minimum of fifteen thousand more men—not a permanent increase to the Regular establishment to be maintained in the piping times of peace (if there is to be such a millennium) but to furnish certain trained and seasoned units in this present emergency. My own thought is that as the situation grows more critical abroad we ought, step by step—not in a single plunge to repeat those past mistakes in our history where we have gotten indigestion from trying to do everything at once at the last moment—but step by step, to do those things which will put us in a little stronger position; to do those things which are most important to be done, so that the military advisors of other governments will recognize our immediate strength and grow cautious accordingly.

SENATOR ELBERT D. THOMAS OF UTAH: Have conditions changed throughout the world, substantially, since the House acted on this bill?

GENERAL MARSHALL: They have changed, I think, materially, sir, and they appear to be growing more critical each day. They make it appear more necessary to fill out our deficiencies in tactical units without delay.

I would like to add one more expression to this statement, and I say this in all sincerity. I do not believe there is a group of people in the United States who are more unanimous in their earnest desire to avoid involvement in this ghastly war than the officers of the War Department. There is not the slightest thought in any of our minds of trying to utilize this emergency to aggrandize the Army, or of making exorbitant demands to put something over, as it were, under the pressure of the situation. We occupy most of our time trying to find some more economical method for improving the National Defense, and the unanimous opinion of the officers I have talked with and come in contact with in the War Department is that we must do everything possible to make it that much more certain that we will not be drawn into this world tragedy.

*   *   *

11

Civil Aviation and the Defense Program

A Talk before the National Aviation Forum,
Washington, D. C., May 27, 1940

~~~~~~

*We should only promise what we can reasonably
expect to achieve.*

I FEEL that it is important that the Chief of Staff should put in an appearance this morning before the National Aviation Forum, to express the appreciation of the Army for the fine coöperation received from all branches of civil aviation, and more especially to make acknowledgment of the tremendous importance of civil aviation to the Army Air Corps.

The President himself has stated that "civil aviation is recognized as the back-log of National Defense in the Civil Aeronautics Act." We have established the principle that the country's welfare in time of peace and its safety in time of war depends to an important extent upon the existence of a highly organized aircraft industry for the production of the planes, and a well established system for their operation for commercial transportation. For almost twelve months we have had under way a tremendous expansion of our Army Air Corps, and I think it is appropriate this morning to mention the unexpected success which has met our first experiment in making direct use of civil aviation schools for the training of Army pilots. Now we are about to enlarge tremendously on this logical procedure, which both stimulates civil aviation and facilitates the development of the Army Air Corps.

Under the direct leadership of the President, our aviation industry expanded last year through the process of greatly increasing the Army air forces. Today he leads in another step of preparation pointing to the further expansion of our productive capacity for military planes. The wisdom of his initial step last year is now clearly apparent to all. Foreign orders for planes have further improved our productive capacity, so it is now possible to make a further stride towards the production of fifty thousand planes a year. At the same time we must consider many other industries which must be expanded to meet requirements in production of items of armament in which we are even more seriously deficient.

During the past week we have all heard a great deal about the training of thousands of pilots, and of the other activities which are believed necessary to further fortify the national defense. I cannot undertake a discussion of the various phases of these matters this morning, but I would like to make few general comments.

The history of our difficulties of the last World War in developing power provides several pointed lessons for our guidance today, and I believe the most important of these relates to the American tendency, under the emotional strain of a great emergency, to assume that vast projects can be completed on a basis of enthusiasm without regard to the practical realities of the problem. In 1917 there was an immediate appropriation of $640,000,000 for the development of air power. So far so good. But there immediately followed a campaign of publicity, probably to reassure or to impress the public, that led the people and the Congress to expect stupendous results in short order. This procedure led inevitably to a tragic disillusionment when the planes and trained pilots failed to materialize in a few months, or even by the end of the first year.

Investigations followed, violent attacks were made on various individuals, some of whom were discredited. The impossible had been promised and the public remained ignorant of the difficulties to be overcome. The country did not realize then, as I think it does not realize today, the long time required under the most efficient procedure, first to initiate a production program and then to arrive at the hour of mass production; the time necessary to train the personnel and to transport the equipment and that personnel to the field of action.

As I recall, America at that time was asked to manufacture in one year, more airplane engines than the entire British output in the fifty-one months of their participation in the World War. We were asked to build more aircraft than the Allies turned out during the entire war. When the smoke of the battle died away almost as much time was occupied in explaining why the planes were not forthcoming for our army in France as had been devoted to the manufacturing effort in this country.

We must approach this present situation in a state of calm determination not to be foiled by the emotions of the moment, or any of the multitude of difficulties which are certain to be involved in a tremendous and sudden expansion.

My thought is that we should promise only what we can reasonably expect to achieve. The impulse of patriotic America is a wonderful thing, but its impatience to overcome the deficiencies of past neglects can be a destructive force. The present situation, whatever the cause, is a matter of fact which cannot be altered by argument. Today all of us must cooperate, must think of ourselves as a team in a united effort to produce the most practical result in the shortest possible time.

12
V.M.I.: Its Traditions and Heritage

An Address at the Commencement Exercises of the Virginia
Military Institute, Lexington, Virginia, June 12, 1940

∼∼∼∼∼∼∼∼∼∼∼∼∼∼∼∼∼∼∼∼∼∼∼∼∼∼∼

*I spoke of this day as being one of high emotions. It is your
graduation day, but it may also be one of the most fearful in
the history of the world. No man can predict the outcome of
the tragic struggle in Europe. . . We are planning and
preparing in every possible way to put this country in such a
state of preparation that we may be spared the agony of war.*

I FEEL that I should preface my talk this morning with an apology
for my complete lack of preparation. The fact of the matter is
there has been no time available to me for anything beyond the
duties of the day. Some months ago when General Kilbourne[10] honored
me with the invitation for this morning, I had thought that the next
week or a week later I would find a moment to sit down and think
over what I might say this morning. But that moment has continued to be of the next week. The week at hand has been filled to
bursting with duties, and those overshadowed by a steadily developing
problem of such vast proportions and tragic possibilities, that I arrive
this morning utterly unprepared to do more than talk to you in a most
informal manner.

This is a day of high emotions to you men of the graduating class; it
is the culmination of your period of preparation for life. You step off this
morning on your own, to make your way in the world. To your parents
this is a morning of profound pride and satisfaction, far beyond any such
previous reactions. Maybe to some of them it is the moment for a sigh
of profound relief. The hazards of youth have not sunk your ship. You
are across the bar and safely started on your way.

To me, for the moment, this morning recaptures my day of graduation.
I think I can clearly recall my thoughts and plans. They were very
personal, of course. I was struggling for an appointment in the Army, to
get into the campaign then in progress in the Philippines; and I was
intent on getting married. I am not quite clear as to whether or not the
Army career was incidental to the marriage problem, a necessary corollary

---

[10]Major General Charles E. Kilbourne, U. S. Army, Retired; Superintendent, Virginia
Military Institute.

with its impressive salary of the $116.67 a month of those days. But beyond those two compelling desires I apparently was indifferent to all other important issues of life. The point is that about six months later I did succeed in securing a commission in the Army, I did manage to marry and I was on my way to the closing phase of the Philippine Insurrection.

I have been attempting to recall this morning just when I first became conscious of the direct influence of my cadet days on my career. In dealwith the men of my first company I did have the super-confidence of a recent cadet officer. I knew my drill, though I was a little vague about matters pertaining to the cooks and kitchen police. The sword I carried at ordinary company formations was the same sword I had carried as a cadet officer, but the Colt revolver on my hip as we filed along in the narrow mountain trails provided an entirely new reaction. It was very reassuring. I think though that there came to me gradually, day by day, in my contact with the other officers, all senior to me, especially with those who showed the debilitating or sometimes demoralizing effect of several years of tropical campaigning an appreciation of what the VMI had given me through its traditions, by its standards of conduct and of responsibility. At retreat formation in some isolated company garrison in the Philippines, I would find my thoughts going back to evening parade with the background of the Brushy Hills and the sunset over House Mountain. These would revive in me the thought of what the Corps, what the Institute expected of a cadet officer in the performance of his duty; also the influence of the reveille ceremony of Newmarket Day had its effect on my course of action. This institution gave me not only a standard for my daily conduct among men, but it endowed me with a military heritage of honor and self-sacrifice.

I spoke of this day as being one of high emotions. It is your graduation day, but it may also be one of the most fearful in the history of the world.[11] No man can predict the outcome of the tragic struggle in Europe. No American can foresee the eventual effect on the Americas. The world we have known may be revolutionized; the peaceful liberty we have accepted so casually may be a hazard in this ghastly game abroad.

All of us hope with all our hearts that you young men may be free to go ahead with the civil pursuits for which you have been in training. All of us hope for a continuation of our blessings on this continent. But no one knows just what the outcome may be. Those of us specifically charged with the duty of safeguarding our defenses are fully aware of the

[11]The date of this talk is June 12, 1940. On this date the German Army entered Paris. Italy had declared war on France on June 10.

vast responsibility implied. We are planning and preparing in every way possible under our law to put this country in such a state of preparation that we may be spared the agony of war. All of us, all of you, I am sure, realize that the day of drum-and-bugle armies is over. And we are determined that if it should become necessary for us to use a club to defend our democracy and our interests in the Western Hemisphere, that it shall be a club of hard wood, and not of rubber hose.

To you men of the graduating class, I would say that though the primary purpose of your training here has been to prepare you for peaceful pursuits, the supplementary course of military instruction you have received makes each of you a source of reassurance to the War Department. You differ from the ordinary graduate in that you are not only trained to serve yourself in civil life and to contribute your services as a citizen to the local community in which you may live, but at the same time you have been specially prepared to serve your country with efficiency as a soldier, as a leader to safeguard the interests of our citizens. In normal times this special education is accepted without comment or thought by the public—rather with indifference, but today by virtue of that training you individually have become of great interest to the public as a very valuable asset to the defensive system of the United States. We can only hope that you will be free to go your way peacefully, and happily. But you are prepared, and that is saying a great deal these days. Good luck to you and God bless you!

13
Building An Army

An Address at the Encampment Banquet of the Veterans
of Foreign Wars, Akron, Ohio, June 19, 1940

〰〰〰〰〰〰〰〰〰〰〰〰〰〰〰〰〰〰〰〰〰〰〰

*The successful army of today is composed of specialists,
thoroughly trained in every detail of military science,
and above all, organized into a perfect team. Today, it is
imperative that cold factual analysis prevail over enthusiastic outbursts. Sentiment must submit to common sense.*

IN talking to veterans I feel free to go straight to the point in discussing the problems of national defense. You men understand the
meaning, the requirements of war, and I feel that you will readily
comprehend the point of view of the War Department.

Today, the United States faces probably the most critical period in its
history. Within the year we have seen the map of the Old World radic-
ally altered in a succession of startling moves. We have seen political
faiths and forms of governments common to our age, placed in jeopardy
or exterminated. Commonly accepted military technique and methods
in the art of war have been consigned to the ash heap. And finally we
here in distant America find ourselves facing the imminent possibility
of being suddenly required to defend the independence of the Western
Hemisphere.

Those of us who are charged with the responsibility for preparing our
defenses are fully aware of the seriousness of the situation and the difficulties of the task. We realize that the soundness of our decisions have
suddenly become of immense importance to the people in this country.
In every way, in every possible manner, we are endeavoring to resolve
our plans in the light of what has occurred, but most of all, on a basis
of sound common sense.

In common with other democracies, the United States has always
been lax in matters of national preparedness, during periods of peace.
Such a policy inevitably results in a convulsive, expensive expansion in
an emergency. Following the World War, efforts to have the condition of
our National Defense abreast of possible developments in the international situation were invariably halted by the steady resistance of
public opinion. The period of boom markets, of the great industrial expansion gave no help to the National Defense. In fact those were par-

[57]

simonious years for the Army. Last week in looking over some old papers I found this paragraph in a letter from General Pershing, addressed to me in China in December 1924, "I find on my return here that the War Department seems to be up against the real thing. The Budget Officer insists on reducing our estimates so that we shall not be able to have over 110,000 men. Just what this means I cannot understand. I do not know what is going to be done about it, but to my mind it is very discouraging."

The blame for this state of affairs cannot be laid to any one individual or political party. It is the result of our form of government, or our sense of security behind what have seemed to be great ocean barriers.

Last February, I stated before a Congressional committee that if Europe blazed in the late spring or summer we should put our house in order before the sparks reached this hemisphere. I also stated that we should proceed step by step abreast of each major development of the crisis abroad. Though this was but a few months ago, yet I was criticized in editorials for expressing such a view. Later, the cut of the War Department appropriation down to fifty-seven planes received considerable public approval. Less than three months later, when the situation abroad burst into a general conflagration, public opinion swung so rapidly in the other direction that I was being criticized for daring to mention so small a number as ten thousand planes. These, incidentally, were for immediate procurement, before Congress would again be in session. Today the American people want the nation to be prepared. They want a large army, fully equipped with the latest vehicles and weapons; and they want this transformation to be accomplished immediately.

Now you veterans know that an army—a large army—can not be recruited, equipped, and trained overnight. It is a long and tedious process, especially as to matériel. The present situation has two aspects, the problem of immediate measures for our security, and the long-range planning for a year or two years hence. Most of the millions of recent Presidential messages and appropriations will bear no fruit for at least a year, and for the majority of items, a year and a half to two years.

Our people must realize that the flag-waving days of warfare are gone. The successful army of today is composed of specialists, thoroughly trained in every detail of military science, and above all, organized into a perfect team. Today, it is imperative that cold factual analysis prevail over enthusiastic emotional outbursts. Sentiment must submit to common sense.

The War Department has long prepared for possible expansions of the Army and has definite plans for a step-by-step coördinated increase. We have started on our way, and are endeavoring to proceed in an orderly manner. Let me strongly emphasize the fact that we must not become involved, by impatience or ignorance in an ill-considered, overnight expansion, which would smother well considered methods and leave us in a dilemma of confused results, half-baked and fatally unbalanced.

If I may leave a message with you, let it be this: The War Department knows what is needed, the American people know that they want preparedness; and the time for endless debate and other differences of opinion is past. We must get down to hard pan and carry out our preparations without vacillations or confusion.

My visit with you, however short, has been a very pleasant interlude in the heavy press of business in Washington. Your very able and genuinely patriotic representative at the National Capital, Congressman Harter, and I must fly back to Washington without delay. I admire your organization for what it stands for, and express my sincere appreciation for the courtesies and kindness you have shown me this evening. If the quarter of a million members of the Veterans of Foreign Wars do nothing more than to promote unity of thought and action in our military preparations, they will have served their country well.

14
Why Selective Service

Statement before the Senate Committee on Military Affairs, on Consideration of S. 4164, a Bill to Protect the Integrity and Institutions of the United States, Through a System of Selective Compulsory Military Training and Service, 76th Congress, 3d Session, July 12, 1940

~~~~~~

We must bring our units and those we are now in the process of organizing, up to a full strength as quickly as we possibly can.

GENERAL MARSHALL: Mr. Chairman [Senator Morris Sheppard of Texas], in relation to this bill that is now before your committee, I would like to say by way of beginning, that the War Department is strongly of the opinion that some such bill is necessary, and particularly at the present time; that the bill now under consideration, which is put forward by the Training Camps Association, is in general accord with the War Department's ideas as to selective service and training; that it can be accommodated to the several more or less minor points that we think should be adjusted by the process of amendment, and that it has in general included the language which has already been the subject of court decisions as to the interpretation and authority under which we might work.

I would like to elaborate a little on the point of view of the War Department in relation to the present situation, and that toward the future.

We are of the opinion, and I am personally strongly of the opinion, that some such measure is immediately necessary. I say opinion, but I might express it more strongly than that. We have the funds and the authority for certain increases of the Regular establishment, which we are now in the process of procuring by way of ordinary enlistment, which will carry us up to a Regular establishment of 375,000 men. The experience of the past has been that there is a very definite limit to how far you can go by way of voluntary enlistments in time of peace, and, naturally, a definite limit beyond which you probably could not go in time of war on the basis of volunteer enlistment.

That experience would indicate that we probably will be able to obtain the 375,000 for which we now have the funds, though there is a certain degree of doubt as to that; but there is no doubt whatever that we will be procuring them at much too slow a rate, in view of the present international situation, as the War Department estimates it.

We are of the opinion—I personally am strongly of the opinion—that we must bring our units, and those that we are now in the process of organizing, up to a full strength as quickly as we possibly can. •

Exactly the same thought applies to the National Guard in the situation today. I do not believe it is possible on any other basis than by some form of selective service to secure the necessary men. Personally, I do not think there is a better, more democratic method for doing it than by some such measure as is now before your committee.

As we see it in the War Department, there are two aspects of this matter: One is the immediate situation of the next six months, and the other is what we should do over a period of years, all of which is, of course, a matter of public policy of the first importance.

Now, as Chief of Staff, with the responsibilities of that position, I feel that the first issue is the dominant one at the present moment, and that with the minimum loss of time we should come to the definite decision as to what is to be done.

As I have said, I do not think we can obtain the necessary men on a voluntary basis beyond those provided under the present appropriations or authorizations, and I feel that we must have more men, and quickly. We must carry our Regular Army organizations now up to full strength, and we must immediately bring the National Guard up to its full peace strength, and then as rapidly as possible to full war strength.

That is the opinion of the War Department. That is also my own personal opinion.

Turning to this particular bill, there are certain propositions in it that we think might well be changed; but those can be discussed in detail by the head of the personnel procurement division of the General Staff, General Shedd, and by the officer at the head of the organization branch of the General Staff, General Andrews,[12] formerly commander of the GHQ Air Force.

I would like again to state that I think this question should be considered very definitely on the basis of the present international situation, and then as a continuation into the future, on probably a somewhat different basis.

I might say that if such a measure is accepted by the Congress, the practical proposition of putting it into effect requires one of two things. Either we must mobilize the National Guard for the purpose of training these men in its ranks, and also in the ranks of the Regular Army units,

---

[12]Major General (later Lieutenant General) Frank M. Andrews, Assistant Chief of Staff, G-3, War Department General Staff.

where we must have more men as quickly as possible, or we will have to emasculate the Regular Army and emasculate the National Guard, at this time, in order to provide the necessary training cadres to handle the new men in the manner that would be desirable. In other words, the training of young men in large training camps on the basis of compulsory training is something that we cannot manage at the present time. We do not have the trained officers and men—the instructors—to spare; also, we do not have the necessary material. We lack the special training set-up at the moment, and we cannot afford to create it. Therefore, we would have to make the first step within the ranks of the Regular establishment, and within the ranks of the National Guard.

That is the practical proposition, and I think there is no escape from that, if such training is to be managed at the present time. We would not dare emasculate existing units in order to provide the personnel to conduct the training, as we would wish to do later on as the system develops.

I do not know whether I have made myself clear, but I will be very glad to answer any questions to the best of my ability.

SENATOR SHERIDAN DOWNEY OF CALIFORNIA: General Marshall, I must admit that I did not quite get the purport of that last statement by you, that you thought that the conditions required the training of this body of men and the National Guard, in the Regular Army. I did not quite understand that.

GENERAL MARSHALL: I meant by that, sir, that if such a bill were passed at the present time we would have to do one of two things, as a practical proposition.

SENATOR DOWNEY: Yes.

GENERAL MARSHALL: We would either have to place these men with the units of the Regular Army—in other words, recruit those units up to full strength, and in the ranks of the National Guard, to carry these units also up to full strength. The new men could thus be trained within those organizations, utilizing their equipment, and their officers and men as instructors.

We would have to do that or we would have to emasculate to a great extent the National Guard and the Regular establishment in order to provide the necessary training cadres to carry out training. A year later the procedure could be different, but today we would not dare, in my opinion, to emasculate the existing organization of either the Regular Army or the National Guard. It would be a dangerous business.

SENATOR EDWARD R. BURKE OF NEBRASKA: There are no unusual difficulties in handling the matter along that line, along the line of the first alternative that you suggest?

GENERAL MARSHALL: No, sir; that is not only a very simple way of doing it, but at the same time it does what I think we urgently need to do at the present time, fill up the ranks of the organizations.

SENATOR BURKE: Is it contemplated that some change would have to be made in the bill as now before the committee to make it definite?

GENERAL MARSHALL: I am not sure the bill as written at the present time would permit that procedure. There probably would be few changes necessary but I want to avoid going into details. One detail concerns the question of pay.

We feel that to pay one of these men five dollars a month, and have him serve in the same company with a man who is being paid twenty-one dollars a month would be destructive of morale. The new man would be an organic part of that unit and we would be trying to make that an effective unit as quickly as possible. . .

SENATOR DOWNEY: I might say this, General. It has been my opinion that we have sadly neglected the Army as to pay.

GENERAL MARSHALL: I am very happy to hear you say that.

SENATOR DOWNEY: And I also have this idea, and this is the point that I am attempting to develop, that this Nation has very terrifically underpaid both its Regular officers and likewise its enlisted men, and the point that I am attempting to make is this: Now, I do start, General, with the idea all things being equal, the man who voluntarily enlists in the Army is a better soldier than the man who is conscripted, other things being equal. I know I would be, personally, and I believe most men would be.

Now, what I am wondering is if in justice and fairness to the men in the Regular Army, we would not be the gainer if we would increase the compensation paid the private soldier, or increase the benefits that he may indirectly derive and thereby tend to build up voluntary enlistments.

GENERAL MARSHALL: I am very glad to hear you say that. So far as the problem of pay rates is concerned, I would say this. For the first enlistment, for the private at the bottom of the scale, I believe that, considering the other things he receives from the Government, the present pay rate is approximately correct; but I think that after that it is not. There are too few privates first class and higher ratings. There should be increases considerably above what we have at the present time.

We are in a very complicated situation in this matter. We must have highly skilled mechanics in the Air Corps—even more highly skilled than in the mechanized forces. If the engine fails in a tank, that is an inconvenience, but if the engine fails in a plane, that may be a tragedy, and in time of peace, a far greater tragedy than in time of war when we accept tragedies as being inevitable.

So there can be no question at all that we must have a very skillful mechanical force for the servicing of planes and for the operation of the planes. You might take this as an example: We build one of these large bombers. They cost around four hundred thousand dollars. What is the purpose of the bomber? It is to bomb. And, how is the bombing managed? It is carried out by a chap, called a bombardier, who uses the bomb sight, about which so much has been written. That is a skillful technical matter. The effectiveness of the four hundred thousand dollar plane depends upon the advantages gained by successful bombing and the lives of everybody in the plane are involved in that operation, and yet one man, an enlisted man, is primarily concerned in carrying out that procedure. We must have a great degree of skill there. We must be able to hold men so trained. If you are in actual war, then you can get almost any quality of men you want in the United States Army. The trouble is we do not have time to prepare them for the things they have to do.

The great tragedy in France during the World War was, as I saw it —and it happened to be my opportunity to see twenty-seven divisions on the battlefield engaged in different types of fighting—the great tragedy was the wastage of the tremendous potential advantage we had in quality of our personnel, because of the very limited opportunity the men had to prepare themselves for what they were trying to do. No one has ever really told the full truth of what might have been, and what actually was; and the fault was that of a nation in not giving these men a fair chance to prepare themselves.

Now, we know that everything must be done at tremendous speed, and that requires that much more skill. If we train for that skill in time of peace, we have to have ratings that encourage men to come in. I have been talking of technical, mechanical skill, yet skill in leadership, which usually has a determining effect on the battlefield, does not receive the pay ratings it deserves.

If we have an act such as this, I think it will do two things. In the first place it would establish the Army on a democratic basis, which I believe would produce a degree of solidarity among our people as to the Army, which would be of great advantage to the Army.

It also would permit us in time of peace to maintain a sufficient military force to secure our position without so much of confused discussion as at the present time, and without the necessity for colossal expenditures, because to maintain large groups of personnel in the military service is an expensive process, and, of course, the inevitable reaction after the period of crisis is one of economy and of emasculation.

We saw that, for example, in June 1920, when after exhaustive hearings the National Defense Act finally was enacted into law providing for 280,000 men and recruiting was started toward that number, another reaction immediately developed. There had been a realization of the vital necessity of proper defense preparations. Then came the reaction for economy and within, I think, nine months, the cutting started, and the Army dropped to 150,000 men. About fourteen months later, as I recall, it was cut down to 125,000 finally to 118,000.

I found a paragraph in a letter from General Pershing the other day when I was looking through some of my papers. He wrote me just after his return from South America. I was in China. He made this comment. He said, "I find on my return to Washington that the War Department is up against it." He said, "The Budget has cut them until they cannot have more than 110,000 soldiers."

He said, "This is a tragic situation and I do not know what is to be done about it. It is very discouraging."

I think that represents the inevitable reaction. I think it will always happen with us.

So if our military establishment is on the basis of high pay, which it must have for the technical men, and particularly for the noncommissioned officers who furnish morale and leadership of our straight combat units, then if there is not some such measure as this to provide most of the men at a much lower cost, the charge will be that the Army costs too much to expect our Government, in its protected situation beyond two oceans, to continue to bear the expense in normal times, and so, the cycle of unpreparedness repeats itself.

*   *   *

15
Expansion of the Air Corps

A Radio Address to the Congress of the National Aero-
nautic Association at Denver, Colorado, delivered over
Columbia Broadcasting System through Station
WJSV, Washington, D. C., July 9, 1940

∼∼∼∼∼∼∼∼∼∼∼∼∼∼∼∼∼∼∼∼∼∼∼∼∼

*If we are to have a mighty air fleet we must have highly
trained men as well as beautifully built machines.*

IN extending long-distance greetings to the Aviation Congress in
Denver, I would like first of all to express the very sincere appreciation of the War Department for the splendid contributions of
civil aviation to the National Defense.

Aircraft manufacturers have been at work constantly improving all
types of airplanes, and, in every instance, I believe, have made these improvements immediately available for our military aircraft.

The facilities of the National Aeronautic Association in experimentation and research have been of tremendous assistance to the Army,
and our fighting planes are equipped with the developments which have
originated in its laboratories. The practical experience of the commercial
air transportation companies has been of great assistance in the design
and operation of military aircraft. For this generous coöperation of all
branches of the aviation industry, the Army Air Corps and the War
Department are extremely grateful.

As you know, the Army is now engaged in a tremendous expansion
of the Air Corps. We cannot reach our goal overnight. It takes more
than a firm resolve and the passage of an appropriation act to build,
arm and operate thousands of planes. Months necessarily must intervene
between the blueprint and the first flight of a new type. The progress
made thus far has been rapid, and the rate of manufacture is steadily increasing. Yet at the same time we have been able to alter designs of planes
on order to include the latest developments resulting from the tremendous conflict in Europe. We are, I believe, securing mass production
of airplanes without freezing progress. Quality has not been sacrificed to
secure quantity. A reasonable balance has been struck in this important
matter. Our expanding industry has made it possible to accelerate production beyond the rate originally thought possible. The production program is based on sound common sense, and I am told that it has had the
enthusiastic support of manufacturers.

If we are to have a mighty air fleet we must have the highly trained men as well as the beautifully built machines. Pilots, mechanics and navigators cannot be improvised, and the efficiency of our air defense will be largely dependent on the quality of the personnel.

The crews to operate and service our new air fleet must be trained in advance of the delivery of the airplanes. With this in view, we have launched our initial training program to provide us with 7,500 new military pilots each year, and for this purpose we have secured the aid of a number of civilian flying schools. The preliminary training of our cadets is being given at these schools and the students prepared for the basic, advanced, and specialized military training at Army schools, like Randolph and Kelly fields in Texas.

At the same time there is being created a large reservoir of potential military pilots and mechanics through the training programs of the Civil Aeronautics Administration and other government and private agencies.

Every branch of the Army is being strengthened. We have embarked on a comprehensive program of rearmament. Private factories and government plants are now engaged in producing equipment that will provide for an army of one million men. At the same time, steps are being initiated to provide productive capacity in the United States to insure the prompt equipment of as many additional soldiers as may be called to the colors in a major emergency.

In all these preparations for the National Defense, it is reassuring and tremendously heartening to feel that we have the eager, enthusiastic assistance of millions of American citizens in every walk of life who are freely volunteering their services and who evidently stand ready to do all in their power to defend our interests. With such support success is assured.

16.
Wastage and War

Statements Before the House of Representatives Subcommittee, Committee on Appropriations, on Consideration of a Second Supplemental Appropriation Bill for 1941, 76th Congress, 3d Session, July 24, 1940

War is wasteful of life, but even more wasteful of matériel.

GENERAL MARSHALL: . . . I have already stated for the record that every part of this appropriation is essential at the present time. I would like to say this in reply to the question that was asked the Secretary regarding trusteeship, not that I am more than a minor trustee. However, I do have a responsibility, and I will probably be the principal trustee when it comes to the period of criticism. I have been very much impressed during my short period as Chief of Staff with the fact that the plans that have been developed in the War Department during the past twenty years, and particularly during the past three years, have been so sound. They have been laid out with such broad vision, that, in general, we have merely had to modify them in the light of recent events. Basically, they were sound. The proposal now before your committee is merely a further step in the execution of those same plans. You have heard us talk up here in the past about the Initial Protective Force. Today we have gone beyond that in matériel and equipment. We have now reached the point of asking you for the matériel, and, particularly, for production facilities sufficient to enable us to maintain a force of two million men in the field. In that original May 16 message, for example, you were asked to provide in critical items the initial equipment, plus a fifteen-per-cent reserve, for the Protective Whittington Plan force of one million two hundred thousand men. By initial equipment, I mean that if you take the various weapons required in a company, and then multiply that number by the number of companies in the force you get the grand total, to which we initially added fifteen per cent for a minimum reserve. That gives us the proposition we were talking about originally. Now, we are going beyond that basis, and under this proposal, we propose the additional matériel needed to maintain troops in the field. I think I should explain the exact meaning of "maintain." The first equipment provided a soldier, such as clothes, gas masks, as well as rifle and machine gun, unfortunately, does not last for a long time.

In other words, the wastage, aside from captures, is tremendous. In my own division, just after the great German offensive of March 1918, there were seventy-two guns in the artillery brigade, and they were firing continuously during the five weeks of action. My recollection is that the rate of fire exploded a gun almost every day. If you multiply the guns disabled by explosions alone by the number of days in action, you will see how the original number of seventy-two grew smaller. There must be a reserve to replace such losses immediately. That was an exceptional experience, but there is always a great wastage concerned with military action. Consider a division of twenty-five thousand men, of the type we had in France. Each month it had to be issued about fourteen thousand new uniforms or suits of clothes complete, with underclothing, shirts, trousers, and so forth. In the case of shoes a little more than that was required or about sixteen thousand pairs a month for the division. Those statistics are accurate. In other words there must be a reserve. Initial equipment is just a beginning. It may take months to procure an item, but lack of it is difficult to explain satisfactorily to soldiers or to the American people. There must be on hand enough reserves to insure continuous supply until production is up to the necessities or demands. I have a note of a division during the Meuse-Argonne that entered the action on the 26th of September and came out on October 2. The report of the inspector general showed that the divisions needed practically an entire reissue of clothing. That was one division. It was not unusual for a division on coming out of action to requisition for from three thousand to five thousand sets of personal equipment, messkits, canteens, gas masks, clothing, and so forth.

I have the record of another division that was in action less than a week, and when it came out it was short 44 machine guns, 504 automatic rifles, one thousand five hundred pistols, and three thousand rifles. Of course, some of that matériel was later recovered. However, it had to be replaced at the time; that is, immediately. We could not satisfy the situation by a lecture on care of equipment or reason for the lack of equipment. Only the actual article would suffice.

I can give you some recent examples of wastage: One of our officers who has just returned from overseas was a personal witness to the landing of German troops from planes at The Hague. The planes landed on highways and in fields of all kinds. The operations offered an excellent illustration of wastage even when matters were running efficiently. The planes came down quickly, one after another, because it was necessary that a sizeable body of men be massed as quickly as possible in order to make good the penetration from the air. In order to avoid any delays, the transport plane would often be ditched right off the road to make way for the next plane. The next plane would disgorge its component, and would be similarly ditched. In many instances these planes were badly damaged. It was more important to land men quickly than to conserve the life of the planes. The officer explained that a large number of planes were deliberately crashed or ditched. There was no time to get them out of the way of the succession of planes that were following, except by this destructive method.

Mr. Louis L. Ludlow of Indiana: Did they try to salvage them at all?

General Marshall: I presume an effort was made later on. The object was to get the men on the ground quickly, and the saving of the planes was a matter of secondary importance. War is wasteful of life, but even more wasteful of matériel.

*　　　*　　　*

17

The National Guard and the Crisis

Statements before the Senate Committee on Military Affairs, on Consideration of SJ Res 286, to Strengthen the Common Defense and to Authorize the President to Order Members and Units of Reserve Components and Retired Personnel of the Regular Army into Active Military Service, 76th Congress, 3d Session, July 30, 1940

I don't think we can afford in any degree at the present time to speculate with the security of this country.

GENERAL MARSHALL: Mr. Chairman [Senator Morris Sheppard of Texas], Gentlemen: For some time it has been the feeling of the War Department that it was urgently necessary that at least a portion of the National Guard be ordered to active duty and recruited up to full strength and seasoned and trained as rapidly as possible.

That is the basis for this particular proposal.

It is our opinion that it is urgently necessary that this be proceeded about as quickly as possible, that we are deficient in organized units trained in a sufficient strength for the necessary defensive measures that we might have to take.

From the viewpoint of the War Department it is very urgent that we be permitted to proceed about the business of developing and training the military forces capable and adequate for the defense of this country in the present emergency along in an orderly and businesslike fashion.

We must know what tools we have to work with. Paper plans will not suffice in the present situation. We must be able, in my opinion, to proceed in a businesslike way to make the necessary preparations; for example, as matters stand at the present moment, the War Department is unable, except in a very limited use of WPA funds, to make any preparation for the shelter of the units that might be called out for training under this measure, and the later in the year with the authorization granted us, the more difficult our situation becomes, because from the viewpoint of construction, the winter is upon us.

It takes three or four months to prepare adequately for the shelter of men, to protect their health, to facilitate their training, after the money is made available.

[71]

In the present situation we couldn't even proceed on an emergency basis because we can't presume an action of Congress.

We are very much embarrassed as the time is passing, the fall is approaching, the Congress has before it a measure for compulsory service; the ordering of the National Guard on active duty, preliminary to the operation of a compulsory selective service act is an absolute necessity.

Therefore, we are growing increasingly embarrassed with the passing of each day, not to mention what, in our opinion, is the seriousness of the situation.

I would like to say this, as the view of the War Department, and certainly my own personal view of the matter:

Our situation today is utterly different from that of 1917. Twenty-odd years ago I don't think anyone felt in any peril in the United States. We could proceed with deliberation, and we could wait until we built cantonments, we could wait until we trained officers, we could wait until we gathered shipping, until we sent troops to Europe and train them after we got them to Europe.

Now, as we see it today, in our judgment the security, the safety of this country depends on having available trained, seasoned men in adequate numbers, and there is no conceivable way to obtain them except by some such measure as this, followed by some form of selective service.

This is but a base of departure to the development of an adequate force to maintain the security of this country; meaning the Caribbean and the Northern Hemisphere at least.

It is a long procedure before anything approximating the finished result is available.

In the present day the very full reports of what is happening in the world, the radio and the press, men can form, to a large extent, their own judgment as to what the situation is. But I am inclined to think that when it comes to estimating what the requirements are to meet the situation, there we are embarrassed by a lack of appreciation of how long it takes to go through these various acts of preparation.

And I am quite certain all of us understand how strong and urgent and vociferous would be the demand should the dilemma arise.

I might put it this way: I don't think we can afford in any degree at the present time to speculate with the security of this country. And that is my opinion as a professional soldier, as Chief of Staff, that is the opinion of the War Department, that we feel is our duty to make clear to the Congress.

*   *   *

SENATOR EDWIN C. JOHNSON OF COLORADO: Is there any plan of rotation for the National Guard? That is, you give certain units a year's training and then bring out another unit and give them a year's training?

GENERAL MARSHALL: That would depend entirely on the situation in the world. I wouldn't attempt to forecast what would be the situation twelve months from now.

I merely say at the moment I think there is an urgent necessity for the President having authority to order out the National Guard. And in order that we may get four infantry divisions, four antiaircraft divisions, and so on, into active service and training as quickly as possible.

Whatever other additional units we may have to protect depends entirely on the situation, but those units we think should have been in training for some time past, and we want to get them in training as quickly as we can.

SENATOR JOHNSON: Will you have equipment and matériel and instructors for all the members of the National Guard as now constituted?

GENERAL MARSHALL: These units, sir, have had instructors with them during their past time of ordinary training and to what extent we can allow instructors to remain with them I couldn't answer offhand, but we certainly should have supervision of all their training.

SENATOR JOHNSON: It will require more active instructors?

GENERAL MARSHALL: I don't think so. They will start in on their training themselves. We will accord them directors, facilities, supervision, higher command, and all that sort of thing.

SENATOR JOHNSON: Will the National Guard be given training in the new machinery of war, the new methods?

GENERAL MARSHALL: Yes, sir. All the new methods that we understand and are trying to put in effect in the Regular units.

SENATOR JOHNSON: Will they be given the instruction that is given to the Regular enlisted men of the Army?

GENERAL MARSHALL: We want to have them trained as a uniform team in the whole Army.

SENATOR JOHNSON: And they will be an active component member?

GENERAL MARSHALL: Yes, sir. That is what we are trying to do, make this unit an integral part of the Army of the United States.

And I would like to interject at this moment the position I have been placed in here in some hearings before some Senate committees in relation to that.

The proposition was put forward that the Regular Army should be increased to 750,000 men. The desire was to obtain a trained force as quickly as possible.

I opposed that. Apropos of what we have just been speaking about, that meant a departure from our present system of National Defense under the act of June 1920. We couldn't have increased the Regular Army beyond the present force that we are organizing except to recruit those men—except to recruit this force up to full strength without either emasculating the Regular units which we must not dare do at the present time, and certainly emasculating the National Guard, in order to obtain the equipment. It would be a most unwise thing to do.

In any case, we were embarking upon a new policy of National Defense, a new system. I did not think that was the right thing to do.

Also, I thought it was an impractical thing to do, because to create entirely new units without a nucleus is a lengthy procedure with a poor result for a long time, and we must not emasculate the existing units in order to obtain the nuclei for the procedure.

So, for the same reasons, I am—I strongly urge that we be permitted to go ahead in a businesslike, orderly way and go ahead with these units to give the effective result as needed. We have been proceeding, I think, on a very conservative basis. It is a question as the time grows late whether we can continue on that basis.

I think it is very important that we be allowed to do this, that the measure be drawn in such a way that we are not unduly restricted, that we do not find ourselves embarrassed in a way that was not intended or not foreseen by the committee at the time.

Frankly, I think you have got to trust us a little bit.

18
Costs of National Defense

Statements before the Subcommittee, Senate Committee on Appropriations, on Consideration of HR 10263, a Bill Making Supplemental Appropriations for the Fiscal Year Ending June 30, 1941, and for Other Purposes, 76th Congress, 3d Session, August 5 and 6, 1940

My fear is not that I am recommending too much but rather that I may find at some time in the future that I recommended too little.

SENATOR ALVA B. ADAMS OF COLORADO: We are taking up HR 10263, a bill making supplemental appropriations for National Defense, 1941. General Marshall, I suppose you are the one we are to look to first for information.

GENERAL MARSHALL: If agreeable to you, sir.

SENATOR ADAMS: I am just speaking for myself, and absolving the other members of the committee from such ideas, I want to say this: I am hoping that you and your associates will clear up an idea that has bothered me. I say, as to these other gentlemen, I am not in any way intimating that they are imbued with these ideas; but after having had very, very large appropriations for defense purposes in accordance with the requests that have come to us in preceding bills, my feeling, as I look over this bill, is that in the zealous desire to make adequate defense preparations, protecting from the hazards of war and invasion, perhaps we are getting a little careless in matters of protecting against the hazards of financial distress.

Now, that disturbed me, and as I say, I am very uneasy over that. I do not want the appropriations against external disasters to go to the extent that they bring internal disaster, and, of course, that might devolve upon the Army also.

I shall be very happy to be convinced that I am wrong in that idea, that we are not sort of shoveling out money with undue liberality, following our fears a little too closely. Again I say that merely is a suggestion from one individual member of the committee.

So, General Marshall, we will be glad to have you, if you will, give us a general statement as to this situation, such statement as you have in mind as you would like to give to us. I am sure you have such a general statement.

GENERAL MARSHALL: When I appeared before this committee in the middle of June, on the First Supplemental National Defense Act, 1941, following the Military Appropriation Act for 1941, Senator Nye [Gerald P. Nye of North Dakota] asked me this question: "General, does it not come down to the point of daily uncertainty as to what the needs and demands tomorrow are going to be, what your needs are going to be?"

My reply was: "I cannot agree with that, Senator, I think the uncertainty lies in the timing in the determination of the rate at which we should proceed. We know our requirements, and we are aware of our deficiencies."

Senator Nye very logically replied:

"But we do not know today and tomorrow how heavily we have got to push the day after tomorrow."

It is obvious to most of us today, I believe, that the safety and future of this country depends and depends solely on the strength of our system of National Defense. We have not come to Congress with hastily improvised plans and statements of requirements.

Each successive request for funds has been made on the basis of deliberate and successive steps toward the accomplishment of War Department plans which have been in preparation for a number of years. Each successive step has been considered necessary in order to meet each major phase of the constantly growing menace from abroad.

The rapidity of events in Europe has forced us to move with approximately equal rapidity, but in doing so we have adhered to our basic plan, and as yet we see no sound reason for departing from it.

The problem has been one of timing, but that, I must admit, has often been more a question of what we might be permitted to do rather than purely a question of what should be done on the basis of national defense. On the latter basis we should have done a long time ago all that we have recently urged doing.

I am keenly aware of the fact that Congress has been called upon to provide tremendous sums for the National Defense. Each time we appear before you, we cherish the hope that the international situation will so develop that further expenditures will not be required this year.

It is not necessary for me to recite the successive military tragedies of the past two months, nor to comment on the fact that each one has brought the possibility of increased danger in the Western Hemisphere. What will happen in the next few months remains to be determined but it is clearly apparent to me, as I believe it must be to most sober-minded citizens, that we can no longer delay in embarking on complete preparations necessary to the maintenance of our national safety. We cannot afford to speculate regarding the security of this country.

These present estimates are for the specific purpose—except for a two hundred million dollar item for commercial items, such as trucks and clothing—of permitting industry to proceed in developing the necessary productive capacity, to do two things: The first is to provide about eighty per cent of the commercial or essential items of equipment for the protective mobilization plan force of approximately eight hundred thousand men in ground units, plus one hundred thousand in the Air Corps and three hundred thousand replacements. The critical items for this force were provided in the Military Appropriations Act for 1941.

There is the further provision to provide critical (noncommercial) items of equipment for eight hundred thousand men in addition to those I have just mentioned, or a force increased to two million men.

SENATOR NYE: General, is that a second eight hundred thousand men?

GENERAL MARSHALL: Yes, sir; that is an addition to the protective mobilization plan force of 1,200,000 men. Provision is also made for a large number of airplanes in order to build up our air force.

These estimates also provide for the development of productive capacity. That means funds for the actual erection of plants which do not exist in industry, the plants to be leased or operated by civilian industry. We propose to build up facilities for the production of reserve stocks of critical items required to equip and maintain in combat approximately two million men.

I think everybody who reads of what has happened abroad is familiar now with the tremendous wastage of war. Consequently, our estimates now provide not only for initial equipment but also for maintenance on a combat status.

*   *   *

SENATOR ADAMS: General Marshall, you may proceed.

GENERAL MARSHALL: Mr. Chairman, I would like to comment on your opening statement of yesterday. I intended to refer to it yesterday at the close of my statement but the necessity for adjournment prevented it.

I would like to say that I agree very completely with what you said, despite the fact that I am a professional soldier and Chief of Staff of the Army. I think it is tragic that we find ourselves in a situation which requires the spending of these colossal amounts of money for purely a war-making purpose.

I think that it is indeed unfortunate that the so-called enlightened peoples of the world should be engaged in devoting such a large part of their resources to nonproductive, war-making purposes.

The spending of huge sums for National Defense is a most serious business. However, I want to be equally frank in saying that I do not see any other solution at the moment. Written history is full of the records of the destruction of peace-loving, unprepared nations by neighbors who were guided by the policy of force of arms.

We must meet the situation that is facing us, and I see no way of doing that except by preparing. Huge sums of money must be spent, but that spending must be done in the most businesslike manner possible. There must be no undue waste. Hasty and ill-considered expenditures must be avoided.

SENATOR NYE: Of course, General, we can entertain a hope that developments abroad in the next few months will be such that we can abandon a considerable part of this program, can we not?

GENERAL MARSHALL: Senator, I am sorry that I cannot entertain any such hope at present. My fear is not that I am recommending too much but rather that I may find at some time in the future that I recommended too little. In fact, if I could feel now that I might expect some day to face an investigation for having recommended too much, my mind would be more at rest than it is at present.

SENATOR ADAMS: General, you mentioned historical situations. Of course, to my mind, we can go back repeatedly to situations such as France, along about 1789 on down. Now, France has broken down, not by reason of war expenditures, but by reason of careless finances. Of course, the whole period following the Napoleonic wars has been followed by bad financing.

We have been running behind. We have not been keeping within our income for some time. We have in these three Army measures, we are appropriating and authorizing contracts for more than the total income of this government in this year just for the Army.

GENERAL MARSHALL: I realize that.

SENATOR ADAMS: Then we have the Navy, and also we have all of our other governmental functions.

GENERAL MARSHALL: Yes, sir.

SENATOR ADAMS: I am uneasy about the effect it will have on people in all walks of life, Army people, wage earners, pensioners, and all of the others. Sooner or later they are going to be paid in a dollar which is not a good dollar any more. It is the small fellow who is going to pay the penalty, if we do break down. As I say, some of us are very unhappy about it.

SENATOR CARL HAYDEN OF ARIZONA: General, I am very happy to

hear you talk about making these expenditures in a businesslike way. Your mention of Congressional investigations brings to mind that shortly after the close of the World War there was a Congressional investigation and testimony about the enormous number of chain harnesses that were bought and never used, and the vast amount of equipment that was then sold for junk after the war was over. We all remember the testimony of General Dawes[13] when he used the famous phrase "Hell and Maria! We were in a war and we had to win it."

But, I saw myself at that time what appeared to me to be just an utter disregard for money. Expenditures were made just on anybody's order at any time, and there was not any close coördination. Undoubtedly very large sums of money were wasted in the World War. With that experience behind us, of course, you are doing exactly the right thing, trying to put this on a businesslike basis.

GENERAL MARSHALL: I hope we can succeed in keeping expenditures on a businesslike basis.

I think the reason we got into the regrettable situation that you just mentioned, was because with no previous preparation of any kind, we were plunged into war. Such a situation makes extravagance and waste unavoidable. You cannot launch suddenly into a huge program of mobilization and procurement without mistakes, waste. The marvel is that we managed to pass through that ordeal with such clean hands.

Senator Russell [Richard B. Russell of Georgia] asked me a question yesterday in regard to the tank program.

SENATOR RUSSELL: Yes.

GENERAL MARSHALL: And, if you recall my answer was that, though we were being pressed to order tanks immediately, we were making certain that we were ordering the best type, based on performance of the past two months in northern France and Belgium. In other words, we are not suddenly going to order all of the harness in the world with the possibility later of having to discard it. We insist on exercising due caution even in the face of the tremendous impatience which is a result of previous unpreparedness, and which comes from a public whose previous attitude has been one of complete indifference.

SENATOR ADAMS: And it comes partly out of misinformation that the public has gotten as to our status.

SENATOR RUSSELL: Of course, human nature is such that the man who

---

[13]Brigadier General Charles G. Dawes was also Vice President of the United States from 1925 to 1929. During World War I General Dawes was a member of the administrative staff of the Commanding General, AEF, and served as Chairman of the General Purchasing Board, and as General Purchasing Agent of the AEF; and later as a member of the Military Board of Allied Supply and as a member of the Liquidation Commission of the AEF and Liquidation Board of the War Department.

complains the loudest because the program is slow will be the one who will curse the War Department the most vigorously if it turns out that they have spent some money that results show was unnecessary after the emergency is over.

GENERAL MARSHALL: I have been criticized to some extent for a supposed overcaution in connection with the development of our air forces.

The problem is to retain the public's confidence in the War Department and at the same time not to move with a haste that we will later regret.

19

Responsibility and Command

Statements before the Senate Committee on Military Affairs, on Consideration of S. 4207, a Bill Providing Uniformity in Temporary Promotions in the Army of the United States in Time of Emergency, 76th Congress, 3d Session, August 20, 1940

Leadership in the field and especially during the hurried organization of the urgently needed new units must not depend on seniority.

GENERAL MARSHALL: Mr. Chairman [Senator Morris Sheppard of Texas], and Senators, for the first time in its history, this country in time of peace is engaged in serious preparation to insure the national security. Vast sums have been provided by the Congress and still greater sums are being asked toward providing the material requirements of an adequate defense.

There has already been a considerable expansion of the Regular Army, and, if the situation continues to become more menacing, there must naturally follow further expansion of the components of the Army of the United States which will be developed through a period of intensive training to meet whatever may confront it.

The expansion of the Regular Army has been carried out without the necessity of increasing the strength of the permanent commissioned personnel. There are certain requirements for temporary promotions that exist at the present time. They were brought forcibly to my attention during my recent inspection trip of units in the field. As a partial result of this inspection I am of the opinion that the provision of temporary rank appropriate to responsibility and command is one of the most important matters in connection with National Defense now confronting the War Department. Leadership in the field and especially during the hurried organization of the urgently needed new units must not depend on seniority.

As an example of our present situation, the Armored Corps of two divisions is commanded by a brigadier general and seven of our divisions are commanded by brigadier generals. A number of colonels are performing the functions of general officers. This unfortunate situation is not limited to the higher grades. There is a shortage at the present time of officers in the grade of captain. We have available first lieutenants of eight to ten years' experience who are commanding companies and who should hold the temporary and appropriate rank of captain.

We must be able properly to organize and train our armed forces as they are expanded; we must place in important positions of command and staff, officers with the knowledge, initiative, drive, and leadership which will assure maximum success in a crisis; the Army prepared in peace must be able to pass to graver responsibilities without possible danger of dislocation incident to necessary reorganization.

Sound military organization and procedure require that these temporary promotions be made at once in order that those exercising increased responsibilities of command and staff may hold grades commensurate therewith.

Legislation now exists by which temporary promotions can be made in peace or war, under the conditions contemplated in the proposed amendment by administrative action of the President, for Reserve officers, including officers of the National Guard of the United States, ordered to active duty. The granting of temporary rank to officers of the Regular Army is limited in time of war. To make the system uniform, authority should be extended to include the Regular Army in order that all three categories may be subject to the same treatment.

*   *   *

A total of 4,697 captains required, and a total of 2,483 available.

There is another point which is very important in this matter. Time is of vast importance, is really the dominant factor.

It is a well known fact that some men, given a year or two years, will do a beautiful job but they are utterly unable to do it in short order and under many difficulties, with the lack of this and the lack of that.

That situation was notorious, I suppose that is the right word, in the AEF where time meant so much.

It is quite evident right now that we cannot afford to place in a position of great responsibility one of these men who works very slowly and deliberately. We must have somebody that will take one of these units and bring about a result in the most expeditious manner possible.

That means we must select the men to give the necessary direction and vigor to units in the field.

Funds have been appropriated in vast sums and additional sums, largely for matériel, are now being considered by Congress, but the development of the plan to use this matériel is of tremendous importance. We are approaching the time where, if the National Guard bill becomes law, we will have to group divisions in the field into army corps.

This will create more vacancies because of the fact that certain division commanders will have to become corps commanders.

It is of great importance that in a large unit such as the army corps, we have a commander who shows vigorous direction, fine common sense, and management in developing the combat efficiency of the unit. We must not have a collection of uncoördinated units each one trying to do its best but without balance or coördination.

Recently we created under existing Army Regulations a General Headquarters which, normally, has as its first duty the direction of operations.

Training in time of war is a secondary function of such a headquarters but in time of peace that is its major function.

I have selected an officer from among the outstanding officers of the Army, mentally and otherwise, to be the Chief of the Staff of that headquarters, in order to remove supervision of training from the War Department.

SENATOR SHERMAN MINTON OF INDIANA: Who is in command?

GENERAL MARSHALL: General Lesley McNair,[14] the former head of the Command and General Staff School at Fort Leavenworth. He has set up headquarters at the Army War College which is ideal for the purpose. He will develop a system of training along proper lines and will control it on a reasonably uniform basis throughout the United States, he dealing directly with the army commanders. The army commanders must in turn deal with the territorial corps area commanders and with the tactical corps commanders.

SENATOR MINTON: This GHQ they are now setting up is just like the GHQ we had in the war?

GENERAL MARSHALL: Yes. GHQ handled both operations and training. Now the training function is of first importance. And we are getting organized. That is, the training direction and training inspection are of great importance. We are trying to organize them on a normal basis right now. I cannot possibly supervise training nor do I want the General Staff to become involved in the details.

The War Department doesn't command. It isn't organized for that purpose, but it should establish policies and exercise a general supervision.

Now this plan puts the direction of training outside of the War Department.

We are going to require more corps commanders. So my great necessity at the present time, in order to produce positive results in the next

---

[14]Major General Lesley J. McNair; later Lieutenant General and Commanding General, Army Ground Forces.

six months, is freedom to select the best commander. As the matter now stands we not only have many vacancies that have existed for some time but also the additional vacancies due to the new units which have been organized since last September.

*   *   *

20

A New Departure: Training a Citizen Army Against the Possibilities of War

A Radio Broadcast over the Columbia Broadcasting System, from Washington, D. C., through Station WJSV, September 16, 1940

It is the feeling of the War Department that the next six months include the possibility of being the most critical period in the history of the nation. . . And for the first time in our history we are preparing in time of peace against the possibility of war. We are starting to train an army of citizen soldiers which may save us from the tragedy of war.

THIS afternoon President Roosevelt gave the final approval to the act of Congress creating a system of selective service for compulsory military training, a great fundamental stride toward the preparation of this country to defend itself, to protect its form of government and its compelling interests in the Western Hemisphere. This morning some sixty thousand citizen-soldiers of the National Guard left comfortable homes, their families and their jobs to fulfill their patriotic mission as members of the Army of the United States.

Within the next ten days most of these troops will concentrate in divisional camps in New Jersey, South Carolina, Oklahoma, and the State of Washington, to start on a period of intensive military training. Along the east and west coasts of the United States, harbor-defense and other units of the Guard will move into camps and commence their training in the handling of heavy seacoast guns and smaller weapons. Antiaircraft regiments will assemble at special firing centers to commence practical training in this vital service. National Guard air squadrons of observation planes will move to air fields to perfect their coördinated training with other branches of the Army.

I wish to emphasize the importance of these preparations. We are at peace with every nation in the world. Nevertheless it is the feeling of the War Department that the next six months include the possibility of being the most critical period in the history of the nation. Ordinary common sense indicates that our preparations should be made accordingly.

The situation today is utterly different from that of 1917. Then we

[85]

were at war—but we foresaw small possibility of military danger to this country. Today though at peace, such a possibility trembles on the verge of becoming a probability. Then we could proceed with deliberation. We could wait until we built cantonments, until we first trained officers later to train the men, until we were prepared to form a field army. We did not need to worry about arms, equipment and ammunition—our Allies were prepared to supply those necessities.

Today time is at a premium and modern arms and equipment must be provided by our own industries—not by allies. We must be prepared to stand alone. We cannot depend on others for protection during a prolonged period of preparation.

Therefore, the mobilization this morning of the first increment of the National Guard is the first long step in the preparation of an adequate army of citizen-soldiers to man our defenses.

Testifying before a Congressional committee last February, I made the statement that our preparations for defense should be carried out in an orderly, businesslike manner, proceeding step by step, in accordance with the major developments abroad; that if Europe blazed in the late spring or summer, we must put our house in order before the sparks reached the Western Hemisphere. Even so, it must be admitted that I only partially visualized the full extent of the conflagration, and the rapidity with which it was to overwhelm the continent of Europe. Yet, at the time, there was severe criticism of that statement as being unnecessarily alarming.

Today the public and the press are demanding action, immediate and all-inclusive, and there is a general appreciation of the hazards of our situation. But I fear that there is not so clear an understanding of just what is required in order to produce the desired results.

The time-consuming process in manufacturing matériel—planes, guns, tanks, and other munitions—is partially comprehended, though impatience and forebodings are productive of demands for miracles to overcome delays due to past public indifference.

Also I fear that we expect too much of machines. We fail to realize two things: First, that the finest plane or tank or gun in the world is literally worthless without technicians trained as soldiers—hardened, seasoned, and highly disciplined to maintain and operate it; and second, that success in combat depends primarily upon the development of the trained combat team composed of all arms. This battle team is the most difficult, the most complicated of all teams to create, because it must operate on unknown ground, in darkness, as well as in daylight, amidst incredible confusion, danger, hardship, and discouragement. It is a team of many parts, the decisive element of which remains the same little-advertised, hard-bitten infantry soldier with his artillery support.

From a foreign source, a distinguished veteran of the recent fighting, we get this comment: "Wars are still fought by men even though they use elaborate weapons. Troops of all kinds must therefore have physical fitness and toughness that will guarantee their vitality and endurance under prolonged strain."

A German general staff officer is credited with this summary of that army's recent campaign. He states:

"Our success is due to close team work between the air force, armored troops, motorized engineers and infantry. Of course, the infantry must finally hold the ground, but all others help to bring it up. Our methods are simple in the extreme; they are understood by every soldier in the Army. Our foot infantry is the best in the world. Their principal job is marching, and the job of every other arm is to keep them marching forward into enemy land." "We move," he says, "on a broad front with armored divisions and air force. Where the initial resistance is too strong for the armored troops to penetrate, it is broken by dive bombers and additional artillery. The way must be cleared for the infantry with whom the final decision lies. This requires perfect communication and coordination between arms; further, it requires a singleness of command and purpose." He is describing a highly organized team, a balanced team, in contrast to a few highly developed specialities each operating somewhat according to its own theory of combat.

The War Department has carefully followed the development of the war in Europe for the purpose of analyzing the reasons for the success of one army or the failure of another. The importance of specialized training is apparent to all observers, but the tremendous importance of seasoned soldiers, welded into a perfect team is the outstanding impression. There is no royal road to such training. It cannot be obtained by reading books or sitting in barracks. The only way we can prepare ourselves for the future is to get out in the open, in all kinds of weather, and take advantage of the lessons forced on nations who are less fortunately situated.

The original recommendation of the War Department that this first increment of the National Guard be ordered into active service last July, was based on the necessity for hurrying to develop a special, seasoned reenforcement for the small body of mobile troops of the Regular Army available in continental United States. Today, the entry of this portion of the National Guard on active duty must also serve another purpose. These divisions, these regiments and squadrons that joined the active Army of the United States this morning, must prepare themselves as quickly as possible to receive and train their portion of the young men selected under the democratic terms of the new law just given force and effect by the signature of the President.

Both the troops of the Regular establishment and those of the National Guard must absorb in their ranks the men of the Selective Service Act and give them their military training. Furthermore, thousands of officers of the Reserve Corps, mainly products of the ROTC in our colleges and universities, are either on active duty or are being called to such duty to provide the necessary additional leaders. In other words, the National Defense Act of 1920, the lesson of our lack of preparation in 1917 and 1918, is being put into effect in a progressive, businesslike manner. The Selective Service Act has added the final touch of authority to enable America to go to work effectively at the business of preparing herself against the uncertainties, the threatening dangers of the immediate future.

The consummation of the War Department plans must be governed by the speed with which adequate shelter can be provided. Until funds were made available the Department could only plan for such important details. Now the problem is the prompt completion of temporary hospitals, sewage and water systems, buildings and other necessities of healthful life. So long as the international situation permits, we will proceed only as rapidly as adequate shelter can be provided. In turn, the trainees under the Selective Service Act will be called out only as rapidly as units of the Regular establishment and National Guard are prepared to receive them—both from the viewpoint of training and of shelter—the first increment probably about the middle of November.

On October 15 it is planned to order a second increment of the National Guard to join the active army—the 27th Division from New York, the 37th Division of Ohio, the 32nd Division from Michigan and Wisconsin, and air squadrons of observation planes from New York, Michigan and Mississippi. Also included will be the entire National Guard of Puerto Rico and Hawaii.

For years the National Guard has been preparing for service in the event of a great national emergency. Today that emergency is recognized, and the first of these troops of citizen-soldiers have reported for duty. Their task is most difficult. They must establish themselves in camp and in the shortest possible time season and prepare their small nucleus of men—about thirty per cent of full strength—to receive and train triple their number.

This means long hours of arduous work. For the officers and noncommissioned officers it means not only hard physical work but also intensive daily study of the manuals covering the latest technique in warfare. It is only through discomfort and fatigue that progress can be made toward the triumph of mind and muscles over the softness of the life to which we have become accustomed.

All this not only takes time, but requires wholehearted effort. It demands a standard of discipline which will prevail over fatigue, hunger, confusion, or disaster. Given the opportunity to prepare himself, the American makes the finest soldier in the world, and for the first time in our history we are beginning in time of peace to prepare against the possibility of war. We are starting to train an army of citizen-soldiers which may save us from the tragedy of war.

If we are strong enough, peace, democracy, and our American way of life should be the reward.

21

The Morale and Integrity of Our Army

A Radio Broadcast over the National Broadcasting Company, from Washington, D. C., through Station WJSV, November 29, 1940

~~~~~~

We ask your assistance in bettering the living conditions for the families of our officers and men, and in guarding the health and morale of our soldiers while they are guests in your communities.

THE past few weeks have brought me so many queries regarding Army affairs that I feel it is desirable to outline the exact status of our military program and the progress that we have made. The majority of the questions have related to the present size of the Army and its organization; to the development of the Air Corps and the training of its pilots and mechanics; to the conditions in our camps, the progress of construction, and to the state of morale among our troops. Since we are at peace with the world, and the basic purpose of our preparation is to maintain that peace, and since this country is undertaking its present comprehensive military program because the American people demanded it, I feel that the more fully informed the American public is, the easier will be the problem for the War Department and military officials in general. Therefore, this brief review tonight of the present status of the Army.

A year ago last summer our active Army consisted of about 170,000 soldiers, 56 squadrons of combat planes, and some 2,500 pilots. There were two small regiments of mechanized troops.

From a purely organizational point of view, the Regular Army had only three half-organized infantry divisions. As for larger organizations, the basic battle unit is an army corps, and there was not one in our army. Furthermore, the troops on active duty in this country, meaning the Regular Army units, were scattered among one hundred or more small posts, making the training of a genuine field army a practical impossibility. As to munitions, such as guns, ammunition, equipment, and motor transportation, we seriously lacked adequate equipment for the organizations then on the rolls, and most of the matériel for which funds had but recently been provided was not due for delivery for many months to come.

Now, I wish very briefly to outline the situation of the Army at this moment, in contrast to that of a little more than a year ago:

Today there are five hundred thousand men in the field undergoing intensive training, and within a very few weeks this total will approach eight hundred thousand. Instead of three incomplete infantry divisions, there are today eighteen under training, with nine more soon to come. The two weak mechanized regiments have grown into an armored corps of two divisions, each of about twelve thousand men.

One cavalry division has had its missing units organized and is rapidly approaching a war strength of about twelve thousand men, with a second division in process of activation. Five partially organized antiaircraft regiments on active duty in July a year ago have been increased to twenty-two complete regiments in the field training at the present time, with more to report in January. Similar changes have taken place in coast defense troops, engineer regiments, communications battalions, medical organizations, and supply trains.

The air force of fifty-six squadrons has been increased to one hundred and nine, and the number of pilots to four thousand. Training schools are now expanding to provide a production rate of about one thousand pilots a month by next summer. The school for air mechanics which was graduating one thousand five hundred a year is now turning out men at a rate of nine thousand a year, and in a few months will have a yearly output of thirty thousand.

As to munitions, American industry is rapidly absorbing the orders for the production of vast amounts of matériel during the next eighteen months. The task is particularly difficult because we are endeavoring to fulfill tremendous orders on behalf of Great Britain, and we are trying to do all of this with a minimum of departure from our traditional democratic method of voluntary coöperation with the Government on the part of industry.

The public, I fear, has been much confused regarding this phase of the defense program by what might be called a war of statistics, incident to the charges and counter-charges of an election campaign. The fact of the matter is, that through the splendid coöperation and energetic direction of the Advisory Commission for National Defense and of the groups of scientists who are working very hard to help us, the munitions phase of the program is getting well under way. We must, however, find methods for speeding up the present rate of production, and no pains are being spared to this end.

One of our most difficult problems has been the hurried erection of temporary shelter at cantonments, for the accommodation of large numbers of troops. A contract to build something within a period of a year is not to be compared in difficulty with the contract which must be completed in three months' time, involving the construction of complete utilities, and roads, hospitals, offices, and barracks for twenty to fifty thousand men. The awarding of such contracts is an exceedingly complicated business, and is only the preparatory step to the equally difficult matter of proper supervision to their completion. With time the dominant factor, this phase of the task has been a very trying one, but we are proceeding more rapidly than we at first thought would be possible. Literally, nothing has been allowed to interfere with the accomplishment of this task at the earliest possible date.

Another difficult matter has been the problem of obtaining large quantities of uniform clothing on short notice. Money for this did not become available until late last summer. Yet we have been able to meet the demands and, given a few months for the development of full quantity production, our problem will be much simplified. This has been a particularly pressing matter from the viewpoint of public opinion, because each mother looks to her son's uniform with a very critical eye, and the young soldier himself feels it is of great importance especially if his best girl happens to be in the neighborhood.

I now wish to bring to your attention two phases of the present situation which are troubling the War Department and for which the Department has no immediate remedy within its power.

There are being established in many portions of the country, particularly in the South and Southeast, tremendous concentrations of troops. In order to provide adequate space for training, it has been necessary to locate these camps where extensive plots of land could be obtained at a reasonable price. The natural result is that only small communities are normally to be found in the vicinity of the largest troop concentrations, with the further result that there is a serious lack of accommodations for the families of the officers and noncommissioned officers. The troops are in the field, it is true, but we are not at war and it is not unnatural, under the circumstances, that many men, wishing to avoid separation from their families for a year, or possibly longer, desire to move their dependents to the vicinity of the concentration areas.

As a result of this influx of families, we find that in some localities, local rents at first doubled, and now in certain areas have tripled, with indications that they will go still higher, apparently on the basis of "charge as much as the traffic will bear." This situation is unfortunate and very unfair, and I can only hope that state and municipal authorities will bring a sufficient pressure to bear to suppress this form of profiteering.

A subject of outstanding importance and one to which we have given extensive consideration is the moral and spiritual welfare of the young soldier. Our Corps of Chaplains, with one chaplain for every 1,200 men, is well organized and will be adequately equipped to provide religious services and training for all denominations similar to those found in the average city parish. The Chief of Chaplains is being assisted by Dr. Paul Moody for Protestants, by Bishop John O'Hara for Catholics, and by Dr. David de Sola Pool of the Jewish Welfare Board. There should be no fear that any young man will suffer spiritual loss during the period of his military service, and, on the contrary, we hope that the young soldier will return to his home with a keener understanding of the sacred ideals for which our churches stand.

However, despite the facilities which exist for the spiritual protection of the soldier, there is another serious problem arising from the establishment of these large camps, and one which troubles me more than any other. I am referring to matters that seriously affect morale, that affect the reputation of the Army, and especially that will affect the future of the young men now in the service. I am talking about the problem of handling tremendous numbers of young men who flood into the small near-by communities over the week ends, or in the evenings when their work is done.

Growing out of our experience in the World War, it had been determined many years ago that we should not have competing welfare organizations on the military reservations, and that the Army should take care of such matters and provide the recreational facilities. Congress has given us the money for the necessary construction and for the operation of such services, and these are being organized in a large way. On the reservations the Army can control matters, but when the soldier leaves the camp our troubles begin.

Human nature being what it is, establishments for the purpose of selling liquor are becoming increasingly active in the communities adjacent to the camps, and in some communities there has been an influx of persons of questionable reputation. Here we have on the one side a sordid business for the accumulation of money, and on the other the interest of every parent in the United States who has a son in the Army, not to mention the responsibility of the War Department to develop an army of the highest quality. This situation must be brought under control before it grows serious.

It is in this field, in the communities in the vicinity of our troop concentrations, that the War Department urgently desires the assistance of every welfare organization in the country. We can manage matters on the military reservations, but, as I have said, we have little authority once the soldier goes to town. Therefore, it is of the utmost importance to the Army that the Red Cross and the YMCA, the Knights of Columbus and the Jewish Welfare Board, the Salvation Army, the various fraternal organizations, and the churches of the community, all coöperate to develop wholesome places for the soldier to go for his entertainment—places where he at least can sit down in respectable surroundings and not have to tramp the streets with the ever-present prospect of getting into trouble.

This question has received continuous thought in the War Department, and much has been done to stimulate the organization of committees of men and women familiar with local customs to coöperate with camp commanders, who have, in turn, been ordered to make contacts with the committees in communities adjacent to their camps.

Here is a field where tremendous good can be done both for the National Defense and for the future of these young men. Here is the field where, it seems to me, an obligation exists on the part of the local communities to do this work. It would appear to be but a matter of good business for communities adjacent to our camps thus to organize for the protection of the thousands of new customers that the Army has brought to their gates. But in a broader sense, there is a moral obligation on the part of both the Army and civil communities to assist these young men to lead clean, sound lives while they wear the uniform of their country.

This is not simply a matter of morals or sentiment. More than ever before, the efficiency of an army depends upon the quality of its soldiers, the men required to operate the complicated machines of this modern age. Soldiers today must be alert, active, and in condition, mentally, morally, and physically to withstand the ordeals of the enemy's onslaught from both ground and air, and still be able to carry the fight to the other fellow.

So, as we report on the progress of the past year in organizing, equipping, and developing our expanding forces, at the same time we ask your assistance in bettering the living conditions for the families of our officers and men, and in guarding the health and morale of our soldiers while they are guests in your communities. Only with your energetic assistance can we insure the integrity of our young army.

22
Living Conditions in the Army
A Radio Broadcast from Washington, D. C., January 7, 1941

~~~~~~

Our new army is assuming definite shape and is well on the way toward becoming the well trained military team which must be formed if this nation is to be provided with security from foreign attack.

I AM appreciative of this opportunity which Colonel O'Laughlin[15] and the *Army and Navy Journal* have given me at the beginning of the New Year to say a few words to the American people who are and should be most deeply interested in the materialization of the present plans for the expansion of our military forces.

As the year 1941 begins, thousands of young Americans, who at this time last year were engaged in civilian pursuits, now wear the uniform of the United States Army and are undergoing intensive military training. And at the beginning of this new year I can report that our new Army is assuming a definite shape and is well on the way toward becoming the well trained military team which must be formed if this nation is to be provided with security from foreign attack.

Everyone in the Army, officers and men alike, are working hard at this task. They are busy from reveille to retreat—hiking, learning to use their weapons, attending schools. They are not only becoming physically conditioned, but are becoming experts in the intricate technical knowledge necessary for the soldier of today where quality counts so much.

Living in a democracy—as we all do and all desire to do—I feel the American public is entitled to full information as to our progress and some of our problems. In my capacity as Chief of Staff I am charged with the responsibility for the training and the organizing of the Army to meet any emergency which may arise. With the uncertainties which exist in the international situation today, time is a precarious factor, but I can give assurance that time is not being wasted and we are further ahead in our peacetime defense preparations than we have ever been in the history of this nation.

A matter on which I wish to speak in particular is that concerning the progress of our Army construction program. There appears to be a misapprehension in the minds of some that this program is not proceeding

---

[15]Colonel John Callan O'Laughlin, publisher of the *Army and Navy Journal.*

as we planned—that it is in effect bogging down, and I wish emphatically to correct this false impression. It is an unfortunate fact that in times of anxiety where time is an urgent factor, accomplishments are overlooked and comparatively minor deficiencies are magnified. It is true that we have had delays in our construction program—snow, rain, floods, countless other incalculable factors have held us up. Those matters are beyond our control and have required revisions in our plans. The tentative dates of induction originally set up for some of our National Guard organizations have been delayed, as have some of the increments of trainees under the Selective Service Act. However, the basic principle which we are following and one which we intend to follow in the future is that troops will *not* be brought into the Federal service until we have provided shelter and ample means to make the men as comfortable as field conditions permit.

These necessary modifications in our plans have been the subject of comment by a well intentioned press. However, we expected both the changes and the comments. As far back as last July while testifying before a Congressional committee with regard to calling out the National Guard, I urged that the appropriation of the necessary funds be expedited in order that the changes in our plans incident to construction work in winter weather would be minimized. This money became available to the War Department on September 9 and very shortly thereafter the necessary contracts had been awarded and the construction work actually started.

I wish that more of our citizens could visit our Army camps to see actually what has been accomplished in many cases under the most adverse circumstances. The construction program which the Army is undertaking at the present time is colossal in scope. The average person living in a community in which he pays taxes, takes for granted the various conveniences which he finds at every turn. He has electric lights, running water, heat, and paved roads. However, he often fails to realize that these conveniences and public utilities were developed successively and over a long period of time, and in no cases were they installed all at once and in a short time.

At the present time the Army is building from the ground up what amounts to forty-four new and complete cities for populations ranging from ten thousand to sixty thousand citizens. In some places we are breaking the ground on scrub-oak prairies for the first time and establishing new water systems, sewage systems, hospitals, railroad trackage, roads, walks, refrigeration, warehouses, laundries, bakeries, electric light systems, telephones, and recreational facilities. These scores of communities are being built simultaneously. Under the best of circumstances this is no small task—but to complete this work on a rush basis makes it infinitely more difficult. In Texas the worst rainfall in fifty years flooded some of our camp sites and halted construction while the land was drained. In the northern part of the United States early snows and freezing weather made construction work exceedingly slow. And we are meeting, in the face of these delays imposed by nature, a building schedule which calls for the establishment of these large communities containing all modern improvements and conveniences, in an allotted time of only four months.

We realized the lateness of our start, we expected these difficulties and are prepared to revise our plans to meet them. And I can say that in the vast majority of our projects the work is proceeding as planned and in several places is ahead of schedule. *Emphatically,* the construction program is not bogging down.

Another matter of which I wish to speak is the conditions under which our soldiers are living in the camps.

In the training areas we have established in the southern part of the United States, the troops are being housed in tents. These tents have wooden floors and wooden sidewalls and are provided with heating stoves. Bathing and washing facilities are placed in near-by heated buildings.

These troops are not living in tents because of failure of our construction program to build barracks, but because in the milder climates barracks are unnecessary and it is actually more healthful, particularly where large concentrations of troops are thrown together in close contact, to sleep in small groups. Our medical authorities advise that in suitable climates this method of quartering is most conducive to good health and the control of sickness. Every camp has a heated hospital with the most modern equipment and the health of our soldiers is a matter of primary concern to the War Department.

While they are training during the winter months our soldiers can expect to slosh around occasionally in the mud and rain, but the clothing which is being furnished them will offer suitable protection against all kinds of weather. I hope it will reassure the parents of the young soldiers who have left their homes to enter the Army, to cite some of the articles of clothing which are provided each soldier when he enters the military service. For instance, he is given heavy woolen underwear, woolen shirts, woolen socks, a woolen coat, a woolen overcoat, a raincoat, gloves, overshoes. In short, he is provided with the necessary clothing which has been determined over a period of years to give him ample protection against whatever exposure is necessary for outdoor winter training.

In addition to his Army pay and clothing the soldier is provided with living quarters, an ample, balanced diet of food and careful medical and dental care.

This tremendous expansion which the Army is undergoing at the present time has taxed our resources to the limit to provide the large numbers of these items of clothing within the short time available. However, I am making a personal effort to see that the issue of this clothing is not a matter of theory, but that the clothes are actually on the backs of the troops in the field. If we feel that it is necessary to delay the induction of troops into the Federal service because the living quarters, hospitals, or articles of clothing are not available for immediate use, it is only because we recognize our obligation to protect the health and well being of our soldiers.

No nation, regardless of the unanimity of effort, can create overnight a large army which would be of any value against a well trained and determined enemy. It was nearly a year ago that, when the international situation required an expansion of our military forces, I stated to a Congressional committee that this expansion should proceed in an orderly, step-by-step manner, with great emphasis placed upon fundamental training and the development of initiative and resourcefulness among the individual members of this great military team.

We have watched military developments in Europe carefully and have modified our plans wherever it seemed advisable. The Officers Reserve Corps is proving to be one of our most valuable assets and the induction of the National Guard is proceeding on a far more orderly basis than existed in 1917. The matter of procurement of matériel and equipment comes under authority other than mine, but we do have sufficient equipment on hand for training purposes alone.

The year 1941 will probably be of greatest significance to the Army and the American people. The Army is working hard at its task and no effort will be spared to consummate our plans of having 1,400,000 men under arms by July 1.

23
The Army and the People

A Radio Broadcast on Army Day over the National Broadcasting Company, from Washington, D. C., April 5, 1941

The world must see in us a nation devoted to one great purpose to meet this crisis in the affairs of mankind.

MY GREETINGS to the soldiers of the Army and to the millions of citizens who are assisting in this great program for the National Defense. Army Day this year finds us engaged in a task vastly more significant than a mere military demonstration. We are, soldiers and citizens alike, in the midst of a huge enterprise, a military and industrial partnership—we are all participants.

During the past six months a momentous change has taken place in our army. The National Guard has been called to active duty for a year of intensive training. Billions of dollars have been put to work for military equipment and construction. A Selective Service Act has been placed in operation. These undertakings in time of peace, however serious the emergency, constitute a great experiment in democracy. They are, in effect, a test of the ability of our form of government to meet an international crisis in a practical manner.

Remarkable progress has been made toward the establishment of a large and vigorous army. During the past winter our men have drilled and worked through all kinds of weather and under all sorts of conditions. The Army now emerges as an organized force, unique in the peacetime history of the nation.

The Honorable James Wadsworth, of New York, testifying on this subject before the House of Representatives, last Wednesday afternoon, made these comments: "Mr. Speaker, the men in our Army are training and working all day, and in their odd moments are laughing—the finest morale I have ever seen." Referring to the *good* food, the *good* order and the *absence* of the dreaded diseases, he added this comment: "Indeed, I think there has been nothing like it in military history. No army has ever made such a record."

This record would have been impossible without the loyal support of millions of Americans. But, much more is required today. There must be a complete unity of spirit and of purpose. The soldier in the ranks making his complete contribution, must be conscious of the full support of the people back home. The world must see in us a nation devoted to one great purpose to meet this crisis in the affairs of mankind.

The Army must have complete support. Without the full coöperation of the mechanic who builds the planes, the machinist who forges the guns, or the farmer who raises the crops, the soldier in the field cannot succeed. Then, with the backing of the American family, of the women he loves and reveres, he cannot be defeated.

24
A Survey of the Army Program Since July 1939

Statements before the Senate Special Committee Investigating the National Defense Program, Pursuant to S. Res. 71, 77th Congress, 2d Session, April 22, 1941

≈≈≈≈≈≈≈≈≈≈≈≈≈≈≈≈≈≈≈≈≈≈≈≈≈≈≈≈

We were also under the difficulty . . . of having to move in anything we did with great circumspection. . . .

MR. HUGH A. FULTON, CHIEF COUNSEL OF THE COMMITTEE: General Marshall, will you tell the committee something of the condition of the Army in the summer of 1940?

GENERAL MARSHALL: Do you desire me to start at any particular date?

MR. FULTON: No. As a matter of fact, you could start earlier than that, if you found it convenient.

SENATOR RALPH O. BREWSTER OF MAINE: At the time he took over. When was it he took over? Why not establish when he took over?

THE CHAIRMAN [SENATOR HARRY S. TRUMAN OF MISSOURI]: You might start from that point, then, in this statement.

GENERAL MARSHALL: Very good, sir.

At that time the money became available for the first augmentation of the Army, and, in personnel purely, the Air Corps. I say "at that time"; I mean on that date, specifically, on which I became Acting Chief of Staff [July 1, 1939]. I had just returned from a seven weeks' absence in Brazil.

The strength of the Army, as I recall, was about one hundred and sixty-nine thousand. When I say "Army," I mean those on active duty. We were to start to build up on the basis of the appropriation then effective to reach two hundred and ten thousand by the following summer. The augmentation involved an increase to approximately five thousand planes and an increase in personnel which would have carried us to the two hundred and ten thousand I referred to a moment ago. The great majority of the individuals authorized in the increase were for the Air Corps, or the supply and administrative services necessary for the proper functioning of the Air Corps.

I became formally Chief of Staff, on September 1, two months later, on the date, incidentally, of the movement of the German Army into Poland, and the beginning of this present war.

Shortly thereafter, as I recall on September 8, the President made a public announcement in the form of a proclamation, I believe, but in any event it created a limited emergency and it authorized an expansion of the Army from the two hundred and ten thousand to two hundred and twenty-seven thousand, the additional seventeen thousand men being ground troops. They also authorized us to create certain deficiencies, which legally could be done, and to specifically enter into the purchase of twelve million dollars worth of motor transportation.

In July of 1939 we had a reasonably adequate garrison in Hawaii, a very deficient garrison of about thirteen thousand men in Panama— there are almost thirty thousand today—some four hundred men, I believe, in Alaska, and a total of ten thousand Philippine Scouts and white troops in the Philippine Islands.

Within the United States we had no field army of any kind. We had the pieces of about three and a half divisions, approximately fifty per cent complete as to personnel, with very little transportation. Roughly speaking, each division constituted a force which when concentrated three or four months later, would permit one regiment to train if all the other troops of the division stayed in camp and loaned their transportation to that one regiment.

We had virtually no corps troops, almost no army troops, or what they call GHQ special troops that are not assigned smaller units. In other words, we had nothing comparable to the United States Fleet, and these troops in continental United States were scattered throughout the country in approximately one hundred and fifty small garrisons.

The authorization of the President in September 1939 permitted us to concentrate most of the ground troops in continental United States for immediate training. The increase of seventeen thousand men permitted us to build up to a peace strength, which is about half of the full war strength, five of the new-type triangular divisions, according to the organization that had then been experimentally developed for the Army. It permitted us to organize mostly from the ground up enough corps troops—that is, heavy artillery, engineers, antitank troops, medical regiments, and signal battalions—for about sixty per cent of those required for a single army corps.

It permitted us to assemble the three hundred-odd tanks that we possessed in some form or other into one place. Also, we added to the mechanized brigade, the only armored force we had, an infantry regiment of two battalions and some small engineer units. That constituted the beginning of a field force. Its assembly was started in the latter part of October and in November.

Except for arms, we had no particular equipment which would enable that force to function. We had to do the best we could with the limited money available in the way of deficiencies that we were legally permitted to create, and it eventually resulted in a force of seventy thousand men being assembled in May for the first peacetime truly large maneuvers ever held in the United States.

It might be of interest to comment here on the fact—

SENATOR BREWSTER: That was May 1940?

GENERAL MARSHALL: May 1940, sir.

It might be of interest here to comment on the fact that it required from October until practically the 1st of May to obtain the motor transportation necessary for those troops, and we could not, even in May, obtain what they called the prime movers to haul the heavy guns and the antiaircraft guns around. The motor industry did their level best for us, and made a tremendous effort to speed production, but it is a long time before production, that is, quantity production, develops, and the maneuvers were delayed from the 1st of April, when we would have preferred to hold them until May. The limiting factor was that we had to get these troops back to their home stations to handle the summer training of all the National Guard and of the ROTC, the CMTC, and of the Reserve Corps.

Those maneuvers, the organization of those divisions, the creation of the beginnings of the first field army corps, tactical army corps, marked the real expansion of the Army.

I think it would be interesting to realize that in all of our planning since 1919 we had to work without the benefit of troops except in our foreign possessions. For that reason we had built up a very elaborate school system, because we had to make good in other ways what can be so much better learned by actually handling troop organizations in the field, as the Navy is able to do with their fleet. They have a much less elaborate school system in the Navy, for the reason that they have something actually to work with, a condition which enables a student to learn his lesson in the best possible manner.

I have gone into some detail as to the development during the fall of 1939 and the winter of 1939-40 because it was the experience we gained from that in the developments of command, of troop requirements, and everything of that nature, which constituted the real basis of further development of the Army.

MR. FULTON: General Marshall, I think you said there were seventy thousand troops in that maneuver.

GENERAL MARSHALL: Yes, sir.

MR. FULTON: Could you tell us why there couldn't have been a maneuver earlier of that number, because the Army has exceeded seventy thousand for the entire period, as I understand?

GENERAL MARSHALL: Yes, sir.

Seventy thousand, under the strength at that time was, a very large number to concentrate in this country, because you have to eliminate all the foreign garrisons, which totaled about seventy thousand, approximately; you have to eliminate the coast defense troops; you had to eliminate the men in the depots, in the headquarters, and in the Air Corps, which was growing very rapidly. I think the Air Corps had at that time probably in the neighborhood of twenty-five or thirty thousand troops. It had had about nineteen thousand at the start of the previous summer of 1939, so when you had seventy thousand you had a very large proportion of a ground field army available in the United States. Certain other troops had been concentrated, notably in Arkansas. We had about six or seven thousand out there. We wanted—I personally wanted—to move those troops into the maneuvers in Louisiana, and I was opposed by the whole staff, because if we did it, we would have to emasculate the equipment of those being assembled in Louisiana to a point where it would not have been a test of the organization we wanted to manage. As it was, we had troops on the West Coast that we didn't bring all the way east. We brought some small organizations east, but to have brought everyone would have entailed a tremendous expense, and the appropriations for the manuevers on our estimates were cut three million at the last moment, which further restricted us in what we were doing.

The greatest cost was the assembly of the people scattered all over the country. We spent comparatively little on the installations for their comfort and incidentally had the coldest winter in twenty-two years while we were doing this.

SENATOR BREWSTER: When you speak of that cut, by whom was that cut?

GENERAL MARSHALL: By the Congress.

SENATOR BREWSTER: Not by the Budget?

GENERAL MARSHALL: No, sir.

SENATOR BREWSTER: The Budget recommended the larger sum?

GENERAL MARSHALL: Yes, sir.

So we had to make use of the equipment then available, meaning motor equipment and matters of that kind. In engineer equipment we were tragically short even for the few engineer units in the Regular Army. They require special machinery for their many purposes and these types require a long time to secure. The troops I have mentioned were not moved in because that would do more harm than good to the experiment we were conducting.

From that time on things began to move with a great deal of rapidity. I might say that in the early spring or the late winter of '40, to give a little picture of the public backing that we were receiving—in the early spring, along in March, our estimates were cut by the House from four hundred and ninety-six to fifty-seven planes; for Alaska, which now has over eight thousand men, and about ten or twelve thousand en route with the garrison going up to twenty-odd thousand in the next few months—we then had less than four hundred men, and those four hundred not where we wanted them—our estimates were cut from twelve million to zero. That was in March of 1940.

I might add that I was severely criticized for daring to mention so small a number of planes as ten thousand about two months later.

We found ourselves in May short some twenty-four million dollars worth of critical items of equipment, needed for the first issue, that is, actually in the hands of the troops, for what we called the Initial Protective Force, not equipment to meet the wastages of a campaign, but just the first issue. We were short, almost completely lacking, in clothing, for example, for a prospective increase of the National Guard from a strength of around sixty men to the company, with one uniform to the man to the number required to equip them to full strength, which would be from sixty to two hundred, for each organization.

We had all those matters to make good if the authorization was granted us, and it seemed to me at the time that the principal trouble, the fundamental trouble, was that the people were not appreciative of the possibilities of the situation. When the German Army made its move into Denmark and Norway, the issue came up to obtain this twenty-four million for this small Initial Protective Force, and on the heels of that came a much greater catastrophe, with a public consciousness that there was much to be done. Just how much I don't think anyone realized.

As you recall, on May 16 the President, in a special message, recommended a sum around one billion dollars of which seven hundred and thirty-two million dollars was for Army equipment. And then three weeks later, about the time Dunkirk was developing, he recommended another sum of around a billion dollars, which included, I think, seven hundred and nine million dollars for Army equipment and matériel.

There is a very interesting sidelight there, I think, in the appreciation and attitude generally that is represented by the fact that between the May 16 message and the May 31 message there was a great change of attitude on the part of industrialists and others as to what might be done, what orders they might be able to handle that we could place with any assurance of their being fulfilled before Congress met again if it adjourned shortly after that and reconvened the 1st of the following January.

We had included in the eight hundred million about all the matériel for which at the moment it appeared that you could actually place orders. But as a result of the tremendous advances of the succeeding few weeks there was a great change of feeling on everybody's part which was reflected in industry, and in the world of industry. They felt that they could make certain deliveries of airplane engines that previously were not thought possible, and that they could undertake orders for artillery and similar items of heavy ordnance, notably antiaircraft, for which a few weeks earlier they didn't feel that under the conditions they could possibly accept orders, with any certainty of carrying them out.

MR. FULTON: Did they explain why they had that difference in estimates over a period of several weeks?

GENERAL MARSHALL: Well, I think it was a general feeling that we had passed from a period of dividend considerations to one of purely patriotic considerations.

MR. FULTON: By the makers of armaments, you mean?

GENERAL MARSHALL: Yes, sir, I do think they did a very fine thing. Those men, of course, have to meet their stockholders. They have to meet a very searching proposition in the business way that you gentlemen know far more about than I do, but that is a purely practical proposition.

Then it became evident that they must accept hazards, definite financial business hazards. That is the way it appealed to me. That is the way the reactions appealed to me. They were willing to undertake things that didn't look like a reasonable proposition to lay before a board of directors a few weeks earlier, when you have to run a business with some view to the success of that business, which is measured in terms of profits in the end.   *   *   *

To return, though, to the end of May and in June, the President, in one of these messages referred to the desirability of authority for him to call out the National Guard. We planned to carry out the induction of the National Guard by increments, and we wanted to bring in four divisions where we had certain facilities in existence and where the induction of these men at that time would not do undue harm in the business world, or in the farming communities. So we selected one division in the Northeast [at], Fort Dix. We had certain facilities there. We had land there. We had our summer training camp set-ups there which we could use, and there was a very small number of troops, only about nine thousand on the rolls in that heavily populated district.

We selected another division to go into Fort Sill, because we had certain facilities there. That was the 45th Division, from Oklahoma, Colorado, and those districts.

We selected another division, the 30th, to utilize the facilities that existed at Camp Jackson, near Columbia, South Carolina, and the 41st Division was in the Northwest. We wanted it near Alaska, and we had a spacious reservation at Fort Lewis, and summer facilities there that we could utilize for that purpose.

Along with that I think were about eighteen regiments, the greater part antiaircraft, a certain number of coast-defense regiments, which we thought should be in the harbors of the Northeast and the Northwest, and along the California coast. We wanted them by July 1. I was under great pressure that summer from the members of the National Guard, who had more or less prepared themselves for this, but the authority did not come to do it.

Those same units were the ones we brought in September 16, but there was a vast difference in the induction, because that was on the edge of the winter, whereas the other would have been July 1, in the summer, quite another matter from the viewpoint of camps and quite an invaluable period to us in building the construction for them against the winter season.

No proposition had been made of any kind by the War Department toward Selective Service. Speaking very frankly, we felt that if that was proposed by the military authorities, it was doomed from that instant, because it would be charged as a measure to militarize the country. We must be the last to appear in that, and besides that, the leadership in the matter naturally had to be with the Commander in Chief, the President.

We were also under the difficulty—I am going to be very frank here, because it is quite a part of the plot from the War Department's point of view—of having to move in anything we did with great circumspection. You may recall that in September 1939, the War Department was attacked on the floor of the Senate for even endeavoring to mobilize our young men for war because we were holding a conference on the Selective Service Committee. We had been holding those conferences, I think, since 1926, first once a year and then, during the preceding four or five years, four times a year. But this particular conference was selected for an attack on us because it happened to be going on in Chicago at that time. The adjutants general from the various states involved and certain public-spirited men of the Reserve Corps who came in for the purpose worked with us, and officials from the War Department, notably the Adjutant General's Department, to go into the whole procedure of how we could suddenly execute a registration should a selective-service measure be passed. We had also gone on the assumption that when the emergency actually arrived, meaning virtually a state of war, the Congress would give us some form of a selective service.

Then the issue was, to what extent we could cut down the time for putting it into practice? That was what we had been going through since 1926, and that was the basis of the attack on us in October 1939.

So in all our moves we had to be exceedingly circumspect, you might say almost naïve, in order not to produce a reaction which would be calamitous in getting the things it was necessary to get. That, I think, comes from the public reaction, which is very normal, and you have to treat it as such, although it makes it very difficult to proceed along ordinary businesslike lines.

We now are speaking of the summer of 1940. We had these appropriations, two of which were effective in June, one an augmented 1941 budget and one the first supplemental bill, the total of which was about two billion eight hundred million. The great problem, then, was how to spend that money in the most efficient and economical fashion. We were still without authority to call in the National Guard, and the selective service proposition was then being put before the public by an element of the Training Camps Association from New York. You are all familiar with the debate.

As I recall, authority was granted on August 27 for the induction of the National Guard.

SENATOR BREWSTER: When was that?

GENERAL MARSHALL: On September 9 the money was provided for housing the Guard.

SENATOR BREWSTER: When was that bill introduced? Do you recall that?

GENERAL MARSHALL: Somebody will have to supply that.

SENATOR BREWSTER: It was sometime in June, wasn't it?

GENERAL MARSHALL: In July I think. The President referred to it in one of his two messages in May. I appeared before the Military Committee of the House, in July, and it was the subject of debate back and forth—

SENATOR BREWSTER: You say it became effective in August, and the money was obtained on September 8 by being added by the Senate to a deficiency appropriation bill that had already been cleared through the House.

But during those preceding three months you knew that the matter was being seriously considered by the Congress.

GENERAL MARSHALL: Yes, sir. We knew that it was being seriously considered, but not acted upon. In August the situation had become so grave as the winter was getting close that the President approved my proposal that twenty-nine and one half million from the emergency fund of the President be made available to the War Department to do something toward preparing camps. At that time it was apparent that if a division was going to be put in the field in the cold climate of the Northeast, meaning Fort Dix, New Jersey, that work would have to be started immediately, so the major portion of that twenty-nine and one half million was applied to the contracts for Fort Dix cantonment for the 44th Division.

Other portions of it were used for the utilities of Camp Jackson, South Carolina, for the 30th Division; to Fort Sill, Oklahoma, for the 45th Division, and Fort Lewis, Washington, for the 41st Division. I don't recall now to what extent any of it was made available for the coast-defense camps for regiments here and there. I think very little.

The actual money for the construction became available on September 9. Meanwhile the selective-service legislation was under debate, and after its passage the money for the construction involved in that was made available by joint resolution which was prepared by the Deficiency Committee of the House during a recess of thirty minutes while we were having a hearing on another appropriation, and that passed within eighteen hours by both the House and the Senate. That made available the money requested for emergency housing for the National Guard and the Selective Service trainees.

What detail do you want me to go into in the further development here, what phases of it?

MR. FULTON: You might take up the step-by-step process of arming an individual and making him into a soldier, the equipment, living accommodations—

GENERAL MARSHALL: Yes, sir.

SENATOR BREWSTER: Wouldn't it be appropriate to show, first, what plans were prepared between May and September, looking to this eventuality, if any?

MR. FULTON: I think General Twaddle[16] will testify about that.

SENATOR BREWSTER: Wouldn't the General have the general outline, as he was responsible for what was done during that period of a general nature, in preliminary planning?

GENERAL MARSHALL: Yes, sir.

I had them go into a survey of their plans as they then existed and their adaptation against the future development of the Army. The important part here is this: What occurred then, I think, on the 10th or 12th of May in Europe, and the collapse of the French Government, was not only catastrophic in its effect over there; it not only completely changed our situation in the world as to security behind the Atlantic

---

[16]Brigadier General Harry L. Twaddle, Assistant Chief of Staff, G-3; later Major General and Commanding General, 95th Infantry Division.

Ocean and the Pacific, but it introduced a departure in warfare, to what extent we could not tell at the time except in the superficial way that you learn from recitations of the press. So it became our business, then, as quickly as we could get hold of it, to find out what actually had occurred, just how this German Army, which accomplished this military feat, operated; how it was organized, and how it was led into combat.

It was quite a difficult matter to get at the real facts, to see in what way any fundamental conceptions had been altered. And in the main they had not been. But quite evidently their application had been decidedly changed, altered. And what was called the maneuver of rupture, which was inaugurated by the Germans on the Russian front in the fall of 1917 and introduced with terrific impact on the Western Front in March 21 to April 3, 1918, had been put on wheels, as it were, to produce a determining result rather than the stalemate into which that attempt fell after April 3, 1918.

The coördination of air with ground, the operation of ground troops with mechanized and armored vehicles, was a new application of a fundamental principle. Up to that time our Air people had felt that the actual participation of air forces on the battlefield itself, with ground troops, was somewhat impractical, that it could operate with much greater effect in the rear of the battle zones, in the enemy's airfields, in which it still must operate with vigor, in the cutting of communications, both the signal communications and road communications, supply and rail heads, and everything of that sort. The Germans introduced air as artillery on the battlefield. To be exact, they coördinated a heavy bombardment preparation with a very rapid movement of ground troops.

It was necessary for us to take every advantage of those developments to get at the bottom of what had really occurred. I might say now that the full information, so far as can be obtained in our present relationships, was not entirely available until about two months ago.

Senator Tom Connally of Texas: General, I don't want to interrupt you, but hadn't the Department had any reports or information two or three years back from their military attachés in Europe as to what the German Army was doing and planning, and so on?

General Marshall: We knew rather definitely what they were doing in the development of a huge air power. We knew definitely that they were developing quite an armored force, but the weight of the tank and the application of the air with the ground, was part of the secrecy of the preparation. That appeared to quite an extent in Poland, but the Polish campaign was really a dress rehearsal. That was a training affair, in a large measure, for the German Army, and they approached the next operation with a tremendous development in effectiveness on what they had exhibited in the campaign in Poland.

SENATOR CONNALLY: Did you have any military observers either with the German Army or the Polish Army in the Polish campaign?

GENERAL MARSHALL: Not actually with the army. They were not permitted. We had attachés in Berlin, and they were taken into Poland some time afterward, at the tail end of the campaign.

I might say that one of our attachés in Germany, the year before Munich, as I recall, reported that the development of the German air power had reached such a point that it would change the diplomatic face of Europe. That was a year before Munich.

But the actual teamwork, the technique, procedure, method, the hazards they were willing to accept—is one of the great parts of this affair. In that method of campaign these features were not exploited until they came into this rupture through Sedan and the move to Abbeville.

We obtained as quickly as we could, sufficient detailed information to give us some grounds on which to profit, and the first step was to assemble all the tanks from the Cavalry and Infantry, pool them and create the beginning of an armored force. I don't know but what it might be a good thing to pause right there to paint the picture of what happens when you do these things.

On July 14 we had no armored force. On July 15 we took the available troops, about four thousand, from the Infantry and from the Cavalry, that were concerned with tanks, or combat vehicles as they call them in their various terminologies, and about four hundred officers. We divided them into two groups of two thousand men and two hundred officers each, designated one the 1st Armored Division at Fort Knox, Kentucky, the other the 2d Armored Division at Fort Benning, Georgia.

Since July 15, to take one division, the 1st Armored Division of two thousand men and two hundred officers, has increased to a strength of eighteen thousand men and in the neighborhood of two thousand officers, and has then been reduced to eleven thousand men and one thousand two hundred officers, in the short space of seven or eight months. The reduction came from the necessity of furnishing the nucleus for another armored division.

The same thing has occurred with the 2d Armored Division. There has been created a school which has three thousand students at the present time and will have turned out twelve thousand men by the summer, trained in motor mechanics, radio, and gunnery and the other things specifically needed on that score. Cadres for the new division have gone out, consisting of three thousand five hundred men for each division with their trained officers. They have gone to their stations and we will have in being by June a force of about twelve thousand to thirteen thousand in each of those armored divisions, making a total of four. But that is the expansion with the consequent attrition we have had to go through in order to produce those units. That is all the school installations that had to be built up, the machinery which had to be assembled, the instructional force which had to be gathered in order to carry that out. Those who have seen the 1st and 2d Armored Divisions have been quite impressed with their military efficiency, yet they are the creation of a few months during which they have undergone what might well have been a catastrophic emasculation in order to produce still further units.

At the present time one of those armored divisions—I happen to remember the figures—has eighty-five per cent Reserve officers, and only fifteen per cent officers of the permanent establishment. That is about the proportion throughout the armored forces; the proportion with the other units that we have created, so-called Regular establishment . . . [is] about seventy-five per cent Reserve officers, and . . . [these units] have been emasculated about four times in the preceding eight months.

The last emasculation was made in order to create the replacement training centers, of which there are nineteen, and they have or will have about twelve thousand men each. All but one of these are now going full blast. I might say your committee can see one here right at Belvoir,[17] and get a good idea of what that means. There we are turning to the normal from the abnormal. Heretofore, we have had to put our men into units to be trained as troops. When the National Guard came into service, some of its men were partially trained, others had to be withdrawn on account of dependencies. We had to add to that the volunteer that had enlisted before the Selective Service Act became effective, and then we had to add to that the Selective Service men, so they went through those three graduations of training within the unit, all of which is an abnormal procedure.

Hereafter the men that go to them will come from these great training centers and will have had three months' intensive training, where they normally would have had about six or eight months under the old peacetime regime, and as much as they would get in four or five months were they with a company unit actually receiving troop development.

Those are the changes in the Regular forces, which are on the increase at the present time, in furnishing all these cogs and training nuclei for these various developments. All of that has happened more or less at the same time. We have had to run schools for these Reserve officers, who are largely about ninety-odd per cent the product of the ROTC, to give them a polishing up before they took over these very important jobs, as

---

[17]Fort Belvoir, Virginia, home of The Engineer School.

you can imagine they must be, when seventy-five to eighty per cent of all of the leaders with these so-called Regular units are from the Reserve Corps.

So our schools—for instance, The Infantry School, at Benning, which involves about ten or twelve different weapons, as well as tactics, has had to go up from one hundred twenty a year to over six hundred every five weeks, and then have those officers go to the units. We are now carrying the additional burden of providing special training for the young officers who have been commissioned from the ranks of the National Guard, and who have not had that technical training that a Reserve officer from the ROTC has before he even receives his commission, and the additional training that we have been able to give them at Sill and at Riley and Benning[18] and Belvoir, and the other special schools, before reporting to the units.

We have gotten over the hump. We have over one million two hundred twenty-five thousand officers and men—one million one hundred fifty-five thousand men; with officers, one million two hundred twenty-five thousand. They are organized in divisions; they are organized in army corps; they are organized in field armies. We have a General Headquarters developed, in contrast with General Pershing's assembling his people in New York on the SS *Baltic*. It consists of a trained staff devoting itself largely at the present time to the training of the men; General McNair and his people are established at the War College and include the largest portion of its faculty, which practically lives in airplanes coordinating this thing throughout the United States so it is on a symmetrical basis. .

*   *   *

SENATOR BREWSTER: How many men did you have in training in this country during the last war?

GENERAL MARSHALL: That varied greatly, Senator, and I will have to get you the statistics on it. At one stage we had two million in France and about one million six hundred thousand over here.

SENATOR BREWSTER: I asked that, addressing myself to the question of whether it must not have been contemplated that we would require very large training cantonments in this country.

GENERAL MARSHALL: It was assumed we would, sir.

SENATOR BREWSTER: And what I am interested in is the extent to which plans for those, both as to location and development, were prepared.

GENERAL MARSHALL: We had our mobilization plans for the sites

---

[18]Fort Riley, Kansas, is the home of The Cavalry School, and Fort Benning, Georgia, that of The Infantry School.

throughout the South, where training could be carried on in any period of the year, and for the use of certain National Guard existing sites in the North if the season of the year permitted us to mobilize those troops at those points.

SENATOR BREWSTER: And in those southern cantonments the sites were selected, you say, in advance?

GENERAL MARSHALL: Approximately, sir; not actually, and I might say in connection with that that we had to follow the same procedure that we did in a great many other things. The actual survey of the site we would not have been permitted—I mean, a basic survey of it—because I don't think there is any doubt about it, we would have been forbidden from going ahead. We would have been attacked from every direction had we done that.

SENATOR BREWSTER: That was a matter of policy?

GENERAL MARSHALL: A matter of public opinion, of Congressional and administrative policy. In almost anything we said, Senator, we were viewed as alarmists. I think the Secretary of War said the other day that if some of these proposals had been made up here they would have examined the officer for his sanity. Our principal instructions to our witnesses were to be very careful that they built the thing up instead of making the flat statement, because those views were practically not tolerated by the public.

In December 1939, I talked in a meeting before a historical group.[19] I didn't have any preparation; I just went into it and talked—one statement I made was that compared to the Navy, which is seventy-five per cent mobilized at all times, we at best were not over twenty-five per cent prepared in the Army. Well, that was just for the purpose of illustrating the difference of the national policy. It was in no way a criticism. It was the national policy that the principal build-up would be behind the oceans and behind the Navy, that our great task was the development of a successful mobilization. What we wanted were a few divisions that were prepared to go anywhere if the Administration and the Congress might decide that we should take action quickly. We had not been permitted to do that.

But beyond that our problem was one of mobilization, of a successful mobilization. The Navy's problem was one of operation. They were already seventy-five per cent mobilized, and at the time I talked they were close to ninety per cent.

And yet the mere statement that my guess was that we were only twenty-five per cent prepared, considering all the motions that we had to go through, was very bitterly attacked in about February 1940.

---

[19]See page 35.

Senator Brewster: I understand your position, then, is that you went right to the edge of what you felt was prudent in preparing plans.

General Marshall: We did what we were permitted to do through the process of the Budget and in keeping with the political party in power. By law I am not allowed to come up here and propose all sorts of things.

Senator Brewster: I am coming to that. But I am speaking now of the latitude which you enjoyed, which of course under the acts following the last war did provide for your making plans.

General Marshall: Yes, sir.

Senator Brewster: But you did not feel free to go forward with locating, for instance, the sites of cantonments?

General Marshall: No, sir.

Senator Brewster: Before we had actually taken action, because of seeming possibly to be a warmonger and an alarmist?

General Marshall: Exactly that. We had superficial estimates on sites, and we had a wealth of data in some respects of what had occurred during 1917-18 as to territory, terrain, and things of that sort, but the actual businesslike engineering survey, and the involvements as to moving people off, what we would be permitted to do, we couldn't go into that at all.

Let me give you two examples that might illustrate the difficulties:

We have a site at Fort Dix. We already had an investment there. Now, the weapons have changed greatly since 1917-18, and also at the time of 1917-18 the artillery practice was not carried on by the divisions. It was carried on somewhere else. Now it is of vast importance that the artillery practice be in close contact with infantry during its whole training period, therefore the artillery range must be close to it, or your training does not progress.

Artillery weapons have increased greatly in range and danger space. Where you could have trained with the infantry weapons of 1917-18, you couldn't do it at all now. About seventy-five per cent of our National Guard target ranges have been thrown out by different range developments in the cartridges.

We go into Fort Devens, Massachusetts and suddenly find that when we extend Devens, an old historic place is located in the center of what would be the impact of all the shooting. Well, now, the issue was this: If the owner stayed on that place, we had to move an entire division away from Devens, because we couldn't train there. There was no question of sparing his house. It was in a danger space. That had to be dealt with right off. Could we be supported in displacing that man, doing him individually, and his family a great hardship, from a beautiful home and his ancestral place with a long history? Yet the whole training of the division at Devens hinged on that one item. . .

SENATOR MON C. WALLGREN OF WASHINGTON: You don't make any recommendations as to locations or sites?

GENERAL MARSHALL: I am just saying that that is my responsibility.

SENATOR WALLGREN: That is your responsibility?

GENERAL MARSHALL: Yes, sir; that is clearly my responsibility.

SENATOR WALLGREN: You know that the Federal government owns considerable land in many of these States?

GENERAL MARSHALL: Yes, sir.

SENATOR WALLGREN: And why—

GENERAL MARSHALL: [interposing] I am personally familiar with a good bit of it, too.

SENATOR WALLGREN: Why can't the Army utilize some of this?

GENERAL MARSHALL: I can have some of my people here analyze the pros and cons of that, but we used as much as we could. There are a great many things, climate, water, the type of land, rock standing on edge. For instance, in most of the great national parks out in the West, with which I am familiar, training would be purely mountain climbing.

SENATOR WALLGREN: Yes; but we have a great deal of public land.

GENERAL MARSHALL: You couldn't train, for instance—take this winter; suppose we had put our army in some of the great spaces, we will say out toward Wyoming and Montana. I would be responsible there, also, to the people for the general freeze-out while we were trying to train. We had to get into a section where we could promote the training, where it didn't cost us an exorbitant sum for the land, and wherever we possibly could arrange it, we used as much Government land as was possible. But let me illustrate: There has been a great deal of talk about a camp down in Georgia, because of malaria threats. The malaria part came up when I started to drain the swamps. I found that we were affecting the duck industry.

These antiaircraft ranges require a tremendous territory, and you naturally have to use cheap land. I didn't feel that we could establish troops in the Mojave Desert for longer than a week at a time. We couldn't put them around El Paso because we already had a great many troops in that area. So we had to go near the coast for two reasons. There is some shooting over water, and we had to find a place where we could get a wide area at a cheap enough price so that we would not be bogged down in a terrific outlay for the purchase of land.

* * *

25
Supporting the Army

An Address Before the Twenty-ninth Annual Meeting of the Chamber of Commerce of the United States, at Washington, D. C., April 29, 1941

~~~~~~

If we have the complete support of the people behind the Army, I think we will have one of the most remarkable armies in efficiency, in spirit, in initiative, and all the fine American characteristics, that has ever been seen in the history of this country.

I FEEL I owe you an explanation in starting this brief talk to the extent of explaining that in the way of prepared remarks, I am completely unprepared. There is a great deal that I would like to talk to you about, but it will have to be in a most informal manner. I did not know until shortly prior to this meeting that these talks were to be broadcast over a national hookup, which to a large extent cramps one's style. However, I will be as frank as I can be under these special circumstances.

We appreciate your interest in military affairs. We have had constant manifestations of the interest throughout this past year. There are two, or possibly three, phases of the National Defense effort that might be suitable for me to discuss this morning, but first, I should like to comment briefly on the state of the Army—the actual, the existing Army. Today there are over a million and a quarter men in active training within continental United States and our overseas possessions. The constantly extending scope of our activities is indicated by the fact that within the past few weeks we have sent increased garrisons to Newfoundland, we have sent garrisons to Bermuda, and we are sending today, I think, or possibly tomorrow, the initial garrisons to Trinidad. Our garrison in Alaska is soon to be increased again by the movement of additional troops to that strategic area.

We have a tremendous training program in progress throughout continental United States; we have all of the eighteen divisions which compose the National Guard in active Federal service; we have nine triangular infantry divisions (a tactical combination of infantry, artillery and engineers) in actual training; we have two armored divisions in full operation; we have two more started this month from a nucleus of four thousand men and about two hundred officers for each one of those divisions. We have a multitude of separate regiments, separate brigades of one kind and another, antiaircraft troops, coastal defense troops, engineers, signal troops, special services of various kinds. The total as I have said, makes a million and a quarter men today, and it will be about a million four hundred-odd thousand by the end of June. Although these men have come through a difficult winter, they are now in more favorable circumstances and have been thoroughly seasoned by a rigorous training schedule.

What I would like to say to you in particular is this. During the past few weeks I have been on two brief inspection trips, of about 3,500 miles each, through most of the states of the South and the Middle Southwest. During the brief survey I have seen probably some four hundred thousand troops at a large number of stations. Everywhere I go I find a remarkably high standard of morale, of enthusiasm, of a willingness to work hard. I find a genuine desire on the part of the men to do their level best in order to produce effective results in the shortest possible time. If we have the complete support of the people behind the Army, I think we will have one of the most remarkable armies in efficiency, in spirit, in initiative, and in all the fine American characteristics, that has ever been seen in the history of this country.

I would like to say just a word concerning some of the complications that go into the making of such an army, some of the things that have to be done. It is necessary that we concentrate on a full period of training for the National Guard so that they can attain the most effective results in the shortest possible time. The Regular Army establishment, eighty to ninety per cent of which is now largely officered by Reserve personnel, has had to go through a period of emasculation, brought about successively by the creation of new units and by the organization and placing in operation of some twenty-two replacement training centers which will eventually carry a total of three hundred thousand to four hundred thousand men, and which already accommodate about twelve thousand men each. The establishment of these replacement training centers transforms our training system from an abnormal basis to a normal one. Hereafter, as the men come out of these centers, they will have had their three months' training as individuals and will be in condition —prepared and seasoned sufficiently—to undertake advanced training in the companies, battalions, and regiments to which they are assigned. From that time on their training with the military units will be the actual regimental, brigade, division, corps, and army training that is absolutely essential, in these days, for the operation of an efficient force.

Until recently we have never had an army corps in time of peace, and actually did not have during the static warfare of the World War except as organized on the battlefield. The nine that we now have is a tremendous progression. I am speaking a little technically and I imagine you ladies understand just as well as most of you gentlemen what I mean by that. I have been very much surprised at how little people understand this phase of the matter, considering how extremely vital it is to our organizational set-up. We have army corps today; we have special troops; they are in the process of being trained as actual teams, and the more efficient they are, the less likelihood there is, I think, of the necessity of their being involved in actual warfare.

The efficiency of any army depends on many different things but one is outstanding and that is morale. You can have all the material in the world, but without morale it is largely ineffective. You must have morale first and foremost, and morale is determined by a great many things. Primarily, it depends, of course, on leadership, on the possession of equipment, and in the long run—on the people back home. The matter of equipment, is of extreme importance in the Air Corps. For instance, having a great many pilots we had an exceedingly difficult morale problem on our hands because they are young men, they are active, they are vigorous, they are restless, they want to get to work, and until recently they didn't have planes. There we have a difficult situation of morale which reacts usually in the press in a number of very specialized, highly instructive points of view.

The same thing applies with equal force to the ground troops and to the state of their equipment. That matter has been handled and we have enough for the training at the present time. We are getting more rapidly, and the more we receive the higher the morale will be.

I now reach the point of talking about your business as it relates to my business. Preparations today for any military effort for defense involve not only men and the proverbial rifle that is hung over the fireplace—but they involve matériel on a vast scale, of which you have heard a great deal; it is a war of smokestacks as well as of men. We need every possible assistance from industry; we need the most expeditious and most completely coördinated assistance that you can give us. We need a symmetrical development, and that means that every sub-contractor, as well as every general contractor or manufacturer and industrialist, must contribute in the same measure of effort and on the same ratio as to time.

You can have a very large instrument, a very impressive instrument, and have it wholly ineffective because it lacks an essential part, and that essential part is often a very small piece of the whole, but it is absolutely necessary to the operation of the main instrument. So this must be a symmetrical development.

I sometimes think that we have an unfortunate habit in the Army of talking about a balanced force. That terminology is not stimulating to thought and people do not understand exactly what we mean. However, in referring to matériel and its relation to industry, we do have great need of a balanced production—which is equivalent to a balanced force in terms of war.

We are in need of all the effort you can manage; the more you do, and the more effectively it is done, the stronger will be our position.

We are also in need, from you ladies and gentlemen, of your influence with the people back home to win their appreciation of what our soldiers are doing in the camps. There is nothing glamorous about training in the mud; there will be nothing glamorous about the long marches in the heat and dust and the difficulties and the hardships that will be involved in the tremendous maneuvers that we will conduct next summer. These young soldiers will do almost anything. I think they *will* do anything, if their efforts are appreciated, and their efforts can only be appreciated if the people at home understand the situation. I am not talking just about the man's family—I am talking about the general public. I feel sometimes that we are diverted from the main issue by so much of statistics about this or that, so much of argument about this delay or that delay, this opinion or that opinion. We have a great Army in the making; it is coming into its own; it needs things, but it needs more than anything else the understanding and appreciative support from every side and on every hand in this country.

26
Morale in Modern War

An Address at Trinity College, Hartford, Connecticut,
June 15, 1941

Today, war, total war, is not a succession of mere episodes in a day or week. It is a long drawn out and intricately planned business, and the longer it continues the heavier are the demands on the character of the men engaged in it.

IT is a pleasure to be here this morning in surroundings that give the spiritual in us a chance to exclude the uncertainties and complexities that harass us in these unpredictable times.

These buildings represent a patriotic contribution of the Episcopal Church to the nation. They house a college whose traditions and environment have enabled her to put a distinctive stamp of her own making upon the young men who have the good fortune to matriculate here.

I can readily understand why that is so when I recall the Trinity men with whom I have come in contact.

Their period of development here not only vitalized the faculties of their minds but also aroused and intensified those latent forces of the soul that the ordinary educational process sometimes fails to reach.

I know that this association with you here this morning is good for my soul. If I were back in my office I would not have referred to my soul. Instead I should have used the word "morale" and said that this occasion increased my "morale"—in other words, was of spiritual benefit to me.

One of the most interesting and important phenomena of the last war was the emergence of that French word from comparative obscurity to widespread usage in all the armies of the world.

With use it took on increased significance—a significance which was not lost in the twenty years following the World War.

Today, as we strive to create a great new defensive force, we are investing the word "morale" with deeper and wider meaning.

I realize that when you read the daily press it would appear, from the headlines, that the War Department is a wholly materialistic institution whose only concern is the development and perfection of a machine—a war machine. You read of OPM,[20] and priorities, and the production of bombers, of pursuit ships, of tanks, howitzers, rifles and shells.

---

[20]Office of Production Management, predecessor of the War Production Board.

You come to the natural conclusion that the machine is the thing—that only steel, in one lethal form or another, absorbs the complete time and attention of the War Department.

It is true, as the daily press points out, that we are applying all of American energy, ingenuity and genius we can mobilize, to the task of equipping our new army with the most modern and efficient weapons in the world—and in ever-increasing quantity. That is our responsibility and you expect us to meet it.

But underlying all, the effort back of this essentially material and industrial effort is the realization that the primary instrument of warfare is the fighting man. All of the weapons with which we arm him are merely tools to enable him to carry out his mission.

So we progress from the machine to the man and much of our time and thought and effort is concentrated on the disposition and the temper and the spirit of the men we have mobilized and we get back to the word "morale."

We think of food in terms of morale—of clothing, of shelter, of medical care, of amusement and recreation in terms of morale. We want all of these to be available in such quantity and quality that they will be sustaining factors when it comes to a consideration of the soldier's spirit.

The soldier's heart, the soldier's spirit, the soldier's soul, are everything. Unless the soldier's soul sustains him he cannot be relied on and will fail himself and his commander and his country in the end.

Today war, total war, is not a succession of mere episodes in a day or a week. It is a long drawn out and intricately planned business and the longer it continues the heavier are the demands on the character of the men engaged in it.

With each succeeding month, with each succeeding year, it makes always heavier and more terrible demands on the mental and spiritual qualities, capacities and powers of the men engaged in it.

War is a burden to be carried on a steep and bloody road and only strong nerves and determined spirits can endure to the end.

It is true that war is fought with physical weapons of flame and steel but it is not the mere possession of these weapons, or the use of them, that wins the struggle. They are indispensable but in the final analysis it is the human spirit that achieves the ultimate decision.

It is not enough to fight. It is the spirit which we bring to the fight that decides the issue. It is morale that wins the victory.

The French never found an adequate "dictionary" definition for the word. I don't think that any "definition," in the strict sense of the word, could encompass its meaning or comprehend its full import.

It is more than a word—more than any one word, or several words, can measure.

Morale is a state of mind. It is steadfastness and courage and hope. It is confidence and zeal and loyalty. It is *élan, esprit de corps* and determination.

It is staying power, the spirit which endures to the end—the will to win.

With it all things are possible, without it everything else, planning, preparation, production, count for naught.

I have just said it is the spirit which endures to the end. And so it is.

That being so I feel that it is quite appropriate and proper for me to speak a soldier's word here, on this occasion, this morning; for I am acknowledging, and gladly emphasizing, in this spiritual place, that the determining factor in war is something invisible and intangible, something wholly spiritual.

This recognition of the potency of the spiritual in war receives full consideration in the War Department. Those of us to whom you have entrusted the task of organizing, equipping and training our great new defense forces never treat it lightly when it touches our planning, preparation and calculations.

You will recall that some time ago the press commented on instructions that went out from the War Department to all commanders in the field relative to the new type of discipline that was to be sought for our citizen armies.

I say "sought" because it is not being "imposed." It has not been found necessary to "impose" it.

The military discipline that many of us here today can look back upon, took the form, in the main, of bodily exercises.

The body reacted to it surely enough. Its appeal was physical and instinctive. It could not be said to have appealed to the spirit and the intellect. It was inculcated by playing upon the lower range of morale qualities—pride, shame, fear and above all, habit.

"Habit" came pretty close to being everything. It was undoubtedly the objective of all that old-fashioned "squads east and west" that you still hang stories on.

This older type of discipline was the objective of all that monotonous drilling which, to be honest, achieved obedience at the expense of initiative. It excluded "thought" of any kind. As an old drill-sergeant put it one day, "Give me control of the 'instinct' and you can have the 'reason.'"

The result of the method was a rigid discipline that expressed itself in a mechanical, subconscious obedience that was, to be just to it, admirable in many respects.

It was born of, and perhaps fitted to, the small professional armies of volunteers who lived under it and accomplished much through it.

But for our new armies of citizen soldiers we have achieved a type of discipline better fitted to the type of man himself as well as to the new tactics that have rendered obsolete not only the shoulder-to-shoulder formations but even the discipline based on them.

"Theirs not to reason why—theirs but to do and die" is out of the picture. Your sons and brothers and friends are being taught why orders must be obeyed; why a faulty command unhesitatingly obeyed will accomplish more than a faultless order carried out half-heartedly or with hesitation; why individuals must submerge themselves in the team of the army is to meet its obligation to the nation.

We are replacing force of habit of body with force of habit of mind.

We are basing the discipline of the individual on respect rather than on fear; on the effect of good example given by officers; on the intelligent comprehension by all ranks of why an order has to be, and why it must be carried out; on a sense of duty, on *esprit de corps*.

From a moral standpoint there is no question as to which of these two disciplines is the finer if you admit that respect is to be preferred to fear; the white flame of enthusiasm to the dull edge of routine; the spiritual to the instinctive.

This new discipline enables me to leave with you the assurance that the men in this Army we are building for the defense of a Christian nation and Christian values, will fight, if they have to fight, with more than their bodies and their hands and their material weapons. They will fight with their souls in the job to do, and we who are here today know that everything, ultimately, depends on the soul—for out of the heart are the issues of life.

The War Department is seeing to it that this Christian army is not asked to live on rations alone. It has enlisted the aid of chaplains by the hundreds and is building chapels by the hundreds (555 to be exact) to give the Army the spiritual food we want it to have.

We know that in creating morale we are creating a living thing that is contagious, that spreads and fastens.

We are building that morale—not on supreme confidence in our ability to conquer and subdue other peoples; not in reliance on things of steel and the super-excellence of guns and planes and bomb sights.

We are building it on things infinitely more potent. We are building it on *belief* for it is what men *believe* that makes them invincible. We have sought for something more than enthusiasm, something finer and higher than optimism or self-confidence, something not merely of the intellect or the emotions but rather something in the spirit of the man, something encompassed only by the soul.

This army of ours already possesses a morale based on what we allude to as the noblest aspirations of mankind—on the spiritual forces which rule the world and will continue to do so.

Let me call it the morale of omnipotence. With your endorsement and support this omnipotent morale will be sustained as long as the things of the spirit are stronger than the things of earth.

27
Extending the Service of National Guards-men and Selectees

Statements before the Senate Committee on Military Affairs, on Retention of Selectees and Reserve Components in the Military Service Beyond One Year, 77th Congress, 1st Session, July 9, 1941

〰〰〰〰〰〰〰〰〰〰〰〰〰〰〰〰〰〰〰〰〰〰〰〰〰〰〰〰

If the term of service of the National Guard and of the selectees is not extended, our present trained forces will largely melt away.

GENERAL MARSHALL: Judging from what I read in the newspapers, I thought you might wish to question me regarding the recommendations I made in the report I submitted a few days ago.

THE CHAIRMAN [SENATOR ROBERT R. REYNOLDS OF NORTH CAROLINA]: By the way, I meant to ask if all of you have received copies of the semiannual report. I think that is what it is; is it not, General?

GENERAL MARSHALL: It is the biennial report[21] covering the last two years.

THE CHAIRMAN: I have a copy, and I asked Colonel Watt [Colonel David A. Watt] this morning if the other members of the committee had received their copies and he was not certain.

GENERAL MARSHALL: I understood that copies were sent to each Member of Congress.

THE CHAIRMAN: Well, I understand that they have not received them, and if you have additional copies I am sure that the members of the committee would appreciate it if you would send each one of them one.

GENERAL MARSHALL: My understanding was that a copy was to go to each Member of Congress.

Did you get any additional copies, Colonel Watt?

COLONEL WATT: No, sir.

THE CHAIRMAN: Well, we would appreciate it if you would have a copy sent to the members, as the only copy I have is that provided for me by Colonel Watt.

---

[21]*Biennial Report of the Chief of Staff of the United States Army to the Secretary of War, July 1, 1939 to June 30, 1943*. Washington: Government Printing Office, 1941. Also incorporated in *Report on the Army: 1939-1943*. Washington: The Infantry Journal, 1943.

Well, General, we are very much obliged to you. Now, are there any other statements that you care to make?

SENATOR HARLEY M. KILGORE OF WEST VIRGINIA: I think I understand your recommendations, but I want to get them clarified. The recommendations are a request for elasticity with reference to the use of not always the Regular Army, but men procured by Selective Service and National Guard for service in the islands. Was that made with any definite thought, or have you any thought at the present time regarding Hawaii or service in any of our possessions, that is behind that recommendation?

GENERAL MARSHALL: There was no implied suggestion in my report that troops be dispatched now or later to any particular area. My recommendation pertained solely to the high necessity of having the Army ready for immediate service.

SENATOR HENRY CABOT LODGE, JR., OF MASSACHUSETTS: In other words, it would give the Regular Army the use of these men on extended service, if necessary?

GENERAL MARSHALL: Much more than that. If the term of service of the National Guard and of the selectees is not extended, our present trained forces will largely melt away. If selectees have to be withdrawn from our Regular units, there would remain only a skeleton of three-year men. For example, the Corps of Engineers has expanded more than 1,000 per cent. There are some eighty per cent selectees to a unit. It is obvious that the trained soldiers that were in the Engineers prior to the expansion have had to be thinly spread throughout the organization. If we had to complete an Engineer unit today with three-year men only, we would have to draw such men from possibly as many as fifteen other units. The result would be that practically all organizations except one would be largely destroyed. Even that one unit would require considerable training before it would operate as an efficient team. In addition to that, the partially trained selectees in the remaining units would be left without experienced guidance, and they too would be going home at an early date.

Under existing limitations of law, almost two-thirds of our enlisted men and three-fourths of our officer personnel will have to be released after completing twelve months of service. The loss of the numbers involved is one thing. The breaking down of practically all existing units is another.

SENATOR KILGORE: May I ask another question?

Do you have any single unit besides a division in the United States Army at the present time that is composed entirely of three-year enlisted men, or are there draftees in every unit?

GENERAL MARSHALL: There are some selectees in every unit, but there are very few in the 1st [Infantry] Division and they could be left behind without disruption.

However, in the 1st [Infantry] Division, in the Northeast, and the 3d [Infantry] Division in the Northwest, about seventy-five per cent of the officers would have to be dropped out because of the twelve-month limitation.

SENATOR KILGORE: You mean seventy-five per cent of them are Reserve officers?

GENERAL MARSHALL: Yes, sir. I have spoken of the 1st [Infantry] Division only. There is a further complication that I probably have not explained clearly. A force for any mission would have to be self-contained and self-supporting. This means that a division, for example, would have with it certain air units, antiaircraft and harbor-defense artillery, engineer, medical, quartermaster, and signal units. There are not enough of these special units in the Regular Army, so National Guard units would have to be utilized. In addition, some of our Regular units are composed of as high as eighty per cent selectees. I am sure that you can visualize the disadvantages of a force composed of Regular Army and National Guard units, all containing Reserve Officers and selectees, and the limitation of twelve months of service applying to all except the skeleton formed by the few professional officers and the three-year men. From the outset the efficiency of such a force would begin to unravel, as it were, as the different expiration dates of service of the various categories of its personnel required new officers and men to be supplied.

I should like to illustrate what I mean with a concrete example of the ordinary administrative difficulties that beset the War Department every day. Some time ago it became desirable to increase the antiaircraft garrison in Hawaii. We had no Regular Army unit available. As you know, our antiaircraft units have had a vast expansion, and the trained personnel had to be spread very thinly throughout the new units. Although we did not want to, it became necessary to send a National Guard unit to Hawaii.

Because of exactly the same situation, and for the same reasons, it became necessary to send a National Guard Coast Artillery unit to Alaska. It would have been more desirable if both of these units could have completed their preliminary training in the United States.

As a result of these moves, this is the administrative problem which faces the War Department today. I ask that you gentlemen keep this problem entirely clear of the larger question as to where our armed forces should be employed, and when. I am discussing solely the administrative problem that faces the War Department.

As the antiaircraft regiment in Hawaii will complete its twelve months of service about the end of August, it must be relieved from duty in Hawaii about the middle of August. To effect this relief, a unit must leave the United States about the 1st of August. There is no National Guard unit available. Therefore, a Regular Army unit must be sent. The Regular Army unit will include at least forty per cent of selectees whose term of twelve months of service will require their return to the United States about eight weeks after their arrival in Hawaii. So, on August 1 we will have to send a unit that should continue its training in the United States, to relieve a unit which must leave on the 15th, and eight weeks later that relieving unit will have to return forty per cent of its strength to the United States. All of these movements require ships, and I need hardly state that available water transportation presents a very serious problem. I shall not discuss the very obvious effect of such personnel changes on the defensive efficiency of the Hawaiian garrison, which is charged with the security of the great naval base of Pearl Harbor.

The same situation applies to Alaska, where a National Guard unit will have to be relieved about August 1. The unit available to relieve that regiment must come from the National Guard, and it in turn will be due to return to the United States four and one-half months later because of the expiration of its twelve months of service. This again demands ship tonnage, and certainly does not encourage the development of an efficient garrison in the now vitally important region of Alaska.

These same problems apply to all of our armed forces, and as they multiply they become insurmountable obstacles to administration. I can find no acceptable solution to overcome the present limitations of law.

Now that I have had an opportunity to observe the reaction to my proposals, or rather to the distortion of my recommendations, it is clear that the public has not understood the nature and purposes of those recommendations. I have been quoted as requesting everything from an AEF to an army of 2,800,000 men. It was clearly written into the report that such broad matters of national policy are for the Congress and the Commander in Chief to decide. I addressed myself to the problem of the readiness of the Army for service. An efficient force, an army prepared for such service as may be required, cannot be arranged under our present restrictions.

It is difficult at this time to determine the exact requirements of the national interest with respect to military personnel. However, in view of the international situation and its rapidly increasing threat to our security, I submit, on the basis of cold logic, that the virtual disbandment or immobilization of two-thirds of our trained enlisted strength and three-fourths of our trained officer personnel at this time might well involve a national tragedy.

SENATOR WARREN R. AUSTIN OF VERMONT: Had you asked Congress to amend the law in the form and substance that would obtain your objective?

GENERAL MARSHALL: No, sir; the War Department has not. I have proposed such action to the Secretary of War. . . .

I feel that we cannot afford to delay and that definite action should be taken at once. Regardless of how difficult it may be to obtain the passage of such legislation, the urgency of the situation, cold logic demands that we meet this situation squarely rather than just drift along from day to day as we are now doing. Time is all important. The public and the Congress have accepted the policy of huge appropriations. This I am urging is far more important today.

SENATOR LODGE: General, what was there behind the advocacy of this one-year term here?

GENERAL MARSHALL: We wanted eighteen months, and one year was a compromise. However, twelve months or eighteen months does not affect the present situation. If the period of service were eighteen months, we would merely have six additional months in which to get out of our dilemma. However, we now have arrived at a condition of affairs that is quite different from the situation that existed at the time of the debate on the Selective Training and Service Act. I do not think that anybody at that time had in mind that, if we had a Selective Training and Service Act, we would release the trained men from our forces on the brink of a national emergency. The law itself is quite clear on that point. The question is, do you think the national interests are imperiled? I do, most decidedly.

SENATOR LODGE: May I direct your attention to the so-called ethical-juridical question involved in the contract or understanding which the Government made with the men?

Now, as I understand it, the Naval Affairs Committee, only last week, refused to extend indefinitely the time for the enlisted men in the Navy and Marine Corps on the ground that they had joined on the promise that they would be enlisted for a certain specified time. That is one category.

Then, too, the National Guard and the Reserve officers, it seems to me, have had the same promise made to them, as I understand it, and a man who is a Reserve officer understands that he has to serve a certain length of time, regardless, and only that certain time for which he signed up.

Then you have the selectee, who was selected and inducted with the understanding that he would be in for only one year.

Don't you think that those categories require separate treatment?

GENERAL MARSHALL: In a sense they do require separate treatment. So long as the present serious situation continues, we would want to hold the National Guard in the service. So long as we are not actually at war, we would want to release certain Reserve officers in order to train more, and we would want to release certain portions of the selectees in order to replace them by the new drafts as they graduate from the training centers. We would not want to continue indefinitely with all of our present selectees and then induct nine hundred thousand more, because that would mean automatically a great increase in the strength of the Army. Incidentally, that latter idea was implied in the latest press comments on my report. They construed my report as indicating that the present army would be increased by nine hundred thousand men. I did not have that in mind at all. However, I do not see the matter of a promise to the selectees in quite the same terms that you express it, because I think every man in the service realized that the twelve months was a training priod, and that if this country became involved in a great emergency, he was going to be retained in the service or recalled to the service as the conditions might warrant.

SENATOR AUSTIN: Would you permit an interruption?

GENERAL MARSHALL: Pardon me, Senator, but may I again read this paragraph from the Selective Service Act?

Each man inducted under the provisions of subsection (a) shall serve for a training and service period of twelve consecutive months, unless sooner discharged, except that whenever the Congress has declared that the national interest is imperiled, such twelve-month period may be extended by the President to such time as may be necessary in the interests of national defense.

SENATOR AUSTIN: That is just what I was going to ask you—that is part of his contract; is it not?

GENERAL MARSHALL: You are a lawyer, Senator, and I am not.

SENATOR AUSTIN: I would say so. As a lawyer, when my son operates under that law, if he does, he undertakes as a part of his obligation to stay right on, beyond the twelve months, provided that Congress passes a declaration that the nation is imperiled and the President basing his promulgation on that act of Congress extends the time. You cannot escape it, that is the language of the obligation and I was greatly surprised to see the press claims that the proposal made by you was a violation of a promise. It does not appear to me to be so at all.

GENERAL MARSHALL: That interpretation had a greater news value.

*   *   *

SENATOR ELBERT D. THOMAS OF UTAH: How about the Reserve officers with commissions in the United States Army, standing on their one-year right? In time of emergency, that right is withdrawn, is it not?

GENERAL MARSHALL: Let me answer that question by giving you an example of the problems with which we are faced. A force was sent recently to Iceland. As you know, Marines are especially trained in carrying out landing operations against hostile resistance. No such situation was in prospect in Iceland, yet the limitations imposed on our Army prevented us from using a force from the Army and necessitated our using the Marines.

SENATOR AUSTIN: I don't quite get that.

SENATOR LODGE: You mean the limitation of a year's service, do you not?

SENATOR AUSTIN: I think if they landed on the west side of the island they would be in the Western Hemisphere.

GENERAL MARSHALL: We were involved in the highly controversial question as to what constitutes the Western Hemisphere. We therefore studied the problem to see how it could be handled without bringing up that question. The 1st [Infantry] Division was considered. It has some four hundred Reserve officers who would have to agree to be relieved from active duty under Public 96, and recalled to active duty with their consent. Presumably most of them would have volunteered.

Had we pursued that course we might have found ourselves in the very unfortunate situation in which part of the Reserve officers had volunteered and part had not. Such a situation would have advertised the convoy before it sailed, and we would have been risking the lives of everyone in it. If you serve notice that you are going to send an expedition of that nature, you are also offering an opportunity to any hostile people to take such action as they see fit. You can picture the reaction of the people of this country and of the Congress, if the War Department had advertised that expedition by discharging some of the men and recalling them to active duty, and as a result of such advertisement having had one or more ships in the expedition sunk? We would not have heard the end of that for the next twenty years, and very properly so.

For a number of evident reasons it was of vast importance that the whole movement be accomplished secretly, and that the entire expedition should be actually safe in the harbors of Iceland before the public was notified of what was being done. As I said before, the limitations imposed upon the employment of the Army prevented its use on a mission which was peculiarly an Army mission. These limitations require the use of Marines on a mission which was not a Marine Corps mission.

SENATOR AUSTIN: Mr. Chairman, it seems to me that we ought to have in our record this simple plain truth—that it does not call for any secrecy —that it appears all through the General's statement and that, under the law as it exists today, we cannot administer the National Defense without wrecking military units by pulling away a high percentage of personnel.

Now is that a fact?

GENERAL MARSHALL: That is a fact.

SENATOR AUSTIN: If it is, then we want it in the record.

GENERAL MARSHALL: I would like to make this further statement: In the present situation and under existing limitations it is almost impossible to have troops available for duties they may be called upon to perform. The time has arrived when we must have a military force that may be employed in any manner that the safety of this country may demand. This further fact should be kept clearly in mind—the largest numbers of selectees are in the Regular Army units; if they are released the Regular Army is virtually immobilized for many months.

SENATOR AUSTIN: Now there is no necessity for keeping that secret.

GENERAL MARSHALL: Not at all. I am relieved to have the opportunity to state it publicly.

*   *   *

28
We Cannot Break Up the Army

Statements before the Senate Committee on Military Affairs, on Consideration of SJ Res. 93, Authorizing Retention of Members and Units of the Reserve Components in Active Military Service, 77th Congress, 1st Session, July 17, 1941

~~~~~~

We are working against a time schedule. We have seen nation after nation go down, one after the other, in front of a concentrated effort, each one lulled, presumably into negative action, until all the guns were turned on them and it was too late. . . . I think failure to authorize the extension of those now in the service would be a fundamental and tragic error.

GENERAL MARSHALL: Mr. Chairman [SENATOR ROBERT R. REYNOLDS OF NORTH CAROLINA]: I am a little at a loss as to just what you want me to address myself. You had a rather lengthy statement by me on the various questions involved in the resolutions under consideration—the retention beyond the original period of twelve months of the Reserve components of the Army of the United States, and of the selectees.

THE CHAIRMAN: In answer to that, General, I might say this, that you made a statement before the Military Affairs Committee the other day.

GENERAL MARSHALL: Yes, sir.

THE CHAIRMAN: A part and portion of that was reduced to writing.

GENERAL MARSHALL: Yes.

THE CHAIRMAN: But, unfortunately, that has not as yet been printed or placed in multigraph form for distribution among the members of the Committee and some members of the Committee have not been provided an opportunity of knowing what you said.

In addition to that, I know you made statements before the House Military Affairs Committee and other committees here on Capitol Hill, but in view of the fact that this hearing relates exclusively to SJ Res. 92 and 93, involving the selectees, the National Guard, and Reserve officers whom it is proposed to continue in the service, we would like for you to make a full and complete statement, as full and complete as you want, without revealing any military secrets, which record will be for the benefit of the members of the Committee who unfortunately are not here but who are detained on other official business, and likewise information for the members of the Senate, many of whom are equally as interested in this important subject as are we of the Military Affairs Committee of the United States Senate.

So, if you will be good enough to proceed, merely bearing in mind that this is for the information of the entire Committee and members of the Senate, many of whom have stated to me that they would not be able to be here, but they would like very much to read all the testimony submitted in reference to these two resolutions.

So, if you proceed upon the theory that you have not made any statement upon it at all, I think that would be better, at least in my opinion, from what I have heard and the many inquiries that have been directed to me by various members of the Senate itself.

I might say, in addition to that, that several members of the House have spoken to me and said that they have hoped to be here during these hearings and if they were not they had hoped to have the opportunity of reading your testimony prior to any time that you might be called to testify before the House Military Affairs Committee.

GENERAL MARSHALL: Very well, Senator Reynolds; I will endeavor to do as you requested.

In the first place, the matter before us is of such public importance and the interest of the public and of the Congress is apparently so intense, that it might be well to go back to my original recommendations in my biennial report, covering the period of my stewardship from July 1, 1939 until June 30, 1941. It may clarify the atmosphere for me to explain that I made the specific recommendations regarding the extension of the twelve-month period of service for the three categories purely on the basis of a military necessity for the security of the country. The Commander in Chief, that is, the President, had no knowledge that I was going to make them. My report was submitted to the Secretary of War and at the same time was released to the press.

The recommendations were dictated by military necessity. I tried to keep as wide a separation as possible between military necessity, the sole basis for my recommendations and political considerations which are matters for the decision of the President and the Congress.

SENATOR AUSTIN: Would you permit a question at this point?

General, I would like to ask if you in that report express the conviction that, from the military point of view, the national interest was then imperiled.

GENERAL MARSHALL: I did so in those very words. I felt that affairs had reached a critical state from a military viewpoint several months ago, and that no more time could be lost without giving the public and the Congress my military opinion of the situation.

As I stated before your committee the other day, sir, some weeks back a report was made to the Secretary of War who, in turn, transmitted it to the President, recommending that action be taken immediately on the basis of our belief, our feeling that the national interests were imperiled and that the existence of a national emergency should be declared.

In my biennial report of a few days ago I endeavored to the best of my ability to keep the issue of the state of readiness of the Army for service entirely clear of other implications. As a matter of fact, however, the reactions of the press, which have had a great deal to do with present public sentiment distorted the report to indicate that I was talking about an AEF which was an absurd deduction as far as I can read my own statement.

I was talking about the state of readiness of the Army for whatever service might be required of it and I stated in the report that questions of where it might be employed or when it might be employed were matters that the President and the Congress should decide. I submitted that the question of the readiness for service in the Army should not be confused with those political considerations.

However, as I have already stated, quite the contrary reaction developed and, so far as I can tell, largely because of a superficial study of the report on the part of the press, I fail to see how anyone could read my report and get an idea that I was talking about an AEF. I was not, inferentially or in any other wise.

When the Congress passed Public Resolution 96 on August 27, 1940, and later, on September 16, passed the Selective Training and Service Act, the purpose was first to build up a military force adequate to guarantee our security, and second, to establish at least on an experimental basis for five years a new military system in time of peace.

At that time we had a force of approximately 175,000 men on active duty, some twenty thousand of whom were in the air service and forty-five thousand of whom were on foreign service. After deducting those men and also the number always necessary for overhead, there remained a pitifully small number of troops in the United States and even that small number was scattered throughout the country.

SENATOR AUSTIN: At that point would you permit an interruption?

I have heard criticisms which conveyed the charge that selectees had been infiltrated into ordinary units and sent away to outlying possessions of the United States in order to force the hand of Congress to the extent of obtaining either the resolution declaring that the national interest is imperiled or amendments such as these that we are considering today; what would you say about that?

GENERAL MARSHALL: Senator Austin, exactly the opposite has been the case. I have been personally responsible for the assignments to foreign service. With the greatest reluctance I was forced to the conclusion that in certain specific cases we must send units upon foreign service which were National Guard units or which had in their ranks Selective Service men. In order to hold these categories to the absolute minimum, we almost destroyed the divisions of the Regular Army in order to provide the troops required.

* * *

I came finally to the conclusion that I had to come out firmly, plainly, publicly, with the request for immediate action in the part of Congress in the shortest possible period of time.

SENATOR AUSTIN: The deadline is indicated in your answer to be around August 1; is that right?

GENERAL MARSHALL: Yes, sir.

SENATOR AUSTIN: That is to say, this legislation, if agreed to, ought to be all completed by August 1?

GENERAL MARSHALL: Yes, sir. There are a great many other involvements that complicate it still more. If the National Guard is to be demobilized, we will have to create a large number of new units. That is a tremendous organizational problem. We have all the plans completed, but we must have a definite decision. We considered that June 1 was our deadline on the decision as to the future of the National Guard.

However, we did not have a decision on June 1. It is now the middle of July and still we have no decision. Right now I would like to add this statement which I think everyone should keep clearly in mind: We are threatened today by a military force which has been built up on the system of, first, drastic training of boys, then a very strict military-training period in labor battalions, followed by a period of intensive military instructions culminating in a series of actual campaigns, with which we are all familiar. That program produces a military force of a very high order containing nothing but skilled veterans. We have been doing our best to build an army only since last fall—only since last fall. We can do a wonderful job in that respect, I believe, if we are permitted to go ahead. We can make ourselves so strong defensively that I believe all our interests can be safeguarded, but we must continue to proceed in the same public-spirited manner that marked the passage of Public Resolution 96 and the Selective Training and Service Act late last summer.

I regarded that legislation even with all the limiting amendments, as a very remarkable piece of work in time of peace in a democracy, behind two great oceans. However, I submit that to stop in the middle of the program when the situation as we see it is grave and critical would be disastrous.

We are working against a time schedule. We have seen nation after nation go down, one after the other, in front of a concentrated effort, each one lulled, presumably, into negative action, until all the guns were turned on them and it was too late.

We have the basis for protective action in the Selective Training and Service Act to meet this threat. There we have the foundation of the entire matter. The whole issue at stake is simply this: Is the situation critical? Is there an emergency?

I say distinctly that such an emergency now exists. Unfortunately, it is not in the national interest to make a public statement of all we know. Such an action would defeat part of our purpose. It might even produce a reaction of public opinion as did the sinking of the *Maine* or the Zimmermann note. We wish to avoid that.

SENATOR STYLES BRIDGES OF NEW HAMPSHIRE: General, may I ask you a question there?

As Chief of Staff of the armies of the United States do you believe the safety of this country would be imperiled—or might be imperiled—I will not say would be but might be imperiled—if the Congress fails to authorize the continuation of these draftees for more than the twelve months' service?

GENERAL MARSHALL: I do, emphatically, believe that it is quite possible, that the safety of this country might be imperiled.

SENATOR AUSTIN: May I ask you one other question along that same line?

The portion of the draft act that precedes immediately that portion which relates to time of service and training also limits the number who can be kept in active training or service in the land forces of the United States at any one time to nine hundred thousand.

GENERAL MARSHALL: Yes, sir.

SENATOR AUSTIN: I want to have you on record regarding your opinion whether the national interest would be imperiled if Congress fails to take the lid off the limitation.

GENERAL MARSHALL: No; not at the moment.

The twelve-month limitation is the more serious, but each limitation presents, from an administrative point of view in the development of the National Defense a situation almost invariably where the cure is very much worse than the bite.

The limitation is inserted for a very particular reason and, almost invariably it operates in exactly the opposite manner.

I would like to give you an example, which was, and still is, a source of great worry. You will undoubtedly recall that during the growing catastrophe in Belgium and France the message of the President on May 16, included a request for an emergency fund of one hundred million dollars cash and one hundred million dollars contract authorization. There was considerable debate about such an appropriation.

I was questioned by the Senate War Department Subcommittee on Appropriations. My statement was—and I was rather severely attacked —that the amount, in view of the circumstances, was trivial, and that I thought there should be no limitations attached to it. The fund has been divided between War and Navy appropriations and the endeavor had been, I believe, to attach to it a minimum of limitations.

However, even with the broad terms under which the fund could be expended, the delay in interpreting certain wording delayed me almost three months in developing airfields in the Caribbean theater.

I was trying to spend the fund as expeditiously and as efficiently as possible but it took three months to get started.

I am now inheriting the further complication out of this of being delayed very seriously in the development of the essential air facilities in —I will risk it—in Brazil, where Pan-American has been improving the fields so that in the interest of hemispheric defense, we shall be able to move air forces rapidly and expeditiously if Brazil should need our help to the points that are of great concern to us strategically.

I think that in these matters you must depend on our judgment and our good faith. I assure you that we do our level best to keep faith with Congress and, of course, that means with the people, also.

You cannot do these things by a fixed rule; it does not work out that way.

We are involved in the problem of 1,400,000 men scattered from the Philippines to Alaska, Newfoundland, and Trinidad, with possibilities of a small force in Iceland, if we are ever able to relieve the Marine garrison as it should be relieved.

*   *   *

SENATOR SHERIDAN DOWNEY OF CALIFORNIA: General Marshall, may I intervene with a question, please?

GENERAL MARSHALL: Yes.

SENATOR DOWNEY: As I understand, if Congress would follow your recommendations here, that would give you, in the armed forces of the United States, approximately 1,400,000 men that you could then hold, according to your discretion, for an indefinite period?

GENERAL MARSHALL: Yes, sir.

SENATOR DOWNEY: Now, General Marshall, will you tell us if you would then have the power to increase the Regular Army beyond that based upon existing laws?

GENERAL MARSHALL: Yes, sir, we would, but I think the expression Regular Army, as you use it is confusing. The effect of a joint resolution is to make a unified army. We cease to have components as all will be in the service under like conditions. We still will be in a position to return members of the civilian components to their homes, on a peacetime basis, but from the moment of passage of the resolution we will have a unified army that can be handled in a far more effective manner than is possible under present limitations.

SENATOR DOWNEY: Yes, but do I understand that there is a certain limitation that would be in existence?

GENERAL MARSHALL: Yes, sir.

SENATOR DOWNEY: That would prevent you expanding the armed forces except upon the three-year enlistment?

GENERAL MARSHALL: Yes, sir.

SENATOR DOWNEY: And to what extent could you expand that three-year enlistment?

GENERAL MARSHALL: There is no limit on the three-year enlistment except the practical one of getting additional volunteers in any large number. Then, too, Congress established the Selective Training and Service Act to permit us to build up a trained reserve. War Department wants to proceed in good faith with Congress to carry out that Act. If the Army were filled up with three-year men, which could not be accomplished, there would be no place for the Selective Service man. The over-all limitation on the size of the Army remains in the hands of Congress because we cannot create a deficiency in the pay of personnel. We can create a deficiency for certain vital supplies, but we cannot create a deficiency for pay. Therefore, the determination as to the size of the Army remains within the power of Congress through the money appropriated for its support.

SENATOR DOWNEY: Yes, but did I understand you, General Marshall, to mean from your testimony that you believe that in the interests of National Defense all limitations should be removed by Congress to your expanding the Army to whatever number, in your discretion, you thought proper?

GENERAL MARSHALL: No, sir; and I want to make it perfectly clear that the amount of money appropriated by Congress limits the size of the Army as we are forbidden by law to create a deficiency for personnel.

The other limitation with respect to personnel which would be removed pertains to the number of selectees. The Selective Training and

Service Act now limits to nine hundred thousand the number of selectees who can be in training at any one time.

SENATOR DOWNEY: General Marshall, what I am primarily interested in, and I think most of the Senators will be interested in this question and a frank statement from you as to your own policy, and that is to what extent beyond this 1,400,000 would you desire to expand the armed forces of the United States?

GENERAL MARSHALL: Congress recently provided in fiscal year 1942 appropriations, 152,000 additional men over and above the present 1,418,000. Those men are all for the Air Corps in order to meet the expanding plane program. I testified before the Committee recently and I repeat now that approximately 150,000 additional men would allow us to restore to divisions the men, and also the units that we had to take away in order to provide base forces and reinforcements that were not under consideration at the time Congress appropriated funds for fiscal year 1942, and would also permit us to organize certain special units which reports on the campaigns of Europe indicate that we should have available. The additional number that we can foresee now is approximately 150,000. You have recently given us 152,000 additional men, all for the increased number of planes that are being procured.

That is the limit, as I see it, at the present time. My principal concern is with the efficiency of the numbers we now have rather than with a great expansion with a possible superficial result.

I would like to say, however, that I am under constant pressure, and have been for the past year and a half, to demand increases in a very large way for almost every purpose. I have remained flatly opposed to such a procedure, because I have felt that there was the time to permit an orderly development instead of a superficial, hasty one. I wanted to go through the difficult first steps of expansion deliberately rather than hastily.

The same idea was applied to money, as to how much money could be efficiently spent, and in the initial phases I was criticized for not asking for enough. My feeling at that time was that the situation resembled a kindling fire. If too much wood were piled on suddenly the fire would be put out. I did not want to put out the fire, I wanted to build it gradually to where it could accommodate large quantities of wood. I have been criticized by a great many people in public life, by a great many experts of one kind or another, because they have felt that I have dealt in too small numbers. But we have tried, and I think pretty well succeeded, in going forward in an orderly way rather than in a hasty, superficial manner. Mere numbers do not interest me. I am interested in efficient results.

SENATOR DOWNEY: May I clarify my mind by one further question, and I hope that will be all I will have to ask you? Do I understand you then, from your testimony so far, that if Congress should follow your recommendation you would then only plan on utilizing approximately three hundred thousand additional selectees in the coming years, plus whatever additional numbers were necessary to take up the casualties in the existing group? Would that express it?

GENERAL MARSHALL: Not quite, sir. Some of them would be three-year men. Casualties in the existing Army would be replaced by selectees but they would not add to the total number, they would replace losses. What I object to is being forced to release men at the specific termination of twelve months. I want to be able to release them depending on where they happen to be located, depending on what the situation of their unit is, and, of course, depending on the development of the national situation. So if we say that we wish to bring in more selectees, we mean that we wish to release more selectees. General Haislip in the Personnel Section wants me to release as many as possible in order to bring in a fresh group. The commanders of units want to hold on to as many as they can because of the time spent in training them. I must reconcile the two conflicting interests.

As to the increase in strength, I have mentioned the 152,000 that Congress has already provided for the Air Corps, and I have mentioned the 150,000 for rounding out our present forces. We must not lose sight, Senator, of the great conflagration in Europe and Asia. Conditions of warfare are changing with great rapidity and I do not want to create the impression that I am committed indefinitely to an army of the size indicated regardless of future developments. At the present time, however, I have no intention of recommending a further increase.

I also would like to add that funds for the latter number of 150,000 have not yet been approved by the President nor by the Congress.

I would like to state, for the benefit of you gentlemen, that it has been difficult at times to get through the Budget and through the President additional numbers, because of their reluctance to approve large increases. I think it is permissible for me to state that the attitude of the President has been against tremendous increases, if it were possible to avoid it. He has always demanded convincing proof of the necessity of the increase.

The President cited—I hope it is permissible for me to quote the President without his specific permission—he cited the other day at a conference at the White House, his having required me to reduce the numbers sent to the various bases, because he would not approve garrisons of the size I recommended. While he recognized the possible necessity of increasing them later, he made us reduce our first estimates. His reaction has been reluctance to large increases, which is quite contrary to the impression that seems to be in the minds of a great many people.

I myself have had to reduce numbers in quite a heavy percentage in relation to one garrison over the remonstrances of the commander of the garrison himself. Had a tragedy occurred I would have been blamed because the commander wanted more, the War Plans Division recommended more, and yet I deliberately cut it. I feel that I had reason to do it. The President in the same way has had to impose cuts on me. His attitude has been one of reluctance to increase rather than a rush to increase.

* * *

SENATOR ALBERT B. CHANDLER OF KENTUCKY: I think you made a magnificent effort, and personally I am not going to be a party to limiting the power and authority of the War Department with some supposed fear that you are going to do something to the people of the United States that ought not to be done. I think it is like a high-school team in my part of the country playing Notre Dame. They want you to release soldiers this fall. Where would we be if we got into the war? I do not believe the President wants you to go into the war, but if you go into it, we cannot win it by training an army and letting it go home. I leave that with you for whatever it is worth to you. You are going to have my support.

GENERAL MARSHALL: I thank you very much, Senator. I was thinking, while you were speaking, of a note someone gave me yesterday, about Mr. Newton D. Baker, for whom I have a higher regard than for any other man I have known because of his integrity, his mental ability, and unselfish purpose. He had written to General MacArthur in 1935, I think, that he knew of no case in history where an Army officer had fomented war in the United States.

I know it to be the fact that the atmosphere in the War Department has been averse to the possibilities of war, more so, I believe, than in any other group of people in the United States. It has been our determination to bring the Army to such a state of efficiency that nobody would dare to interfere with our freedom of action.

* * *

SENATOR JOSH LEE OF OKLAHOMA: General Marshall, if you have erred, in my opinion, it has been on the side of being conservative. I have had the feeling, in the times that you have appeared before our Committee, that you have reduced your own estimates in numbers of men and amounts of money, yielding somewhat to the pressure of those who do not believe that we should adequately defend this country. Do you believe that our chances of staying out of war will be increased by the increased strength of our military establishment?

GENERAL MARSHALL: I am strongly of that belief, sir. I know that every effort is being made right now by the most skillful propaganda agencies ever developed in the history of the world to take advantage of all of our deficiencies, of our debates in regard to them, and of our delays in perfecting our defense. Organized propaganda against us is one of our most serious considerations, Senator. It is rather difficult to talk about it, because there are diplomatic considerations. One of our most serious problems is the tremendous propaganda service all over Latin America organized by countries that are not only our enemies but the enemies of Latin America as well. This propaganda takes notice of everything that occurs in this country, magnifies it, distorts it, twists it to develop in the minds of those people a feeling that we are not only ineffective but that we are completely torn apart by dissensions. This propaganda is carried out in a most skillful way, but nevertheless, in a very open way, and on a tremendous scale.

SENATOR LEE: Then the confusion and weakness that would follow our failure to follow your recommendation in continuing the selectees would be seized upon immediately by the propaganda agents, the Axis agents in this country, in your opinion, and that would increase America's chances of war?

GENERAL MARSHALL: Yes, sir; I think failure to authorize the extension of those now in the service would be a fundamental and tragic error. It is difficult to prophesy in these days, but the release of these men at this particular time would defeat the effectiveness of a large portion of the vast amounts of money that have been appropriated. You would lose face immeasurably in the minds of other peoples who should be associated with us. Not only can our failure to take action be magnified and distorted, but those who know what is required for the development of an effective military force, would feel that half of their campaign had been won. Each step we have taken toward providing for our defense, each deliberate move we have made in that direction in time of peace, such as the Selective Training and Service Act, such as ordering into the Federal service of the National Guard, has had a profound effect on nations that are hostile to our purposes. We must not forfeit that advantage. We must not sacrifice the tremendous strides that we have made.

SENATOR LEE: In your opinion, if we fail to extend the time of the draftees, would it weaken America's prestige abroad?

GENERAL MARSHALL: Most decidedly, sir.

SENATOR LEE: And thereby increase the chances of war?

GENERAL MARSHALL: I think so, Senator.

SENATOR LEE: General Marshall, when you came before us in the first instance and asked for legislation drafting men into the military service, you prefaced your statement with the remark, I believe, that a grave danger confronted this country. Is that not true?

GENERAL MARSHALL: That is correct, sir.

SENATOR LEE: In your opinion, is that danger greater or less today?

GENERAL MARSHALL: Far greater, sir.

*   *   *

29
The National Emergency

Statements before the House of Representatives Committee on Military Affairs, on Consideration of HJ Res. 217, HJ Res. 220, and HJ Res. 222, Joint Resolutions Declaring a National Emergency, Extending Enlistments, Appointments, and Commissions in the Army of the United States . . . and for Other Purposes, 77th Congress, 1st Session, July 22, 1941

≈≈≈≈≈≈≈≈≈≈≈≈≈≈≈≈≈≈≈≈≈≈≈≈≈≈≈≈≈≈≈

An emergency exists whether or not the Congress declares it. I am asking you to recognize the fact. . . . I am not asking you to manufacture a fact.

GENERAL MARSHALL: Mr. Chairman [Representative Andrew J. May of Kentucky], I have no prepared statement. I have already testified twice before the Senate Committee on Military Affairs. The first hearing has been printed, and I assume some of you have read it. I do not know just to what extent I should repeat myself, but I can be guided in that by your questions, if what I say now is not sufficient for your purposes.

I would like to begin with a reference to my biennial report covering the period of my first two years as Chief of Staff. The recommendations submitted in that report were made by me at that particular time and in that specific manner because the situation was so serious that, in my opinion, it had to be brought before the people of the United States. My recommendations were based on military necessity only, and I was especially concerned that they be made in a manner that was clearly nonpolitical. I consulted no one with respect to them and no one knew that I was going to make them. I thought that my action was in the best interests of national defense.

At first there were a number of instances where the statements published in the press were not based on an actual reading of the report, but rather on a hasty glance at headings of sections of the report. One example was where I grouped certain specific recommendations under the heading "Legislative Restrictions." Apparently that heading was read at a glance and the conclusion reached that I was recommending an AEF, and it was so circulated on the press wires. I was doing nothing of the kind. So far as I could express myself I was definitely trying to eliminate any such idea from my recommendations, because it involves a most important matter of public policy that should be settled only by the President as Commander in Chief, and the Congress. I specifically endeavored to keep all political questions entirely clear of the problem of the necessity for the readiness of the military forces for whatever service might be required of them.

I believe now that almost everyone is familiar with the administrative problem, the administrative impossibility of managing the Army under the present limitations. I have repeated in my report, I have repeated twice before the Senate Committee on Military Affairs, I have repeated in conversations with legislators, and in informal discussions, the complications involved in the direct business of operating our army. . . . The Congress last August and September took a step in further developing our military policy as laid down in the National Defense Act of 1920 which even with its limitations put National Defense on a much sounder basis than formerly. The law as it stands on the books today points the way clearly to what the further moves should be.

I have been disturbed by suggestions that we go back to the Civil War proposition of bounties, or volunteers, and quack remedies or compromises of that character. I beg of you gentlemen not to repeat the colossal errors of that day. You have the laws on the books; you have your future course defined in those laws. The answer is plain, as I see it. Are the national interests imperiled? Does a national emergency exist? As I said before and as I say now again, in my opinion a national emergency decidedly does exist; in the opinion of the War Department, it does; in the opinion of the President, it does. He has already declared an unlimited emergency which, however, does not affect the military forces, because under the laws governing the Army a national emergency must be declared by Congress.

Our book of rules on personnel is a most complicated affair. I never fully understand it; I have to have General Haislip[22] and his corps of pick-and-shovel men explain to me almost continually the legal complications involved in any military action.

You have laid down for yourselves in the law a course of action which is logical, which is in contrast to the history of our past errors, and which meets the present situation. I am most concerned over temporizing, over expediency, over a patchwork solution, when direct action is so clearly indicated.

Under half measures it is exceedingly difficult to develop military forces because soldiers are only human; they read the papers. Like all of us humans, with a little encouragement they can feel very sorry for themselves. I have been one of them myself, have intimately associated

---

[22]Brigadier General Wade H. Haislip, Assistant Chief of Staff, G-1; later Lieutenant General, Commanding General, XV Corps and Seventh Army.

with them. As an illustration I would like to recite an incident that occurred shortly after I joined my first regiment, almost forty years ago. I found myself on the coast of Mindoro in the Philippines. An insurrection was going on and I was out with a detachment of the 30th Infantry. We were quite isolated, and without any service to help morale. No town, no ice in the tropics, no pay for four months, and not even a book or magazine supplied.

I, as a 21-year-old lieutenant, became the commander of that section of the country, the highest command I held for about thirty years. Among other things, I had to coal the boats that arrived periodically, and one of those contracts to economize in funds, made by the Quartermaster Department in Manila protected the crew against handling the coal until it was delivered on the deck of the boat. That passed the buck to the soldiers as someone had to handle that coal. Their pay was thirteen dollars a month. They worked from the coal pile on the edge of the jungle to a little flat-bottom boat—we had only one—and rowed that through three-quarters of a mile of heavy surf to the ship, and laboriously transferred the coal to the deck of the ship. One day while working in a torrential rain, a tall, lanky soldier from the mountains of Kentucky paused in the middle of his shoveling job, with this comment: "I didn't see nothing like this on that damned recruiting circular." My old first sergeant suppressed a laugh, and flashed back the order to "Keep your mouth shut and shovel coal; that's your job." That gave me a lasting impression of the Regular Army; what discipline meant, what dependability meant in times of difficulty.

THE CHAIRMAN: Was the first sergeant from Kentucky, too?

GENERAL MARSHALL: I may have moved him into that State from Tennessee, Judge, when I thought of your constituents. [Laughter.]

The first sergeant was from America. Almost any reaction can be gotten from young men under given circumstances. There is always a certain degree of grousing that seems to be inherent in the soldier, but does not detract from discipline if it remains within the bounds of his unit. But there are times when the leader must command, "Keep your mouth shut and shovel coal; those are the orders."

There are many disagreeable tasks that our army has accomplished without comment, without notice or appreciation, throughout a long period of years; there is a great deal that is going to be difficult and hard to do in this program. But today, to have the men stirred up and agitated by outside influences is a most unfortunate business because under those conditions soldiers are very apt to begin to feel sorry for themselves. The business of the soldier, as I have found it, involves mud, or extreme heat, and irritating dust. It involves missing meals, long marches, bad weather, insects, and discomforts. It involves a great many inconveniences; it interferes with social affairs and sometimes it very seriously affects personal relationships. All of that is inevitable and is part of the life of a soldier. We have tried in every way in this expansion to avoid the worst of these, to an extent that has never before been attempted. The men have been kept in a perpetual state of agitation from this and that report or discussion. Yet we came out of the winter with the highest morale I have ever seen in United States forces.

At the present moment we are undergoing a very depressing, a dangerous experience. Yesterday afternoon I received a radiogram from General Drum [Lieutenant General Hugh A. Drum] that he had issued these orders as Commander of the First Army:

> There appears to be an organized effort from some source outside the Army to have petitions signed by members of the military forces and sent to the Congress in an effort to oppose legislation proposed by the War Department to continue the service of the National Guard and the Reserve officers in the service. Any such action by those in military service violates the provisions of Army Regulations.

As you have read in the press, some of those young men were led into this business. We cannot continue to ignore such actions. We must treat them as soldiers; we cannot have a political club and call it an army. I regard these disturbing activities from outside the Army, gentlemen, as sabotage of a dangerous character. I do not wish to be held responsible for the development of the Army under such conditions. We must enforce disciplinary measures to offset such influences, if the Army is to have any military value of dependability as an army. Without discipline an army is not only impotent, but it is a menace to the state.

I do not want to see our young men victimized, misled into unsoldierly conduct; I want to see them handled so that we can build up a splendid American army. I cannot bear the burden of responsibility of maintaining the discipline and morale of our army in periods of uncertainty and agitation such as is now going on. There is enough uncertainty at best in the military service, but today we have the additional legislative uncertainties, together with a broadcast of seeds of discontent. We ask you to reach a decision, to settle this matter, and leave us the opportunity to train and develop the Army for our national security. I realize the difficulties of your problem, but the logical solution, to my mind, is so unmistakable that I do not see how sound, acceptable argument can be developed against it, unless you definitely determine to change our military system and maintain a large professional army.

*   *   *

THE CHAIRMAN: Now, General, it is being argued and carried in the press and in the Congress and elsewhere that Congress made a contract with the draftees to remain twelve months and then be sent back home. I would like to call your attention to subsection B of section 3 of that act, which reads:

Each man inducted under the provisions of subsection (a) shall serve for a training and service period of 12 consecutive months, unless sooner discharged, except that whenever Congress has declared that the national interest is imperiled, such 12-month period may be extended by the President to such time as may be necessary in the interests of national defense.

Now I thought you stated, if I did not misunderstand you, you preferred that Congress pursue the simple remedy of passing such a resolution, declaring that the national interests are imperiled, rather than to undertake to amend the act. Was that your suggestion?

GENERAL MARSHALL: That is my suggestion.

THE CHAIRMAN: I think I quite agree with you on it, although I have not stated that as a final conclusion.

GENERAL MARSHALL: I was going to make more than a mere suggestion because if the Congress attempts a patchwork procedure, it will probably do permanent, serious harm to the development of the Army. If you delay three, or four, or five, or six months in finding a solution you are just postponing the problem. In reality, you are doing more than that because you are putting me in the very difficult position of trying to develop an army subject to all sorts of limitations, agitations, and uncertainties. You gentlemen must admit that it is disturbing to have these questions remain long in a state of uncertainty, of debate, and of public misrepresentation in one way or another.

I have received, quite naturally, an extreme reaction since my biennial report was issued. Most of it followed the newspaper headlines to the effect that I was recommending an AEF for Europe. Nobody suggested where I was going to get the necessary ship tonnage for such an expedition. Apparently no one read the recommendations in my report. I would like to read the classification of that mail into the record. Of unfavorable comments, I received 241. Sixty-three came from New York State, and 53 of those from New York City. Twenty-four came from Illinois, and twenty of those from the city of Chicago. Eighteen came from California, nine of them from San Francisco, and eight from Los Angeles. Sixteen came from Pennsylvania, and ten of the sixteen were from the city of Pittsburgh.

A large number of those unfavorable communications were postcards couched very much in the same language. Certain of them came from specific districts. For example, quite evidently a large number of the postcards came from a particular little group in Brooklyn, apparently of German stock. A large number came from the vicinity of Passaic, New Jersey. One hundred and seven of the unfavorable comments stressed the abrogation of a supposed contract or promise to which you have just referred, Mr. Chairman. Fifty-five or twenty-three per cent were marked by extreme personal abuse or threats of violence against the President or Chief of Staff. Twenty-one per cent condemned the AEF and another ten per cent were distinctly anti-British.

In the opinion of those who analyzed the mail, the following points gave evidence of collusion: Frequent and exact duplication of ideas and themes. That was particularly true in the postcard campaign. Frequent duplication of phraseology, sometimes exact and sometimes slightly varied in terms, from the same locality. Frequent expressions over German signatures, of Bund and Christian Front attitude. There was a petition bearing twenty names obviously all written by three or four individuals. There were a number of instances where two or more letters were written by the same person and mailed from different post offices.

These people labor under a confusion of information and opinions, correct and incorrect, as to what the terms of the law actually are and as to what, of course, the degree of the emergency is.

It is, I think, out of the question for me to spread on the open record all of the facts in our knowledge. There are two general types of information. One comes from a great many small items that must be put together like a jigsaw puzzle which indicate with reasonable clearness, a general line of action which threatens our best interests. Then there are other items of information which are direct and complete in themselves and conclusive as to purpose.

I am under pressure to inform the people, at least to give our representatives in Congress this information. I believe, gentlemen, that such an exposure would be most unwise.

THE CHAIRMAN: You may reserve those.

GENERAL MARSHALL: I have received, quite naturally, an extreme reaction since my report, I believe, to the fact I thought such action on my part would be decidedly against the public interest. In the first place, there is the great risk of stirring up a violent reaction on the part of the public. I referred to the fact that we had had several instances of that kind in our history. My hope is that we can meet the issue in a calm, businesslike manner. My purpose is solely the security of this hemisphere. I am interested in America, and, because I am interested in America, I am also interested in the British Fleet, to put it coldly and selfishly. I do not want to see us stumble into a line of action. I want to see this country take deliberately, and I hope wisely, the various precautions and measures that the Axis Powers hope we will not take. Their disappointment or discouragement is my desire. They are capitalizing on our debates and delays; they are capitalizing on the difficulties we are experiencing in crystallizing our army and our people into a unified force and not a collection of differing groups. They are advertising our weaknesses in a tremendous campaign of distortion and misrepresentation, which started two years ago, at least, and which now has reached a maximum of intensity in the Latin-American countries.

I want to see us proceed in the wisest way we can determine upon and not have us stumble along, aimlessly, hoping against hope. In other words, I want to see us protect ourselves against errors of our own choosing.

To me there is a wide difference between a national emergency, and a state of war. A state of war does include a national emergency, but a national emergency does not necessarily include a state of war. A frank recognition of the existence of a national emergency gives us the authority to take the necessary measures, to fortify ourselves against trouble, to place ourselves in a position of such strength that our voice in this troubled world may possibly be determining.

THE CHAIRMAN: General, I think as leader of the armed forces of the United States I should ask you one question, in order that you may be placed in a proper light before the public.

As I remember it—and I think the hearings will disclose it—when you appeared before this Committee last year to advocate the Selective Service and Training Act, you then urged and argued very vehemently to the Committee that anything else than a three-year training period would perhaps be unwise, but you accepted the other as a compromise?

GENERAL MARSHALL: No, sir; I said I regarded eighteen months as the minimum.

THE CHAIRMAN: That is right.

GENERAL MARSHALL: I went on to say that I would be willing to compromise on fifteen months but that we must have at least twelve months. I went from cold military reason to plain political expediency. I wanted the Selective Training and Service Act to pass and for that reason alone I was willing to compromise.

THE CHAIRMAN: I remember it very well now, since you recall it to me.

GENERAL MARSHALL: Of course, there should be a well understood proportion between the number of three-year men and the number of selectees. What I am fearful of is a mandatory type of legislation that will tie our hands and force us into an inflexible procedure which is against efficiency or impracticable of administration. Allow me to illustrate what I mean. Some months ago I directed that fifty per cent of the Reserve officers on active duty be released after completion of the twelve months' period of service. What we were trying to do, what General Haislip and the Personnel Division were urgently pressing us to do, was to rotate the officers on active duty so that we could bring in and train some thirty thousand Reserve officers who had not yet been called to active duty. The commanders in the field are more or less opposed to that procedure. The strongest protest came from the head of the Armored Force, who wanted his percentage of turnover decreased to twenty-five per cent, because of the special nature of his force. I compromised on forty per cent. I wanted, and the Personnel Division wanted, to bring in other Reserve officers in order to build up a trained reserve of officers. Such a plan also permitted us to attend to cases of hardship; it permitted us to systematize our selection and development of officers. It had the great advantage of being able to be carried out without destroying efficiency, because we did not have to meet a deadline like, for instance, the two-year foreign-service tours in the Philippines. We must get men back to this country before the expiration of the two years or be in violation of the law.

Exactly the same idea applies to the selectees. My report was distorted by assuming that I was proposing to increase the Army by nine hundred thousand. I had no such idea. We do not want to increase the Army by nine hundred thousand at this time. We could not take that additional number at the present time because of lack of shelter; also, we must stabilize our existing units in order that their training may be completed. We prefer to have our existing units reach as high a state of efficiency as possible, rather than to take them apart spread them into a larger number, and start all over again. I had a similar problem in the development of the Armored Force. We had two divisions almost a year old and two additional divisions organized just this spring. Our plans provided for two more this fall if the matériel could meet that schedule. Could we afford to draw cadres for these last divisions from the first two, or should we leave those two intact and untouched, and make the second two organized this spring assume the burden of the development of the remaining two divisions? The answer should depend on the international situation and should not be compromised by some legal stipulation.

We wish to pass the selectees out of the service as rapidly as we can after they have completed their twelve months of service. We definitely wish to take the older men out as rapidly as we can, and we think we can almost meet a deadline with respect to them. We think we can release some of them ahead of time, both to our advantage and also to theirs. We are settling hundreds of cases a month now of selectees who we are returning home before the completion of twelve months' service for a variety of reasons. You are familiar with the procedure. When a case of hardship comes to our attention, it is sent to the local Red Cross chapter nearest the man's home. They make an investigation of the case, and also consult with the local induction board. A military review is made of the facts in the case, and the War Department makes a decision in the matter.

The units of our field forces have different priorities, depending upon probable tasks that have been assigned them and also depending upon their location. In those divisions that are on a low priority as to the possibility of use, we can proceed with speed in the replacement of selectees. In those divisions engaged on special work or located so that sea transportation is involved, we might be behind schedule. We want to be able to use our own judgment in applying a flexible rule. If we are compelled by law to meet a mandatory deadline we will be in a hopeless situation and will have to do many things actually against the public interest. There has been a good deal of talk at cross purposes. The very things that have been talked about in opposition to this resolution are the very things that we want to do not as incidental to the immediate public demand but for our own purposes. We want to bring in new selectees so it follows that we must release men in order to make room for them.

The same idea applies to the officers in the National Guard. We want to release, on the completion of twelve months' service, a number of those lieutenants in the National Guard who received commissions without adequate preparation. We can also relieve hardship cases among the officers of the Guard. Those released can be replaced by Reserve personnel; and by what we know is going to be the perfectly splendid product of the officer candidate school. I have been told that the first group at The Infantry School is the finest looking lot of men ever assembled there.

I can handle our men on a fair basis, but if you say "on September 22 you must do this," then I say that you may be imperiling the national interest. You must trust in my good faith, in our professional common sense. I have tried to be very frank. The War Department has been scrupulous in its efforts to meet, as far as possible, the desires of Congress. Though encompassed with too definite and too numerous laws, we have not tried circumlocution or evasion.

THE CHAIRMAN: General, if I understand your position, it is simply this: That you are trying to build an armed force sufficient for the adequate and proper protection of the United States and the Western Hemisphere and that unless this legislation is enacted you will have military problems arising that you cannot solve without it.

GENERAL MARSHALL: That is entirely correct, sir. . .

MR. CHARLES I. FADDIS OF PENNSYLVANIA: General, I notice in your report, you make a statement to this effect, that you believe the material phase of this program is much better understood than the personnel phase.

GENERAL MARSHALL: Yes, sir.

MR. FADDIS: That is, of course, very dangerous in this country. I believe that the people will become firmly entrenched in the viewpoint that we can meet this situation merely by an output of matériel. And if we do as you would like to have us do under the circumstances, it would certainly increase the appreciation of the people of the United States in the personnel phase of the situation.

GENERAL MARSHALL: Yes, sir.

MR. FADDIS: Furthermore, I notice in your report—

GENERAL MARSHALL: May I add to that?

MR. FADDIS: Surely.

GENERAL MARSHALL: One of the great difficulties we labor under is that the public does not understand that matériel is worthless unless there is a highly trained personnel to operate it. People do not see the difference between a force in France in 1918, in a stabilized sector, and the fast-moving tactics of the new World War. They do not recognize what an army corps is, nor what a tremendously complicated agency it is; how much territory it covers, nor the difficulties under which it operates.

The difference in our problem as compared to that of the Navy, for example, is this: Only a team can fight a ship and it requires much technical preparation to develop that team, both as to the individual's knowledge of his job, and as to coördination among the members of the team. The team has to be so developed that despite the shock of battle, explosions, and so forth, it will continue to function according to a prescribed procedure. However, nobody runs from a ship, because there is no place to run, and hiding in the hull is of no advantage. The ship is full of buttons and fixed gadgets that the electrical companies have built into them. And, Mr. Faddis, I think you will agree with me, that you never saw a button on a battlefield. There communications are not welded or built into the structure. They are scattered over the face of the earth. Your first glimpse of a modern battlefield would be when you plunge forward on it. You do not see the artillery unit that is supporting you. You may never see it in your lifetime, yet it is the unit that has to pour down the artillery fire at the place and the time you need it.

There is an added complication, in complete contrast to the naval problem. A hostile vessel will lie somewhere between the horizon and your ship, and you fire directly at it. We have the problem of practically never seeing our target straight to the front, because as far as possible the machine guns and the other weapons fire from enfilade, and are behind the hill or cover to your front. All of which presents a tremendously difficult problem and all of which requires a tremendous development of technique and the highest standard of discipline. Our men must be hardened and trained until they will respond to orders to do what they think is not humanly possible to do.

We have had some tragic examples in our history of good men, sound men, being involved in humiliating reactions on the battlefield and the very same men performing magnificently at a later date, when they had been thoroughly organized and trained. We had such situations in the Civil War. In fact, most of the Union Army ran into the arms of Congress I think after the First Battle of Bull Run. And yet later on those same men did some of the heaviest fighting and took the heaviest punishment in the history of the world. But it took years to develop that state of discipline.

The personnel phase, as you say, has been dwarfed by the matériel phase. The public interest has been focused on statistics, on huge sums in billions, and in debates as to whether the schedules are all that they should be, as to whether the weapon is the right type or not.

*   *   *

MR. FADDIS: Do you not believe the reason for that is this, that they are guilty of exactly what they accuse the War Department of being guilty of, all the time, in that they are always thinking of the next war in terms of the last war.

GENERAL MARSHALL: Yes, sir.

MR. FADDIS: The public has its mind fashioned on the World War and the systems and methods used in the World War. The public in general has failed to grasp the idea that warfare today is geared to the spirit of the times, the machine age.

GENERAL MARSHALL: Yes, sir.

MR. FADDIS: Further along that thought, I gather that the actual training program has been badly broken into because it has been necessary to reach into the various outfits you had when it started, and take out valuable personnel and transfer them around to the new increments as they came in, and that it has been necessary as to many of these units to break them up and make them into units of a different character because of the change in the methods of warfare.

For instance, I see in your report where you broke up seventeen cavalry divisions, I believe it was?

GENERAL MARSHALL: Four cavalry divisions.

MR. FADDIS: Seventeen cavalry regiments, I believe.

GENERAL MARSHALL: Yes, sir.

MR. FADDIS: And you made them into mechanized cavalry and tank units and field artillery and so forth. So that has interfered with the training program up to this point. And because of the necessity of this reorganization and because of the necessity of reaching in and getting valuable officers and noncommissioned officers, and transferring them around, our training program really has not reached the state of efficiency that it might have if that had not been necessary.

GENERAL MARSHALL: Yes, sir, that is correct. The National Guard infantry divisions were kept as clear of changes as possible in order to give them a full opportunity for development. The special units that you refer to were converted into corps cavalry, half mechanized and half horse units, and also into antiaircraft units. All Regular units had to provide cadre after cadre for the development of new units or for the setting up of the great replacement training centers—all of which interfered very seriously with the program of training. We are just now coming out of the woods.

MR. FADDIS: That is all.

MR. LESLIE C. ARENDS OF ILLINOIS: How large an army do you think it is necessary to have to defend the Western Hemisphere?

GENERAL MARSHALL: Under present conditions, over and above the 152,000 additional men for the Air Corps already provided for, we need about 150,000 more men. Specifically, we do not want to create additional divisions at the present time. We wish to avoid that, if it is possible to do so. We want to improve the quality of the divisions we now have. We want to establish one basically sound force. It may be that later on, if the situation becomes more serious, we will have to add additional divisions. But we would do that in the rear of our present force, which we now have well on the way to dependable efficiency and without breaking up present units.

The additional 150,000 men are needed to restore to units men taken away in order to provide signal, engineer, antitank, and other special units that we need but for which we have had no authorization. Also we need men to replace those taken out of divisions to garrison the leased bases for which no men had been provided.

If the situation develops into actual operations there would be a number of units that would have to be hastily created, such as port units, military police companies, engineers, and elements of that sort. But as matters stand now, we do not want to increase the present number of divisions of the continental army, except for the Armored Force.

MR. ARENDS: In other words, a million and a half or 1,700,000 more would be sufficient.

GENERAL MARSHALL: About 1,700,000. There have been proposals that we take on nine hundred thousand selectees in addition to those that we wish to hold in service. We do not want to do that. In the first place, we have not the shelter. In the second place, such an increase is not needed at the moment. We will want to induct as many of the authorized nine hundred thousand as we need, but we will want to exchange them for others that we will release from active service and send back home.

MR. ARENDS: In other words, if these selectees remain in for a longer length of time, the induction will be slowed up with these new selectees?

GENERAL MARSHALL: It will be slowed no more than is necessary. We have gone ahead in July and August to an overstrength in order to level off the numbers in our three-month training centers.

MR. ARENDS: Just one other thought I had in mind. I can see from your standpoint the desirability of a declaration of a national emergency. But I think it goes even a little further than the Army. I think the national emergency goes pretty wide, probably beyond the Army.

GENERAL MARSHALL: There is now a national emergency in regard to everything but the military forces. The President has declared an unlimited emergency, but this does not affect the Army and Navy.

MR. ARENDS: But not declared by Congress.

GENERAL MARSHALL: No, sir.

MR. ARENDS: I think there is a great difference between that and a national emergency declared by Congress. That is all.

MR. CHARLES R. CLASON OF MASSACHUSETTS: General, I would like to ask you this. How many men would you expect to have in all branches of the Army by July 1, 1942, under your present plan?

GENERAL MARSHALL: About 1,700,000.

MR. CLASON: Then, on the theory either you are not going to keep these selectees in very long, whom you now have in—that is, much longer than one year's service, or else you are not going to induct many new men.

GENERAL MARSHALL: We are not going to keep the present selectees, all of them, for an indefinite period. We are going to bring in as many new men as are needed to replace the ones we release.

MR. CLASON: What I am trying to avoid is a fixed rule which cannot be applied without damage to the Army. Following your theory, then, certain inductees, if they happen to be unfortunate enough to get into certain regiments, may be held on for two years, while others, who were brought in at the same time, and are equally needing the training are likely to get out at the end of twelve months?

GENERAL MARSHALL: Even a young man at isolated Dutch Harbor would not be held for such a long period as you mention.

MR. CLASON: I thought your idea was that you want to keep up the regiments, filled to their enlisted strength, by using the selectees and keeping them there?

GENERAL MARSHALL: We have already filled them up to full strength with selectees.

MR. CLASON: You wish to keep those men in those particular regiments?

GENERAL MARSHALL: Not indefinitely, but we should not be compelled to release them at the end of twelve months. There is a regiment in a division in Texas, we will say, for which there is no immediate prospect of special employment. It would be very simple to meet that problem. A certain percentage per month could be released and they would be replaced by others coming from the training centers, men of the new nine hundred thousand authorized under the terms of the Selective Training and Service Act.

MR. CLASON: On the other hand, you keep Regular troops in the Philippines and in Hawaii and in the Panama Canal Zone except for a number possibly less than 4,500. If that is true, and those places are all built up and well established fortifications, it seems to me, that if they need the presence of Regular troops, certainly the Army which is going into Iceland or going into Brazil, ought to be made up only of Regulars, well trained, and not men who are merely inductees, who have had from three to six months of training.

GENERAL MARSHALL: How are you going to get the Regulars?

MR. CLASON: As I understand, under the records which were before this Committee the last time we had hearings, you can get approximately thirty-five thousand new enlistments every month.

GENERAL MARSHALL: I said the largest number we ever received was from July to September 1940, under the impetus of the Selective Service debates, and under the greatest recruiting campaign we had ever undertaken, and that number averaged about thirty-nine thousand a month. Men are going out all the time at the end of their service so that the number of enlistments does not represent the net gain.

MR. CLASON: Surely.

GENERAL MARSHALL: So while we are enlisting thirty-nine thousand, we are losing somewhere nine thousand. In other words the net would be thirty thousand and we actually have requirements for six hundred thousand three-year men.

MR. CLASON: Where are you going to put those six hundred thousand men outside of continental United States? It would take only a very small fraction of the number that would go to Iceland or to Brazil, unless you are thinking about an expeditionary force.

GENERAL MARSHALL: Mr. Clason, we have our numerous bases and our regular overseas garrisons and we have got to maintain a continental army. I must not transfer from our home forces all of the experienced soldiers, the three-year men.

I have to provide three-year men for the huge Air Corps, which is struggling to get such volunteers right now, even though it is a very popular service. Your scheme, I think, means attempting an impossible proposition.

The Air Corps must have seventy-five per cent three-year men. The Armored Force has to have a substantial nucleus of three-year men.

Then there are other requirements. Each of the triangular divisions must have a nucleus of three-year men. The National Guard divisions must have a similar, dependable corps or nucleus of three-year men. Otherwise, we would have merely a training school, instead of an army. Training schools are necessary, but there must be an army, too.

Then there are the outside or overseas considerations: the Philippines, Hawaii, and Panama. Those garrisons require three-year men.

The conditions and requirements add up to an impossible problem for solution on a volunteer basis. And besides, please keep this in mind. Volunteering is an uncertain proposition, and we are not in a speculative situation. We are preparing to stand off a highly professional crew. We must know within reasonable limits what we are to have in men.

MR. CLASON: Since September of last year, has any attempt been made, any real attempt, to secure as many voluntary enlistments for three-year terms as the Army could get?

GENERAL HAISLIP: Yes, sir. We have been trying to get up to a strength of five hundred thousand three-year men and have not got it yet. We have 476,000 three-year men in the Army now.

GENERAL MARSHALL: And we must have a minimum of what?

GENERAL HAISLIP: About 640,000.

GENERAL MARSHALL: That is the very minimum we must have, and we are working toward that.

MR. CLASON: General, if I understand the statements made by officers in the Army, about selectees and the National Guard, apparently many of them are anxious to remain beyond the twelve months' time. Has any attempt been made to ascertain if that is so?

GENERAL MARSHALL: Mr. Clason, such an action would involve the question of a national vote, as it were. We must not use political methods within the Army. They are highly desirable for a democracy, but not for an army. That sort of thing is going on now and is wrecking morale. All sorts of agencies are working upon the individual soldier to stir up dissension. No such army can be depended on to defend America.

MR. CLASON: How many troops do you need in Iceland, for instance?

GENERAL MARSHALL: I must not tell you that.

MR. CLASON: How many do you expect to have in the bases you secured from the British?

GENERAL MARSHALL: I do not want to give out that information, sir. We have 125,000 men on foreign service at the present time, and there must be a further increase.

MR. CLASON: Do you think it is fair or proper to send selectees with only a few weeks' or months' training into Iceland, where they might be involved in war, since they are in contact with the enemy?

GENERAL MARSHALL: No, sir; I do not think it is fair or proper to do so and I think it is most unfair to the War Department to put it in the position of either doing it or failing to provide the necessary security. I am resisting such action because we cannot afford to send men to such distant localities and then have to bring them back by boat a few weeks or months later.

MR. CLASON: Well, you would send Regulars there?

GENERAL MARSHALL: Mr. Clason, I am trying to get a unified army and you are trying to have a collection of classified groups.

MR. CLASON: No, I am wondering why a year ago, when the question was brought up, you did not get a Regular Army of as many three-year enlistments as possible at that time, when they were coming into it?

GENERAL MARSHALL: Well, we did, but the minute the Selective Service debates ceased, enlistments went down. We cannot build up large forces on a volunteer basis. Our history proves conclusively the wastefulness of such a procedure.

MR. JOHN MARTIN COSTELLO OF CALIFORNIA: General, do not you think a lot of those men who might otherwise go into the Army are getting jobs in industry?

GENERAL MARSHALL: You have brought up a very serious problem. We are not at war and the men in the Army are giving us their services for small pay, not small in terms of soldiers' pay in other parts of the world but very small in terms of the wages now being received by other men in industry.

One serious consideration pertains to the possible future of the National Guard. We have had to make up our plans for the return of the

National Guard at the end of twelve months, because of that requirement in the law. What happens when a National Guard division goes home? It returns to its State status and becomes a State unit under the Governor; it ceases to be in the Army of the United States.

The Federal government has a contractual relationship with the Guard under which it provides regulations for its training, its type of organization, its arms, its uniforms, its equipment, and the pay of its members for certain prescribed drills, and camps.

The Guardsman himself is at perfect liberty to go beyond the boundaries of the State. Take, for example, a division recruited largely from a farming district. When it returns to its home district the men will disperse toward the jobs at high pay which are to be found in the industrial centers. That division will be washed out, and will cease to have a value as a military asset.

The very fact that this is a great industrial program introduces a complicated situation in the development of an army while we are still on a peace basis.

MR. CLASON: I thought the argument or the reason why we do not have more volunteers was that the trouble is not on account of our national interests being imperiled from abroad, but due to a change in economic conditions, which is an important one.

GENERAL MARSHALL: I do not agree on that, sir. From my point of view, that is not a correct statement of the cause.

*   *   *

MR. CLASON: With reference to this eight hundred thousand figure, the eight hundred thousand Regulars were going to be secured with this Selective Service Act remaining in effect, were they not?

GENERAL MARSHALL: I do not think that we could possibly get them.

MR. CLASON: What effort is being made to secure them at the present time, as compared with what was done a year ago between August and September?

GENERAL HAISLIP: Colonel Stuart [Colonel LaRhett L. Stuart], will you answer that question?

COLONEL STUART: To get three-year men in the Army, The Adjutant General put on a very intensive recruiting campaign. He tried radio broadcasts, paid advertising, and everything else. In addition to that, there had been much discussion in Congress and in the papers about Selective Service and many men were trying their best to get into the service of their own volition, instead of waiting to be drafted. The recruiting went up in July to thirty-two thousand men, and on up to forty-three thousand men in October. In November it went down to twenty-four thousand and at that time we also took them in for one year—anything, to get them in.

In November, when we took in our first selectees, the recruiting dropped down to twenty-three thousand or twenty-four thousand, and it has averaged about eighteen thousand to twenty thousand since then— because of two reasons, primarily: The big pressure of getting in first, which all Americans want to do, was off: The Selective Service Act was law and, as they were subject to induction, they waited for that. There was no incentive to volunteer. Another thing was the high rates of pay that were being paid in industry on the outside. And the whole history of recruiting has been that the higher the rates of pay on the outside, the harder it is to get recruits and the poorer the quality of the recruits. I imagine if we made a graph of the recruiting records and a graph of the pay rates, we would find that when the one went up, the other went down exactly in proportion.

Mr. J. Joseph Smith of Connecticut: General, if the national interests were not imperiled, it would be all right to let them go out?

General Marshall: Yes, sir.

Mr. Smith: If the law states it is imperiled, you could plan on that; if the national interest is not imperiled, you could plan on that?

General Marshall: Yes, sir.

Mr. Smith: And if the national interests were not imperiled, then they could be replaced?

General Marshall: Yes, sir.

*   *   *

Mr. Clason: General Marshall, do you make any distinction between the need for the National Guard and for the selectees?

General Marshall: No, sir.

Mr. Clason: You think one is just as essential to keep in the service as the other?

General Marshall: Yes, sir.

Mr. Clason: The National Guard apparently, according to your report, on page 8, was particularly necessary in order to provide what really amounts to a skeleton organization for the training of the selectees?

General Marshall: Yes, sir.

Mr. Clason: I understood this morning that you felt that the selectees might be allowed to leave the service very shortly after the twelve-month period.

General Marshall: Yes, sir.

Mr. Clason: Would you expect the same of the National Guard?

General Marshall: Generally, as to individuals, but not as to units, sir.

Mr. Clason: How about the selectees? They are not units, are they?

General Marshall: They are individuals.

Mr. Clason: They are individuals.

General Marshall: I am speaking about the organizations of the National Guard regiments, brigades, and divisions. When I speak of selectees, I am talking about individuals. And I would like to say, also, Mr. Clason, that when I spoke about the National Guard being necessary for the training of the selectees, I was talking about it in that light because at that time we had no replacement training centers nor did we have the personnel to create them. Replacement training centers had to be officered by Reserve officers, and they had to be trained in order to be able to function. We utterly lacked the necessary amounts of matériel for the centers. That matériel existed in the hands of the National Guard. The officer force and the noncommissioned officer force were present in the National Guard. So, as a plan for the prompt building up of the Army, not for its development over a period of years, it was essential from that point of view alone to utilize the National Guard by bringing it into active service. Otherwise, we would have had to emasculate it by taking away its equipment, and psychologically, destroying it.

However, we needed their regiments and divisions. We had been working on them for twenty years, trying to build up their efficiency, trying to train staffs. I personally worked with division and brigade staffs and with the divisions generally of the National Guard. That had been part of my duties during the period of twenty years following the World War. It seemed to me aside from the fact that it was not in accordance with the national policy—it seemed to me out of the question to abandon all of that development when we needed an armed force as quickly as we could get it.

If you recall, in the early summer, when the National Guard issue first came up, I spoke to you gentlemen specifically about our urgent desire to bring in a first increment of four divisions, and I think twenty-five separate regiments, antiaircraft and coast artillery. We wanted to put them in summer camps the 1st of July; we wanted to get them started on a schedule of intensive training because in case of an emergency we would have needed them urgently for specific assignments.

I would have you keep in mind also that, at that time, we did not know whether or not the British Empire would be in existence at the end of the next six weeks or two months and whether or not we would find ourselves with the Atlantic completely open to naval forces hostile to our interests.

All of those things came into the picture at that particular time—training possibilities, matériel, the necessity for having units available for specific purposes.

I recall saying then that we wanted to develop deliberately, and, again to use the phrase that I have used too much, we wanted to do things in a businesslike manner.

We wanted to start with a modest increment. We did not want to bring all the Guard in at once. We have never wanted to do that.

Now, today, we do not want to let them all go out at once. I am not now speaking solely of the National Guard organizations. If the National Guard is sent home now, it is automatically necessary to create new units, and if that decision is made, it will change our military policy. It will eliminate the National Guard from further serious consideration as a factor in the National Defense. It will have to be placed in a much lower category for the immediate defense of this country, and it would be necessary to maintain large forces of some other kind.

Whether that other force is composed of some units of three-year men, some units of fifty per cent three-year men, and other units of twenty-five per cent three-year men, depending on the degree of readiness necessary, the organization of such a force would constitute a new national policy. You would be nullifying the National Defense Act of 1920. The Selective Training and Service Act is merely an amplification of the National Defense Act—a system that was wanted at the time of its passage, but which could not be voted. These are the reasons we are not considering at the present time the sending home of National Guard organizations.

The selectee should enter the ranks of the National Guard exactly as he goes into the ranks of the Regular Army, from the replacement training center, after the completion of three months of individual training.

Once he is with his unit in the present situation, his period of service should depend on developments. If there is a prolonged period of uncertainty, such as we now have, we wish to continue the rotation of the selectees as far as possible, in order to bring new men in for training. The longer we freeze the men in the ranks of the Army the more difficult it will be to maintain their morale, unless real trouble starts. Then morale takes care of itself.

I would like to read an extract from my testimony before the Senate committee on July 17, which has not yet been printed. Is that agreeable to you, Mr. Clason?

THE CHAIRMAN: Go right ahead, General.

GENERAL MARSHALL [reading]:

The President has deemed it expedient to declare an unlimited emergency concerning civil functions and the War Department, and I personally, now believe it to be urgently necessary in the public interest for Congress to declare the existence of a national emergency.

In answer to a question of Senator Austin's, I made this reply: Senator Austin, on questions of legislative strategy, I am a layman, a novice. On the urgency of the situation, however, I do not regard myself as a layman nor as a novice, but rather as a highly responsible military agent of the government.

There is no doubt in my mind whatsoever about the existence of an emergency.

The declaration of an emergency does not create it. An emergency exists whether or not the Congress declares it. I am asking you to recognize the fact—the fact that the national interest is imperiled and that an emergency exists. I am not asking you to manufacture a fact.

Because an emergency exists it is necessary that authority be granted to hold National Guard units, Reserves, and selectees in the service beyond twelve months. The emergency creates this necessity. What form of statute you enact is unimportant so long as it authorizes that which the national interest requires. That is, the creation and maintenance of a strong, ready, armed force. One which can respond to whatever may be required. Not a force fettered by inelastic rules. And, if I may say so, rules do not recognize emergencies, nor do emergencies permit the existence of hampering rules.

MR. CLASON: It seems to me—and I was wondering what your position might be—that the Congress might well consider the two groups in two different resolutions because it seems to me that the National Guard is in an entirely different position from the position of the selectees. It is contained in a different law, contained in a different wording, and with an entirely different background. One is by nature a voluntary group, the National Guard; the other is a drafted group.

Do you not feel that that would be a better way; and that the two types of men are in different positions?

GENERAL MARSHALL: Practically all of the National Guard units have from thirty to fifty per cent of selectees in their ranks. So the one includes the other. Practically all of the National Guard units have a certain number of Reserve officers. All of the National Guard units have the three-year volunteers of the National Guard and the original officers commissioned in the National Guard.

My problem is to create an army out of all of these different categories, several of which have not yet been mentioned. We also have the Regular Army Reserve. This is another category and a special law refers to it. We have brought the Regular Army Reserve into active service.

We have the Reserve officers in three different categories. We have the National Guard officers, and three-year enlisted men who are a normal part of the Guard. We have National Guard officers who have been given temporary commissions from noncommissioned rank and who will go back to noncommissioned grades at the end of the emergency. We have the officers who have been commissioned, on three, four, five or six weeks' preparation, in the National Guard, either as it was preparing to come into Federal service or shortly thereafter.

We have the Regular Army units, with everything in their ranks but the National Guardsmen. But the larger units such as the army corps, include a number of National Guard organizations.

So we have a veritable mélange, a complete interweaving of all components in the Army, with separate laws applying to each.

I submit that the most effective service you can render the National Defense at this time is to permit us to create a united army, that I can treat as an army, and eliminate the forced special consideration of various groups.

As the Army exists today, I need a lawyer constantly at my side, but lawyers and legal complications are inappropriate to a battlefield.

I am utterly sincere in this. The other day I told a number of the leading Members of Congress that the way to go at this matter is to recognize the emergency and do it boldly, and squarely, without quibble or circumlocution. We are in a most serious situation, and I cannot believe that we will benefit by any evasion of the fact. An army at best is a very difficult instrument to create, and to maintain at high efficiency. A scrambled army, an inefficient army is both costly and a dubious investment. That is my sincere reaction, Mr. Clason.

*   *   *

30

Our Mission in the Army

An Address at the American Legion Convention, Milwaukee, Wisconsin, September 15, 1941

∼∼∼∼∼∼∼∼∼∼∼∼∼∼∼∼∼∼∼∼∼∼∼∼∼∼∼∼∼∼∼∼

Criticism, justified, or otherwise, is to be expected. In fact, it is as inevitable as a Congressional investigation, but when its nature and purpose is to cause disunity within the Army, I say, direct such criticisms at me personally, but leave the Army alone.

THIS National Convention of the Legion finds our country in the midst of a tremendous defense effort. It finds the Army at a momentary climax of the most extensive and strenuous peacetime training program in the history of this, or possibly, any other country.

A great deal of water has gone over the dam since your first convention in 1919. Unfortunately it carried with it, by way of erosion, most of the military power created by your youthful vigor and your willingness to serve the country in those other critical days. Obsolescence had a similar effect on matériel.

Since the transition of your men from the ranks of the Army to the ranks of the Legion, your organization has fathered and has urged, year after year, military policies and appropriations which if they had been accepted by the people and the Congress, would have found us in 1938 so strong in being and so powerful in immediate prospect, that the influence of this country might have given a different turn to the tragic history of the past two years.

No other group of men and women in this country can render such powerful support to the War Department as yours, and at no other time has this support been so necessary as it is today. In the past you have urged adequate appropriations for defense. Today, money is not the acute problem—the Congress has been ready to provide the desired appropriations. What we lack and what we must have is an understanding by every family in America of the gravity of our situation. They should understand what it takes in discipline, in training, and in time to make a dependable army, and they must realize what infinite harm can be done through ignorance of military requirements and unwitting coöperation with agencies working in the interest of potential enemies.

The problems of preparing our present military forces are quite different from those with which you men were familiar in 1917. In those days the matter of equipment was solved by the tremendous productive capacity which had been developed in England and France after three years' concentrated military effort. Our troops were sent overseas barehanded, versed only in the basic training of the soldier. Divisions were equipped in the field, trained within sound of the guns along the lines held by our Allies. Corps and armies were actually organized on the battlefield. Units were placed in the line at our convenience. Tactical errors, the results of faulty leadership, were not fatal, although unnecessary losses resulted, since they were localized by the very nature of the sector warfare of that period.

The technique of 1917 is outmoded today. The specialized training for a particular type of operation gives way to the necessity for perfect teamwork in fast-moving operations over any type of terrain. A high degree of technical and tactical knowledge is necessary, from the individual soldier to the commanders of the highest units. Skilled initiative is a mandatory requirement. The complicated coördination of fire power, ground and air, must be managed at top speed, and for a surprising variety of weapons, with little or no opportunity to rehearse the procedure or to gain familiarity with the ground.

The training of this modern Army has been steadily progressive in nature. The soldier is given thirteen weeks of basic military education, including specialized training for his branch of the service. He is then assigned to a tactical unit where he passes through a period of unit training. The man who entered the Army last fall is now engaged in a final phase of training—that is, field service as a member of large military units. These maneuvers have been in progress all summer, with constantly increasing forces until they are now culminating in the operations of three field armies, involving three-quarters of a million men.

It is difficult to overemphasize the importance of the maneuvers. You veterans who served in France will recall the fog of battle and the utter confusion which often prevails when large military forces come to grips; you probably remember the tremendous difficulties of ammunition and food supply; the great strain placed on field communications and the difficulty of their maintenance; I know you realize the stern necessity of willing obedience and firm discipline. In actual battle these matters are of decisive importance and they cannot be simulated on the parade ground. The present maneuvers are the closest peacetime approximation to actual fighting conditions that has ever been undertaken in this country. But what is of the greatest importance, the mistakes and failures will not imperil the nation or cost the lives of men. In the past we have jeopardized our future, penalized our leaders and sacrificed our men by training untrained troops on the battlefield.

The maneuvers also constitute a field laboratory to accept or discard new methods of applying fundamental tactical principles. They enable us to perfect close liaison between combat aviation and ground units. They permit of test of a possible solution to the secret of defense against tanks. By actual field operations we are determining the proper tactics for the employment of armored units. The development of our mechanized reconnaissance units is being accelerated by experience with the difficulties and uncertainties created by masses of troops operating over wide distances. Opposing divisions are kept in the dark as to the size, equipment, and other capabilities of their immediate opponents. The results at times have been startling. In some cases divisions would have been annihilated; in others they would have been captured. On the field of battle such events would be tragic. Today they are merely mistakes. We can correct them, replace the ineffective leaders, and go ahead. As an insurance policy against whatever operations our troops might be called upon to perform, the cost of these maneuvers represents a trifling premium to pay. Tremendous sums of money have been spent on our national defense effort, but I know of no single investment which will give this country a greater return in security and in the saving of lives than the present maneuvers.

Although we have streamlined the Army, blistered feet and aching bones are still the lot of the recruit, and heavy burdens and long marches the rôle of the majority of the soldiers. Tank and truck travel may be fast but it is far from luxurious, really a severe hardship, which the men must be trained to endure.

Strenuous as the past year has been on the troops, we will find that all but a few have gained weight and that despite the tremendous increase in the size of the Army during the past year, the death rate has actually decreased from three per thousand to two per thousand. Although we moved hundreds of thousands of men from all parts of the United States into tent camps in the middle of winter, the sickness rate in our Army camps was, and is, generally below that of the average civilian community. Our soldiers probably constitute the healthiest group of individuals in the world today.

Along with the progress of the past year, we have encountered problems that have taxed our ingenuity to the extreme and there is one in particular which I wish to discuss tonight. It is a very serious matter for it strikes at the tap root of military efficiency.

Although the President has proclaimed a state of emergency, the Army for all practical purposes is still operating under peacetime conditions. Perhaps it is this unusual, unprecedented situation which has resulted in a lack of understanding by the public as well as parents of soldiers and the soldiers themselves, regarding fundamental military requirements. The power of an army cannot be measured in mere numbers. It is based on a high state of discipline and training; on a readiness to carry out its mission wherever and whenever the Commander in Chief and Congress decide. Any compromise with *those* requirements and *that* purpose not only minimizes our efforts but largely vitiates our development of military power.

This army belongs to the American people—it is their army, your army. What it does, what it is, are naturally matters of personal interest to all of our people; not only to those who have relatives in uniform, but to every citizen depending on the army for security. Despite the pros and cons which have attended every issue debated during the past year, whether on the floors of Congress, in the press or over the radio, I am certain that everyone is in agreement on one point—that is, this country must have the best army in the world.

Now, as veteran soldiers, I submit to you men of the Legion the impossibility of developing an efficient army if decisions which are purely military in nature are continuously subjected to investigation, cross-examination, debate, ridicule, and public discussion by pressure groups, or by individuals with only a superficial knowledge of military matters, or of the actual facts in the particular case. I submit that there is a clear line of demarcation between the democratic freedom of discussion which we are determined to preserve and a destructive procedure which promotes discontent and destroys confidence in the Army.

As Chief of Staff I am largely responsible for the military program and for the decisions of subordinates. Mistakes have been made and it is to be expected that more will be made. However, I am certain that we in the Army are the most severe critics and also that we can best detect deficiencies and we are better prepared to determine the method for their correction.

Please have these considerations in mind. A sane, a wonderful step has been taken by this country in adopting a policy of preparing its military forces in time of peace as the wisest of precautionary measures in the face of a world crisis. The very fact that the nation has shown such unprecedented foresight in a military way presents the most serious difficulty for those responsible for the development of the army. With a clear-cut task before us well known to the troops, the development of the Army would be comparatively a simple matter. But *must* we *declare war* in order to facilitate training and morale? *Must* you *burn down* the building in order to justify the Fire Department?

The local posts of the Legion can do much to bring the people at home to a better understanding of the requirements of the situation. Even you

veterans probably do not realize the result of appeals of the young man
angling for a home-made cake or bragging to his parents or his girl of the
hardships he endures, or grousing over the failure of his leaders to recognize his particular ability by immediate promotion. The War Department at times receives a veritable avalanche of criticisms or pressures
resulting from such ordinary soldier reactions as these. The incidents in
themselves are often amusing, as in the case of the mother who com-
plained that her son wasn't getting enough to eat, and we found her boy
had gained sixteen pounds in twenty days. But the total effect is really
serious. As I read confidential reports from abroad there is a startling
similarity between our present situation in this respect and that which
affected the late lamented army of France. Criticism, justified or otherwise, is to be expected. In fact, it is as inevitable as a Congressional
investigation, but when its *nature* or *purpose* is to cause disunity within
the Army, I say, direct such criticisms at me personally, but leave the
Army alone. Don't tear down what you are striving so hard to build up.

Let me cite an example of what I mean. Take the matter of a separate
air force. Because we are convinced that the establishment of a separate
air force would not only be a grave error but would completely disrupt
the splendid organization now in process of building, we are accused of
being unprogressive, jealous of prerogatives and incredibly short-sighted.

On the basis of cold-blooded analysis of facts, the matter has been
studied in great detail by the War Department during the operations in
which foreign nations are now involved. I can assure you that nothing
has developed as a result of the present set-up in the United States. Com-
parisons are drawn that two nations whose air forces have attained the
greatest success have so-called separate air forces. Here again we encounter a confusion of facts. Consider, for instance, the case of our
friends, the British. Except for the gallant and truly remarkable defense
of the British Isles which is a special problem having little application to
our problem of hemisphere defense, the lack of unity of command between the air and ground forces has courted disaster in virtually every
operation they have undertaken. In the operations in Belgium, and
France, in Norway, in Greece, in Crete and in the Middle East this lack
of unity of command has remained a continuous, unsolved problem. In
fact, the British have found it necessary to modify the separate air arm
idea with respect to naval aviation. More recently they have been improvising special groups to operate more closely with ground troops.

The ex-democracy of France had a separate air force which operated
on a basis similar to that which some individuals are now proposing that
we adopt. France was defeated and reduced to a state of vassalage in a
five-week's campaign. The Italian Air Force which nurtures the theory

of total war from the air and which has so-called independent control has yet to be effective in the present war. Contrary to popular belief, the German Air Force is not independent of the ground arms in the generally conceived sense, but is closely coördinated by means of a system of command and staff over and above all civil departments, which would not be acceptable to a democracy such as the United States. The German government is geared throughout for the primary purpose of making war through a superlatively centralized form of control. Hitler is Commander in Chief, but he operates through a Chief of Staff of a Supreme Staff which plans, directs, and controls the operations of the Army, Navy, and Air Force, and is responsible only to the head of the government. Through this machinery a campaign is planned, the organizations—air, ground, and naval—are allotted, and a commander is designated. He organizes and trains this task force and at the appointed time carries out the campaign with every available resource of Germany in support. He may be a ground officer, an air or a naval officer. But he is in sole charge of every phase of the operation.

It is needless to say that the American people are not likely to establish a military oligarchy for this country, and lacking such an organization the German system would be ineffective. As a matter of fact, we have adapted to our own use a set-up that approximates that of Germany as closely as is possible under our system of government.

Just a year ago the President gave final approval to the Selective Training and Service Act and to legislation authorizing reserve components to be called into federal service. The importance of these two measures for the National Defense was tremendous. They constituted a reversal of the historic and almost tragic policy that the United States should prepare for war only after becoming involved in war. Our peacetime military force was maintained for minor transactions, not to meet a first-class foe; a perilous policy, and one of extreme extravagance in men and money when the emergency arose. The greatest security which this nation can possess is a powerful navy, backed by a well trained army, together so strong that no foreign nation will dare to provoke a war. The army is now in the making, but it must go through another winter of training under field conditions before it is fully prepared; and it must have the understanding and support of the people at home.

You gentlemen are practical soldiers. You can understand the difficulty of handling large masses of men under conditions of warfare. You recognize the meaning and importance of discipline. You realize how easy it is to tear down, and how difficult it is to build it up. During this emergency the sound policies of the Legion have been a tower of strength to the War Department and to commanders in the field, and it is to you that I look for the support necessary to the accomplishment of our objective.

The spirit and determination that were yours twenty-three years ago, in the Meuse-Argonne, at St. Mihiel, or in a training camp at home, must be instilled in the men of this new army. You can understand this and I know you will help. There is a further responsibility which I place upon you. I look to you to educate the people at home as to the necessities of the times. Without a united country it will be impossible to build the type of army we must have. We cannot build the best army in the world unless the people of this country are behind it.

I am a soldier and I have spoken to you as one soldier to another. I have but one purpose, one mission, and that is to produce the most efficient army in the world. Given the American type of soldier and our war industries operating at top speed; given your aggressive support on the home front, it can be done, and it will be done in time.

31
The Challenge of Command

An Address to the Graduates of the First Officer Candidate School, Fort Benning, Georgia, September 18, 1941

~~~~~~

Warfare today is a thing of swift movement—of rapid concentrations. It requires the building up of enormous fire power against successive objectives with breath-taking speed. It is not a game for the unimaginative plodder. Modern battles are fought by platoon leaders.

YOU are about to assume the most important duty that our officers are called upon to perform—the direct command of combat units of American soldiers. To succeed requires two fundamental qualifications—thorough professional knowledge and a capacity for leadership. The schools have done all that can be done in the limited time available to equip you professionally, and your technique of weapons and tactics should rapidly improve with further study and actual practice. However, they cannot provide you with qualities of leadership—that courage and evident high purpose which command the respect and loyalty of American soldiers.

You were selected as officer candidates because you gave evidence of possessing these qualifications. Whether or not you develop into truly capable leaders depends almost entirely upon you personally.

Your school work has been under ideal conditions from an instructional standpoint; but when you join your organizations, you will find many difficulties and deficiencies complicating your task. There will be shortages in equipment, for example. These are being made good as rapidly as possible, but so long as they exist they are a challenge to your ingenuity and not an invitation to fall back on an overdose of close-order drill and the other necessary but stultifying minutiæ which so irked the Army of 1917 that we still suffer from the repercussions.

Warfare today is a thing of swift movement—of rapid concentrations. It requires the building up of enormous fire power against successive objectives with breath-taking speed. It is not a game for the unimaginative plodder. Modern battles are fought by platoon leaders. The carefully prepared plans of higher commanders can do no more than project you to the line of departure at the proper time and place, in proper formation, and start you off in the right direction. Thereafter, the responsibility for results is almost entirely yours. If you know your business of weapons and tactics, if you have inspired the complete confidence and loyalty of your men, things will go well on that section of the front.

There is a gulf between the drill ground or cantonment type of leadership and that necessary for the successful command of men when it may involve the question of sacrificing one's life. Our army differs from all other armies. The very characteristics which make our men potentially the best soldiers in the world can be in some respects a possible source of weakness. Racially we are not a homogeneous people, like the British for example, who can glorify a defeat by their stubborn tenacity and dogged discipline. We have no common racial group, and we have deliberately cultivated individual initiative and independence of thought and action. Our men are intelligent and resourceful to an unusual degree. These characteristics, these qualities may be, in effect, explosive or positively destructive in a military organization, especially under adverse conditions, unless the leadership is wise and determined, and unless the leader commands the complete respect of his men.

Never for an instant can you divest yourselves of the fact that you are officers. On the athletic field, at the club, in civilian clothes, or even at home on leave, the fact that you are a commissioned officer in the Army imposes a constant obligation to higher standards than might ordinarily seem normal or necessary for your personal guidance. A small dereliction becomes conspicuous, at times notorious, purely by reason of the fact that the individual concerned is a commissioned officer.

But the evil result goes much further than a mere matter of unfortunate publicity. When you are commanding, leading men under conditions where physical exhaustion and privations must be ignored; where the lives of men may be sacrificed, then, the efficiency of your leadership will depend only to a minor degree on your tactical or technical ability. It will primarily be determined by your character, your reputation, not so much for courage—which will be accepted as a matter of course—but by the previous reputation you have established for fairness, for that high-minded patriotic purpose, that quality of unswerving determination to carry through any military task assigned you.

The feeling which the men must hold for you is not to be compared to the popularity of a football coach or a leader of civic activities. Professional competence is essential to leadership and your knowledge of arms, equipment, and tactical operations must be clearly superior to that possessed by your subordinates; at the same time, you must command their respect above and beyond those qualities.

It is difficult to make a clear picture of the obligations and requirements for an officer. Conditions of campaign and the demands of the battlefield are seldom appreciated except by veterans of such experiences. The necessity for discipline is never fully comprehended by the soldier until he has undergone the ordeal of battle, and even then he lacks a basis of comparison—the contrast between the action of a disciplined regiment and the failure and probable disintegration of one which lacks that intangible quality. The quality of officers is tested to the limit during the long and trying periods of waiting or marching here and there without evident purpose, and during those weeks or months of service under conditions of extreme discomfort or of possible privations or isolations. The true leader surmounts all of these difficulties, maintaining the discipline of his unit and further developing its training. Where there is a deficiency of such leadership, serious results inevitably follow, and too often the criticism is directed to the conditions under which the unit labored rather than toward the individual who failed in his duty because he was found wanting in inherent ability to accept his responsibilities.

Remember that we are a people prone to be critical of everything except that for which we are personally responsible. Remember also that to a soldier a certain amount of grousing appears to be necessary. However, there is a vast difference between these usually amusing reactions and the destructive and disloyal criticism of the undisciplined soldier.

Mental alertness, initiative, vision are qualities which you must cultivate. Passive inactivity because you have not been given specific instructions to do this or to do that is a serious deficiency. Always encourage initiative on the part of your men, but initiative must of course, be accompanied by intelligence.

Much of what I have said has been by way of repetition of one thought which I wish you gentlemen to carry with you to your new duties. You will be responsible for a unit in the Army of the United States in this great emergency. Its quality, its discipline, its training will depend upon your leadership. Whatever deficiencies there are must be charged to your failure or incapacity. Remember this: the truly great leader overcomes all difficulties, and campaigns and battles are nothing but a long series of difficulties to be overcome. The lack of equipment, the lack of food, the lack of this or that are only excuses; the real leader displays his quality in his triumphs over adversity, however great it may be.

Good luck to you. We expect great things of you. Your class is the first of which I believe will be the finest group of troop leaders in the world.

32
Lend-Lease

Statements before the House of Representatives Subcommittee, Committee on Appropriations, on Consideration of the Second Supplemental Appropriation Bill for 1942 (including Lend-Lease) 77th Congress, 1st Session, September 29, 1941

〜〜〜〜〜〜〜〜〜〜〜〜〜〜〜〜〜〜〜〜〜〜

Wherever we can furnish matériel without detriment to our own military requirements, against the possible collapse of the powers fighting the Axis countries, it is definitely to our advantage to do so . . .

THE CHAIRMAN [REPRESENTATIVE CLARENCE CANNON OF MISSOURI]: General Marshall, have you a formal statement you wish to present?

GENERAL MARSHALL: I have a brief statement; yes.

THE CHAIRMAN: You may proceed.

GENERAL MARSHALL: Mr. Chairman, the War Department allocation from the defense-aid estimates now before you is $2,255,575,667. This sum is requested under the provisions of "An act to promote the defense of the United States" approved March 11, 1941 [HR 1776], as essential to meet the more urgent and immediate requirements submitted by the United Kingdom, China, and the American republics.

The actual items of equipment and material, and the money value thereof, included in these estimates in general provide for shortages of equipment and supplies originally requested in connection with the Defense Aid Supplemental Appropriation Act, 1941, but on which action was suspended because of lack of funds. There are but few new items included in the estimates.

Agencies of the War Department have carefully reviewed the list of items submitted to the Department as requirements of the countries seeking aid under the provisions of HR 1776. The review has been made with the following basic principle in mind:

First, with reference to the type of material requested. In almost every case it has been determined that the items of equipment and the material requested is either of United States standard type or of a type which could be used by the United States Army in case it were not required, due to some future contingency, by the country to be aided. There are of necessity certain exceptions to this principle caused by the specific requirements of the countries concerned. Effort is made, however, to keep these exceptions to a minimum and to restrict them for the most part of components or accessories, rather than complete items of military equipment.

Second, as regards the ability of industry to meet military-production requirements. Full consideration has been given to the position of our existing armament program before agreement has been reached on the requirements submitted by the countries to be aided. In general, it has been determined that the production of the items required will complement the production of similar items on order for our own forces, and thus will assist in increasing the productive capacity available to our own forces.

Third, as regards the need of the countries requesting aid for the items requested. Each request received in the War Department is carefully scrutinized by the War Plans Division and the Supply Division of the General Staff. The principal consideration is to determine whether or not the procedure is to our eventual advantage; and to what extent the items can be supplied from stocks available for transfer under the terms of Section III a (2) of HR 1776, without detriment to our interests.

As stated by the Secretary of War, an agency has been established within the War Department to consider and submit recommendations upon all requirements submitted by foreign countries. This agency is known as the Defense Aid Supply Committee. On it are representatives of the office of the Under Secretary of War, the Supply and War Plans Divisions of the War Department General Staff, War Department supply arms and services concerned with the procurement and distribution of the equipment, War Department users of the equipment, and representatives of the country to be aided. All of the items included in the estimates now before you have been considered by this committee which has unanimously recommended their procurement.

There are two categories of items in these estimates about which I wish to speak specifically. The first of these is that of spare parts. In the haste to get production of complete items, the matter of obtaining spare parts is proving difficult.

It is our experience that most manufacturers under contract for the production of defense items desire to establish a record in the production of complete items. In accomplishing this they avoid the complications involved in diverting a portion of their facilities to the production of spares. While this may be satisfactory for the moment, with respect to our own forces—which are just receiving this new type equipment for the first time—it is an entirely different story when it becomes necessary to maintain this equipment on distant fields of battle. Even with respect to the items which it has been possible thus far to transfer to the countries to be aided, there has been a serious difficulty in obtaining sufficient spare parts to keep the equipment in action. After a considerable study of the wastage factors involved and those being experienced by the countries to be aided, it has been determined that it will be necessary to finance in dollar value roughly forty per cent of the original cost of items for spare part purposes. The amounts in these estimates for such purposes are not nearly that great, largely due to the fact that spare parts are not at this time so readily obtainable. The estimates make provision for what is considered the minimum essential pool of spare parts which must be set up at this time for transfer to those countries which have equipment furnished from Defense Aid, in order to assure the continued operation of such equipment in combat.

The second category, of which I specifically wish to comment, is that of miscellaneous items. There are thousands of miscellaneous component items which are needed by the countries to be aided, such for instance as special type containers to permit loading of equipment and ammunition in special vehicles; materials for manufacture of explosives; radio parts; parts for modernization of existing equipment; ammunition components, such as primers and fuzes; and standard hardware. The Defense Aid Supply Committee of the War Department has been clearing requests for miscellaneous items of equipment at the rate of about ninety million dollars per month. Contrary to expectations, there has been no slowing up of this rate. Because of the exhaustion of the funds provided the War Department from the Defense Aid Supplemental Appropriation Act, 1941, it has in some instances been necessary to forego or cancel the purchase of complete items of military equipment in order to provide sufficient funds for miscellaneous purchases. The items contained in the estimates under the heading "Unspecified future requirements" make provision for this purpose. The sums requested under these items are based upon a ninety million dollar per month rate being maintained through the period to February 28, 1942.

The War Department has foreseen the necessity for additional appropriations for Defense Aid purposes from the time the original requirements for Defense Aid were presented to the Department. The allocations made to the War Department from the amounts appropriated under the Defense Aid Supplemental Appropriation Act, 1941, were inadequate to meet the demands upon the Department by those countries approved for aid under the act. The amounts proposed in these estimates are still inadequate to meet those requirements of the countries requesting aid which have been recommended after careful consideration by the War Department agencies concerned. The items included in these estimates represent in money value less than half of the outstanding requirements reported at this time by the countries to be aided. From the War Department viewpoint there is an immediate and pressing need for the funds in these estimates if the Department is to meet the responsibilities placed upon it under the policy established by the Congress in the enactment of HR 1776, and thus furnish its maximum contribution under the act toward aiding those countries which are assisting in the defense of the United States.

One final point in closing. The items covered by the funds requested in the estimates represent actual stated requirements of certain countries now at war. Obviously, information concerning these requirements would be valuable and of assistance to their enemies. It is, therefore, essential that the greatest possible secrecy be preserved by all concerned as regards the specific requests contained in the estimates.

I urge you to grant the estimates as requested.

THE CHAIRMAN: General Marshall, what is the military aspect of the Lend-Lease program presented in this estimate; that is, to what extent will it serve the purposes and objectives from the military point of view?

GENERAL MARSHALL: Wherever we can furnish matériel without detriment to our own military requirements, against the possible collapse of the powers fighting the Axis countries, it is definitely to our advantage to do so. For example, with reference to the present tremendous battle going on in Russia—the estimates now before you make no specific provision for aid to Russia and while we have not a great deal we could provide at this time, and what little we do have would take a long time to ship, all must realize that whatever we do to keep the Russian Army in the field aggressively resisting the Germans is to our great advantage. It would increase the chances of a successful end to the war; it would hasten the early conclusion. Our assistance will not only contribute directly to the safety of the Western Hemisphere but will shorten the period of tremendous expenditures for defense. If the present conflict drags on through a period of years you will certainly have a constantly mounting bill of expenses.

The German scheme of campaigns from the start has been a tremendous effort to settle the war quickly, brutally, rapidly. They were defeated in 1918 due to the fact that they failed to carry through the French and Russian campaigns to quick conclusion in 1914 as planned. They had almost completed the encirclement of the French armies when they were forced to withdraw some of their divisions and send them to fight Russia. To sum up as an illustration of the question, it is axiomatic that anything that can be done to keep Russia fighting makes a mighty contribution to what we all are endeavoring to bring about—an early termination of the war by the destruction of the German war machine, through attrition or dispersion, through defeat or by the collapse of the German Government.

THE CHAIRMAN: You say in your statement that there is an urgent and pressing need for this appropriation?

GENERAL MARSHALL: Yes.

THE CHAIRMAN: About how soon should it become available?

GENERAL MARSHALL: Mr. Chairman, you are getting into a very technical field for me. All I can say is that even with the present marked efficiency of the Ordnance Department it takes a long time to put the money to work. Time is required for all the necessary minutiae that is incident to placing Government contracts. I am certain that it is essential that they know definitely that this money will be available in order that they may go ahead with contracts for this new equipment as rapidly as possible.

This whole struggle has been one of providing matériel. The course of this war is so unpredictable in every way, and particularly as to requirements of weapons and matériel that we must not be on the short side. The Congress has adopted a policy, in the original Lend-Lease Act. I think it would be a great mistake to temper or delay the procedure under the present policy. Rather abandon the policy entirely. That is your choice. Our Army has suffered steadily from such delays. The British suffer today and risked their national existence by similar delays.

MR. D. LANE POWERS OF NEW JERSEY: That delay has not been the result of any action on the part of Congress, has it, General Marshall?

GENERAL MARSHALL: Not in connection with Lend-Lease; no.

MR. POWERS: That is what I mean.

THE CHAIRMAN: General Marshall, you say that we must not be on the short side. You mean by that, I take it, we must provide at this time ample appropriations that will shorten the war and that will make it less expensive in the end?

GENERAL MARSHALL: We certainly will not shorten it by delays.

THE CHAIRMAN: As a military man and as the one who has perhaps made a closer study than anyone else in the country, you think we should proceed with the use of our every resource and with as little delay and little parsimony as possible.

GENERAL MARSHALL: That is an excellent statement of the way I feel about it, except the last three words, "As little parsimony as possible"; I think, "with as much efficiency as possible."

THE CHAIRMAN: And if we are to proceed efficiently we must have money.

GENERAL MARSHALL: Yes; if the program is to be a success.

MR. CLIFTON A. WOODRUM OF VIRGINIA: General, I want to ask you just one or two questions. This bill pending before the Committee, of course, as you have indicated, is to implement the Lend-Lease policy designed by the Congress in the passage of HR 1776. I was very much interested and gratified with the statement and recommendation several times in your statement that these materials are to be sent to the British when they do not in any way weaken our own position for our own defense.

GENERAL MARSHALL: Yes.

MR. WOODRUM: In that light I want to call your attention to an item, if you have not already seen it, that appeared in the *Washington Post* on the front page of September 28, that is, yesterday, and an article along the same line in today's *Washington Post*. It states:

> United States may stop draft, send all arms output to Russia, Britain. Supplies inadequate for larger Army here and help to foes of Nazis, too.
>
> The induction of selectees into the United States Army may virtually be halted in the near future, the *Washington Post* learned yesterday.
>
> No decision to suspend induction has been reached, but high officials, it is known, are at least seriously considering such a suspension.
>
> If the decision should be in the affirmative, it would mean a temporary "freezing" of the Army at a figure considerably below the size once contemplated, which was 1,750,000.

The articles goes on to point out that the present strength of the Army, as of September 18, including the Regulars, National Guard, and Reserve officers and Selective Service trainees as one million five hundred ninety-seven thousand eight hundred ten. It further points out that it is contemplated to release about two hundred thousand of those that were first in, reducing the strength down to around one and a quarter million.

If any such policy as contemplated in this article is seriously considered by those high in authority it would mean instead of building up the Army as contemplated, decreasing it to a million and a half men, stop giving them further material and sending it abroad. I would like you, if you feel like it, to comment on that, as to whether there is any such policy in contemplation or what you think of such a policy if it is contemplated.

GENERAL MARSHALL: Mr. Woodrum, I know of no such contemplated policy except from reading a series of articles in the papers which look like—

MR. WOODRUM [interposing]: A build-up?

GENERAL MARSHALL: A build-up of some sort with which I am unacquainted. I would say that it would be a particularly tragic procedure from several points of view: It would serve notice, for example, to German officials that they could ignore the military might of America. A vast power now in the offing could be ignored in their calculations, not to mention the devastating effect of such shuttling about of a broad national policy.

This should never be allowed to happen. The German leaders should always have before them the constantly growing power of America to thwart their plan of world domination. We must not thus lightly and suddenly abandon a great governmental policy designed for our security in this troubled world. You cannot engage in the business of building a vast machine such as this emergency army and then sweep it aside because of the news of the week, the situation of the moment. Incidentally, omitting the recruits or selectees undergoing basic training, the administrative overhead, the coast defense, air forces, and overseas garrisons, we have left a very small force—our field army, only thirty-five divisions.

MR. WOODRUM: In other words, and I would assume this without your saying so, it is your hope that we do not in any sense of the word abandon the present program.

GENERAL MARSHALL: Absolutely.

*   *   *

MR. JOHN TABER OF NEW YORK: Now, General, to what extent do you personally go over the items that are presented by the purchase requests?

GENERAL MARSHALL: Actually I saw the original list. I examined the totals, considered the types of the articles to see if they were asking for things not usable by us, or which would seem to complicate our production problem. I assured myself that the items they were asking for fitted in in general with what we required and would add to our defensive power if we had to use them. Further, I assured myself, through my assistants who followed it from the technical side, that what was being asked for as to type fitted in with our general picture of production development. Then I discussed quantities with the officers of the War Plans Division of the General Staff in order to obtain their views as to the necessity for the requisitions submitted.

We have reports from our own observers in the countries requesting aid. They are organized as staff groups and they inquire into everything to see that we are not being requested to supply matériel and equipment which cannot be made use of by the countries submitting the requests.

After that discussion and superficial examination by me, General Moore [Major General Richard C. Moore] then takes it up, as Deputy Chief of Staff for supply and as a member of this committee to which I referred. He carefully goes over the requests with the War Department agencies concerned with the Assistant Chief of Staff G-4, and with the various supply services, including the Ordnance Department under General Wesson [Major General Charles M. Wesson, Chief of Ordnance] and in the case of airplanes and related equipment with the air force under General Arnold. Then it comes back to me.

MR. TABER: Do you have any means of checking on it to see whether the British actually need the things they ask for?

GENERAL MARSHALL: Yes, sir.

MR. TABER: I have not found anyone yet who was able to give us any picture of that situation. If you could give us a statement about that I think it would be very helpful to the Committee. We have not had anybody who could give us that satisfactorily at all.

GENERAL MARSHALL: I will try to do that.

[The statement is as follows]:

The general method followed in checking all lend-lease requirements is described below:

The basic factors involved are:

(1) Our own needs.

(2) Consideration of present over-all organizational objectives of Great Britain and her associates with their general strategic purpose and schedule of development.

(3) Equipment now on hand to meet this objective, including maintenance and reserves.

(4) Equipment now being produced in Great Britain and associated countries.

(5) Schedule of expansion in units.

(6) Experience as to maintenance and reserves required.

The above indicates the bases, in general, upon which the War Department General Staff checks requirements both for Great Britain and for other countries to be aided. Much of the information must necessarily be obtained from British and other sources and is subject to change as the strategic and tactical situation varies. However, the War Department scrutinizes each program and each request for the purpose of determining how best to serve our own interests as well as meeting the requirements of the nations to be aided. To assist in accomplishing this purpose military observers have been sent to all principal theaters and to other areas which may later become scenes of combat. These observers are our representatives, and as such they report conditions as they see them from our own viewpoint. They visualize present and future needs not only for the initial issue of equipment but for its proper operation and maintenance as well.

Decision on requirements in some cases is necessarily made without as much information as is desirable. However, the general strategic situation confronting Great Britain and her associates has been and is such that strategically justifiable needs have so far exceeded available supplies of critical items.

MR. GEORGE W. JOHNSON OF WEST VIRGINIA: General, you need production more than you do money, do you not?

GENERAL MARSHALL: We need money, but we need production too.

* * *

33
The Citizens' Defense Corps

A Radio Broadcast on the Citizens' Defense Corps
from Washington, D. C., November 11, 1941

*We should set ourselves with determination to
see this thing through as a united people.*

THE anniversary of the Armistice of 1918 is a day of renewed tributes to the memory of those who made the great sacrifices of the last war. It also has been the occasion for rejoicing over the victorious conclusion of that war.

Today's anniversary finds us with little reason for rejoicing. Instead we have reached a moment in our history, I believe, when the civilian should definitely take his place in the general preparation of the country to meet the tragic circumstances of these fateful days. The Navy on the seas and the Army in our distant outposts are prepared to do their duty. Behind them a powerful military force is rapidly being developed. Industry is now moving into high speed production of munitions. Finally, today, on the twenty-third anniversary of that futile armistice, the President inaugurates a week to prepare for the organized coöperation of civilians in our defense effort.

To organize the home front for the protection of the civilian communities, a new arm—the Citizens' Defense Corps—is in process of formation. Somewhat like the Army with its various arms and branches, this Corps has its air-raid wardens, its auxiliary police and fire fighters, its first aid and hospital service, its Signal Corps and Motor Corps, its engineers and other special units. Men and women to form these ranks will do so voluntarily along with their normal daily tasks. The details of organization have been or will be explained to you by local committees, by speakers on the radio, and through the medium of the press.

Mayor LaGuardia[23] has been charged by the President with the tremendous task of organizing this corps of citizens. At the outset he is faced with the problem of convincing one hundred thirty million people whose shores have seen no invader for a century and a quarter, of the need for this step. He must convince them of the necessity for organizing against any eventuality.

Mr. LaGuardia has asked me to give you my opinion as to the im-

[23]The Honorable Fiorello H. LaGuardia, Chairman, Citizens' Defense Corps, and Mayor of New York City.

portance of this task he has undertaken. From the standpoint of the soldier, the urgency of this project is difficult to overemphasize. An Army is no stronger than the people behind it. Soldiers require the whole-hearted support of their home folk. They are entitled to it. They must have it. Furthermore, soldiers need to be reassured that measures have been taken to care for their families, to protect them in an emergency.

We pride ourselves on being an energetic and determined people, not easily duped and far from gullible, but we live in a free land and with such kindly relations to one another that we fail to appreciate the dangerous possibilities of the present situation. We should realize that the more we, as a nation, influence the course of this war, the more important it becomes for us to protect every phase of our national life against the efforts of the Axis Powers to deter or to weaken us. The difficulty of arousing our people to a clear understanding of what must be done varies, somewhat directly, with the distance of their homes from the Atlantic and Pacific seaboards. And yet that apparent security of distance presents a great weakness to the German mode of procedure.

We must be prepared on the home front against both the direct methods of sabotage, and against the direct and subtle methods of propaganda. It is not difficult for the inhabitants of coastal communities to recognize the necessity for organizing an air-raid warning service. It is more difficult to convince people in the interior of the country that some of the most serious schemes for destructive action against our interests are possibilities in their midst.

It seems best to speak very frankly on this particular subject. The Government today is constantly on guard against damage to our industries or their products, but we must be prepared for a sudden and widespread attempt at sabotage directed against the entire munitions industry, including the critical utilities and transportation facilities. Nothing should be taken for granted. We should assume that at a given moment wholesale sabotage may be attempted by the far-reaching organization which has secretly and ceaselessly been planning for just such an occasion. We must be prepared against the confusion that so easily can be created in large centers of population, and we must be organized to look after our people at home in any emergency, whatever the nature.

However, while not minimizing the seriousness of the possibilities just mentioned I personally am more concerned over the effects of the clever methods of Axis propaganda which for a long time have been directed against the development of our entire defense program. A portion of my daily mail is more or less a direct repercussion of such German scheming. The letters come from families who are worrying about their boys in the Army, who have been led to believe, for instance, that the soldiers lack food, lack proper shelter or medical attention. They come from members of Congress who have been similarly misled. This process of misrepresentation and distortion has been carried on with persistence and skill. Sometimes the results are seriously disturbing.

Let me give you an example. Last summer, incident to the democratic process of Congressional debate on the question of the extension of service, public interest centered on the Army; everything concerned with the troops—their training, the conditions under which they were living, and the state of their equipment—were the subject of widespread discussion and publicity. In this connection I wish to read an extract from the instructions issued by the German Ministry of Propaganda last April: "It is more effective," these instructions state, "when the American press provides propaganda for our mill than if we do it ourselves."

Now, what happened last summer? The debate was on, the criticisms of our good faith and judgment were naturally frequent, and the more unfavorable reactions of individual soldiers were broadcast. Mass desertions were reported to threaten the Army in October.

Throughout the press of Latin America we found comments and conclusions seriously prejudicial to our interests, being given wide publicity, along with clever distortions of the facts. I read similar articles in the Italian papers, assuring their people that a breakdown of military preparation in this country was in progress. But the cleverest move to capitalize on this golden opportunity for sabotage was a rumor skillfully planted among the men in National Guard units that a large number of soldiers, more than a thousand, had deserted *en masse* from a certain Regular Army division. The men had been fed this particular rumor because such an occurrence in the Regular Army was indicative of a general breakdown in discipline. The actual fact in this matter was that the division in question had one lone desertion in the period referred to. And yet there had been spread throughout a large part of the Army this carefully planned attack on the soundness of our military organization. Back at home, mothers were confused and prejudiced to an extent that was both pathetic and alarming. In certain districts known to have a number of people opposed to the strengthening of our means of defense, the reactions to this propaganda were increasingly evident.

There have been many examples of this same general nature, examples of skillful borings from within to weaken the power of the Government. We no longer live in a "snug, over-safe corner of the world." We cannot continue to be naïve and credulous. On the contrary, we should set ourselves with determination to see this thing through as a united people. For these reasons, I believe that the Citizens' Defense Corps will serve a vital purpose in completing our general organization for the security of America, and I am sure that it will exert a strong influence in combating secret and destructive efforts to divide and confuse our people. I urge the whole-hearted coöperation of the leaders in every community to complete the organization of the Corps.

PART TWO

The Nation at War

34
The Day After Pearl Harbor

An Address at the Conference of Negro Newspaper
Editors, Washington, D. C., December 8, 1941

〜〜〜〜〜〜〜〜〜〜〜〜〜〜〜〜〜〜〜〜〜〜〜〜〜

*It is now only a few hours since this nation was attacked
by one of the great armed forces of the world. . . . I
know that this news has brought to all our people a new
realization of our common destiny as free men.*

I AM GLAD to welcome you gentlemen to the War Department.
It is now only a few hours since this nation was attacked by one of
the great armed forces of the world. Great as our efforts in the interest of National Defense have been during the year which now draws
to a close, events of the past day have brought to us the sterner realities
of actual war.

Those of you who have come from a considerable distance in order to
meet with us here today left your home while we were still a nation at
peace. Today we have been saddened by the news of other homes on
American soil, in one of the great strategic outposts of our nation, blasted
by the ruthless and treacherous hands of those whom we have so often
befriended in the past. I know that this news has brought to all our people
a new realization of our common destiny as free men.

You gentlemen have long served as the leaders of a large and important
group within our democratic system. History has brought you new responsibilities, and new opportunities for service. Never has the press
of our country been called upon to play a greater part in the functioning
and the strengthening of Democracy than now lies before it. It is more
essential than ever before that all our people have prompt and uninter-
rupted access to the truth, and all the help that wise editorial interpretation can give them.

When Judge Hastie [Judge William H. Hastie, Civilian Aide to the
Secretary of War] first informed me of this conference, I gave careful
thought to the more extended remarks which I hope to be able to make.
This is the first press conference I have had for a long time, and I know
that newspaper men are always looking for news. The thing which I
felt might interest you most was the activation of one, and I hope two
Negro divisions, in the very near future. There are details still to be
worked out, including the always essential one of appropriations. We
shall include as many Negro officers as can be employed with due regard

to the numbers available, and the needs of existing military units. Younger officers are being trained in the Officer Candidate Schools, and will be assigned to tactical and other units as commissioned.

As this conference progresses, you will learn something of the internal organization of the War Department, particularly those agencies concerned with personnel and the broad problems of human relations. But even more important, we shall have a chance to learn, also at first hand, your own views on many subjects of common concern to us all.

Judge Hastie is to be congratulated upon the great contribution which he has already made to a better understanding between the War Department and the Negro public. He came to us with a national reputation as a brilliant jurist. He and his associate, Mr. Gibson [Mr. Truman K. Gibson, Assistant Civilian Aide to the Secretary of War], have made many friends within the Department, and have accomplished a great deal toward the solution of problems in which I am as sincerely interested as any of you gentlemen.

You will understand the urgency of official duties which prevent my spending as much time with you as I had hoped to do, but I shall follow with great interest the reports of this conference.

I feel now that your action at this particular time, taken, as you put it, on the grounds of having everybody in one unified army of soldiers taking orders, is a very fine patriotic action.

35
Getting Down to the Business of War

An Address at the National Council Dinner of
the Reserve Officers' Association of the United
States, Washington, D. C., January 9, 1942

*I have been greatly encouraged in the midst of these extremely
difficult days by the evidence of the fact that the organization
and the planning that have been set up have been sound.*

COLONEL HOLLERS, Senator Connally, Senator Schwartz, Representative Thomason, [24] Gentlemen: I haven't decided yet just what I might say. There is so much I would like to say to you that it is a rather difficult business for me to determine here at the moment what would be appropriate for me to talk about other than my own expressions personally as to your Association and the Reserve Officers generally.

We are in the midst of war. Our whole attitude, our whole method of approach to the business of the day has changed. We are united. We all have a common intention and purpose, and, of course, an overwhelming interest in how we will successfully do what we must do to meet whatever is yet to happen.

However, I have been greatly encouraged in the midst of these extremely difficult days by the evidence of the fact that the organization and the planning that have been set up have been sound. I can't go into details now, naturally, but tremendous business has been carried on during the past three weeks so smoothly that it just was hardly commented on, vastly proportioned according to plans that haven't been easy to approximate to the immediate situation. Difficult? Yes. But war is difficult, all of it, in all of its manifestations. But I have been greatly encouraged at the smoothness and directness and rapidity with which we have been able to roll, once we knew we were at war.

I might mention (because it can do no possible harm to speak about it publicly) that among the various things that have been set up that people don't appreciate at all are, for example, our great ports of embarkation. You were familiar with Hoboken in the first World War and what that meant in terms of tonnage of shipping, individuals, great tri-

---

[24]Colonel James P. Hollers, Officers Reserve Corps, President of the Reserve Officers' Association; Senator Tom Connally of Texas; Senator H. H. Schwartz of Wyoming; and Representative R. Ewing Thomason of Texas.

umphs of transportation of armies abroad. It might interest you to know that six months ago the port of embarkation of Brooklyn was handling a greater tonnage than was handled on the average in 1918. Organization of ports along the East Coast and along the West Coast has progressed so extensively, with the depots and all of the things that go to make them, that we have been able to go ahead wherever it was necessary without fumbling and without 'delays and without confusion. I mention that as merely one manifestation of organization, because it is not at all harmful to talk about publicly.

I have been very much reassured and impressed by the fact that the very staffs that we have organized during this period of preparation, which has involved so much of an advance from literally nothing at all in the continental United States to what we have today, that we have been able to avoid what has always been our dilemma in the past—improvising here and improvising there. We have trained staffs; we have experienced commanders. They have all had their experience, and we have been able to move them here and there without any difficulty at all and by a single telegram instead of a hundred for each little minor adjustmenet of that kind, which was the case in previous experiences of ours in war time.

So I feel that we have made tremendous progress. I feel that the organization is sound. And even in the turbulent days which come with the declaration of war, if you choose to call it that, we were able to straighten our house out and get down to smooth business within twenty-four hours. That has been a great reassurance and encouragement to me. Not that there isn't plenty of business, not that there isn't far too much business, but we have been able to keep our heads well above the floor, and it is regularizing and systematizing smoothly and more smoothly each day.

For the benefit of some of the older Reserve officers who feel they have not been in the picture because we were taking the first and second lieutenants in a great majority of cases, I have some information with regard to the mobilization of Reserve divisions. Our mobilization plans for some years have been established on the basis that the initial mobilization of the first Reserve division was to have occurred on M plus 120 [120 days after war is declared]. Actually the initial mobilization of Reserve divisions, three of them, will start twelve days ahead of the scheduled date. The cadres have been arranged, the commanders have been selected and will be assembled within the week. The actual induction of the divisions will start on March 25. That is fifty-two days ahead of time. That is the start of our war mobilization. We have certainly been on a mobilization basis for a long time in a material way, and in a personnel way to quite an extent, but now we are starting the full mobilization of effort, which involves everyone in the Army, in the Reserves not yet called to active duty in the Army, and in the country at large. That has not been difficult to arrange. The only thing has been to get the approval.

When I speak of three divisions, that is only the basis. All the trimmings and all the supporting units and everything else are to go along. It is all in the cards, all arranged, and all can be done. All the various people pertaining to it are now going into special schools for that particular preparation for that particular job, so that there will be nothing of confusion, there will be nothing of lost motion, and there will be everything of expedition and speed. We ought to do a better job than we ever dreamed of doing in the past.

I am very glad that it was possible for me to get here tonight. It looked dubious for the last thirty minutes, but it worked out all right and I am here. I appreciate very much the opportunity to be with you, the reception you have given me, and I want to say to you gentlemen of the Reserve Officers' Association that I know the War Department is tremendously appreciative of your attitude. I am personally not only appreciative, but keenly aware of the fact that without this Reserve Corps, which has had its stimulus in the Reserve Officers' Association, we would have been lost in the necessities of today.

When you think of the size of the Army in the continental United States (when I became Acting Chief of Staff I think it was probably somewhere in the neighborhood of one hundred ten thousand officers and enlisted men) and that now we are on the road in the next month or two to one hundred forty thousand officers, you get some idea of the magnitude of the effort. When you realize that of our divisions that have been developed and that have gone through the hurly-burly of these maneuvers (which were magnificent training opportunities such as I believe have never been attempted before by armies), that of all these so-called divisions, ninety per cent of the officers were Reserve officers, there is something to be said for the system that we have built up during time of peace and for its dependability and its workability.

We have passed to the point in the last week of putting the whole Army on a single, solid, unified basis. We have gone in the past two years through various steps. Difficulties? Yes. Misunderstandings? Yes. But the thing is we have gone through these steps, and we have now reached the point where everything is unified, everything is on one level, everything is on the same promotion basis, and we have just one army.

I am keenly appreciative of the support that the War Department—the Army—the nation—has received from this Association, from your leaders who have come to see me frequently, and of the fact that you have kept the broad vision of this problem in your minds. You have seen with us what our broad problems were, and you have kept out of the picture all the little various human but exceedingly trying, and interfering, reactions of the individual case. We owe a great deal of gratitude and we are greatly appreciative.

36
Defenses of the Western Hemisphere

An Address at the Opening Session of the
Inter-American Defense Board, Pan-American
Union, Washington, D. C., March 30, 1942

∾∾∾∾∾∾∾∾∾∾∾∾∾∾∾∾∾∾∾∾∾∾∾∾∾

*The highest degree of protection we can furnish the Western
Hemisphere will result from an offensive elsewhere.*

APPROXIMATELY a year and a half ago, the Chiefs of Staff of the
Latin-American republics visited the United States as guests of our
government and it was a definite privilege to take them on an inspection tour of our military establishments. From a military viewpoint,
the visit was a profitable one, but, in my opinion, the greatest benefit
derived was the friendly personal relationships which the military leaders
were able to form. The meeting of the Inter-American Defense Board
will also, I hope, promote understanding and good will among the military leaders of our closely related nations and it will afford to all of us
the opportunity to renew valued old friendships and establish new ones.

As you know, we have assembled in accordance with a recommendation of the recent meeting of the Ministers of Foreign Affairs of the
American Republics, held in Rio de Janeiro. That recommendation
provided for "the immediate meeting in Washington of a commission
composed of military and naval technicians appointed by each of the
Governments to study and to recommend to them the measures necessary for the defense of the Continent."

This meeting has a very special significance since it is the first time
that military representatives of all the Americas have met for the purpose of studying the defense of the Western Hemisphere.

From the military standpoint, the protection of America is of primary
importance to the United States. From our viewpoint a hostile landing,
a bombardment of the coast, or the loss of shipping on the part of our
neighbors affect us exactly as though similar occurrences happened on
our coast, or and to our own people. The advent of the airplane and the
speed of modern warfare has shortened time and space factors to the
extent that distance is no longer a form of security. We view the defense of each country in the American hemisphere and the integrity of
its possessions as a matter of greatest importance to the United States,
and any military action which is directed against the United States
equally as against the attacked neighbor.

We have all seen the tragic fate of nations which waited too late to take adequate and precautionary defensive measures. Let not us make that mistake ourselves. We must prepare the defenses of our critical areas as speedily and as strongly as possible: eliminate hiding fifth columns and sinister subversive activities. We must all help each other and consider our defensive measures in the light of the common cause and frankly face realities. Without delay, we soldiers must show the way to our countries, not only how to defend our nations and the heritage of our American tradition, but also to make sure there will be no challenge to our strong position and united strength.

Unquestionably, a matter of outstanding importance to you gentlemen is the assistance which you can receive from the United States in the form of munitions of war. We fully realize the great importance of supporting you in this respect, and for that purpose we consider your requirements in virtually the same light as our own. Certain commitments which were made some time ago have necessarily been altered because of the sudden change in the world situation. Here in the United States we are involved in the conduct of warfare on a world-wide scale. We are involved in the conduct of military operations in the Southwest Pacific, a distance of approximately seven thousand miles from our own shores. We are involved in assisting our allies in Europe and in the Pacific area who at present are bearing the brunt of attack by a vicious military machine. It is imperative that we deploy our resources in the vital theaters at the moment of necessity. Emotions or desires must not divert us from concentrating on the great task before us—the launching of a major offensive against the enemy. The highest degree of protection we can furnish the Western Hemisphere will result from an offensive elsewhere. Our ability to furnish supplies to our Latin-American neighbors is considered substantially on the same basis as our ability to furnish equipment to units of our own forces which are not actively engaged. As Chief of Staff, I am on the receiving end of numberless requests for allocation of means, and it is a necessary daily procedure for me to refuse or modify requests for additional units, equipment, and weapons from our own American commanders who naturally feel that their own requirements are paramount.

In view of the unprovoked attack which was made on the United States, it is most fortunate that by our preparation and advance planning our industries began their transition from a peace basis to a wartime basis before we were actually involved in war. It takes time to develop huge war industries but it is reassuring to me, and I am sure it will be reassuring to you, to know that in a very short time the most modern and unmatched munitions of war will come off our unrivaled manufacturing lines in a virtual flood, and we will be able to fulfill our commitments to our troops, allies and associates in our common cause of liberty. I should however, qualify this by the statement that our policy must be flexible and designed to furnish the equipment where it will be most needed and the course of the war may make it necessary to alter our present plans as you, as military men, I am sure will well understand.

It is well to remember that victory is dependent on putting the largest number of competent, well equipped, capably led soldiers in the right place at the right time. We, I know, realize that winning the last victory is what counts rather than a few preliminary battles in the campaign.

In closing, I wish to say that it is a great pleasure to have you with us in the United States. It is my firm belief that the exchange of views here by this distinguished group of military leaders on hemisphere defense, will assist us toward eventual victory. Our mutual coöperation of effort, our unity of purpose and our unswerving determination will defeat our enemies and keep the Americas free forever.

37
West Point and the Citizen Army

An Address to the Graduating Class of the United States
Military Academy, West Point, New York, May 29, 1942

‿‿‿‿‿‿‿‿‿‿‿‿‿‿‿‿‿‿‿‿‿‿‿‿‿‿‿‿‿‿‿‿‿‿

*We are determined that before the sun sets on this terrible
struggle our flag will be recognized throughout the world as
a symbol of freedom on one hand and of overwhelming power
on the other. . . . There is no possible compromise. We
must utterly defeat the Jap and German war machines.*

I APPRECIATE the honor of being here this morning, but I would
like you young men to have a sympathetic realization of the fact
that it is an obviously dangerous business for a soldier to make a
speech these days. Nevertheless, I welcome the opportunity to talk for a
few moments to you First Classmen on your day of graduation, and to
the other members of the Corps who will carry the flag after you have
gone.

Two weeks from now you join a great citizen army. In physique, in
natural ability, and in intelligence, the finest personnel in the world.
In their eagerness to work, to endure, and to carry through any missions,
they are all that could be desired of soldiers. They but require the modern tools of their profession, the support of the people back home and,
most of all, understanding leadership. Preparation for that task of leadership has been the purpose of your course at the Military Academy.

Your predecessors have usually endured long years of slow promotion.
They have suffered professionally from our national habit of indifference
to military precautions. You will enter the service under quite different
circumstances. Your opportunities will be great and they will be soon,
but your responsibilities will be far greater and more immediate.

In a few days you will find yourselves among thousands of officers
who have recently won their commissions in a rigorous competition
unique in the annals of our army. These officers are splendid types.
They understand from personal experience the tasks, the duties and
the daily problems of the private soldier. They have received intensive
training in the technique of weapons and in minor tactics. They won
their commissions because they proved conclusively in a grueling test
that they were *leaders*, and that they had the necessary intelligence and
initiative. Already they are familiar with the concentrations and move-

ments of large masses of men. Many of them have participated in maneuvers which extended over a period of months and involved hundreds of thousands of troops operating over tremendous areas, covering in one instance an entire state. In other words, you will be in fast company; you are to join virile, highly developed forces. You will meet the citizen-soldiers of America at their best and, by the same token you will have to work very hard to justify your heritage.

Within the past three years our military establishment has undergone a tremendous growth. When I became Chief of Staff, the active Army consisted of one hundred seventy-five thousand men and twelve thousand officers. Today it numbers almost as many officers as it formerly did soldiers. During the past four weeks alone it has been increased by three hundred thousand men, and this expansion will continue until by the end of the year there will be nearly four and a half million in the ranks.

A large part of this expansion is taking place within the Air Forces. In spite of the high speed with which it must be accomplished, we know that our pilots represent the flower of American manhood, and our crews the perfection of American mechanical ingenuity. These men come from every section of the country, and pilots have been drawn from almost every college and university in the land. No finer body of men can be found. They are consumed with a determination to carry the fight into Germany and Japan—the same determination that inspired Jimmie Doolittle and his gallant band. Yet splendid as is this personnel, a unified air force should have a proportion of officers whose viewpoint, moulded by four years in the Corps of Cadets, includes a full understanding of those military intangibles which are epitomized in the motto of the Corps. Here, then, is one of the most important reasons for the introduction of a flying course into the Academy's curriculum. Last spring I insisted upon the rearrangement of courses in order that our new air force should include as soon as possible a large number of commissioned flyers imbued with the traditions and standards of West Point.

The path we have followed in preparing the Army during the emergency has not been an easy one. It has not been traversed overnight, and it has been uphill all of the way. During the period prior to Pearl Harbor, my most difficult task was to progress with the mobilization and training of the Army despite the confusion, to express it mildly, that was spread throughout the ranks by a nationwide debate regarding the necessity for organizing such an army, as to whether or not there was an emergency which justified it, and as to what our national policy should be.

Current events remind me of questions which were put to me by members of Congress prior to December 7, as to where American soldiers might be called upon to fight, and just what was the urgent necessity for the army that we were endeavoring to organize and train. In reply I usually commented on the fact that we had previously fought in France, Italy, and Germany; in Africa and the Far East; in Siberia and Northern Russia. No one could tell what the future might hold for us. But one thing was clear to me, we must be prepared to fight anywhere, and with a minimum of delay. The possibilities were not overdrawn, for today we find American soldiers throughout the Pacific, in Burma, China, and India. Recently they struck at Tokyo. They have wintered in Greenland and Iceland. They are landing in Northern Ireland and England, and they will land in France. We are determined that before the sun sets on this terrible struggle our flag will be recognized throughout the world as a symbol of freedom on the one hand and of overwhelming power on the other.

The state of the public mind has changed. Many of those who were in confusion have come to a clear conclusion as to what we must do. Our people, solidly behind the Army, are supporting wholeheartedly every measure for the prosecution of the war. The calm and the fortitude with which they accept the vicissitudes that are inevitable in a struggle that goes to the four corners of the earth are very reassuring. And our greatest reassurance comes from the courage and fortitude of the wives and parents of those who fought to the last ditch in the Philippines.

I do not know of anything which has impressed me so much with the present implacable state of mind of the American people as the letters I received from the wives and mothers of those men in the Philippines who went down in the struggle, either as casualties or prisoners. Their heroic messages of fortitude and resolution are an indication of the fact that this struggle will be carried to a conclusion that will be decisive and final.

Your utmost energy, aggression, and effort, backed by high and unselfish purpose, will be required to bring this struggle to a triumphant conclusion. There is no possible compromise. We must utterly defeat the Jap and German war machines. You will notice I omit Italy.

It is on the young and vigorous that we must depend for the energy and daring and leadership in staging a great offensive.

I express my complete confidence that you will carry, with a proud and great resolution, into this new army of citizen-soldiers at their American best, all the traditions, all the history and background of your predecessors at West Point—and may the good Lord be with you.

38
Lowering the Draft Age to Eighteen Years

Statements before the Senate Committee on Military Affairs, on Consideration of S. 2748, a Bill to Amend the Selective Training and Service Act of 1940, by Providing for the Extension of Liability, 77th Congress, 2d Session, October 14, 1942

~~~~~~

Everything we did in the World War was more or less on a stabilized basis, at least up to the last week or ten days. Then our troops deployed in delimited sectors and in trenches, with a degree of training that was lamentable. We can't take such risks in this war. Everything must be a highly geared, a highly trained machine, everything about which is exceedingly complicated. Youth is required. . . .

GENERAL MARSHALL: Mr. Chairman, I have no prepared statement. General McNarney has one, and will go into details; also General Edwards [Brigadier General Idwal H. Edwards], head of the Training Division of the General Staff, has still more details; and, of course, General Hershey [Major General Lewis B. Hershey] is here to discuss the Selective Service phase of the matter.

I have listened to the Secretary of War testify before the Military Affairs Committee of the House this morning, and I think I might well summarize the approach that he gave to the matter.

In the first place, the plans of the War Department are for the purpose of producing, during the calendar year 1943, the largest air force, with supporting troops, meaning the engineers, signal corps, and so forth, that it is possible to organize with the plan production and transportation facilities in view. That, we find, involves approximately two million two hundred thousand men.

We are planning and our estimates contemplate the development of a highly trained ground force, including armored divisions, airborne divisions, and some six hundred thousand antiaircraft troops. This force will absorb a total of three and one third million men actually in organizations, training or overseas.

In addition, approximately one million men will be engaged either in training others or in being trained as individuals in training centers for later assignment to combat units in accordance with the expansion of the Army during 1943 or to replace casualties.

Further, about one million men will be involved in the Services of Supply, commonly called the SOS. These figures total, in our estimates, for the calendar year 1943, an aggregate of seven million five hundred thousand men by January 1, 1944, including four million two hundred thousand now in the service.

The Secretary referred this morning, before the House Committee to a confusion in the public mind and apparently in the press and elsewhere, as to just what we were doing and why we were doing it. He mentioned that there had been talk of a thirteen million-man army, and of a ten million-man Army, when actually we had arrived at the present figure for 1943 many months ago; in fact, as early as April of this year.

Another source of confusion is the frequent and ill informed references to a "mass army." I am not certain as to what those who talk of a mass army mean. There is certainly no great mass in what I have referred to as ground forces. It is an integrated army, balanced as nearly as we can calculate our necessities, for offensive action outside of the Western Hemisphere.

Also, it has been implied that the War Department has ignored the transportation difficulties and intends to accumulate a mass of men in this country which could not possibly be transported to the overseas theaters of operations. Nothing is probably further from the fact.

I presume that all of you gentlemen finish your day with the Lord's Prayer as I do, but even then my thoughts involve ship tonnage and transportation and these are among my first waking thoughts. The calculations pertaining to ship tonnage are as involved as integral calculus and relate to all our plans, because it is our purpose to keep the war outside of the Western Hemisphere. Also, it is our determined purpose that our efforts will be directed toward offensive operations—all of which necessarily involve shipping.

Therefore, we must analyze all the factors as to the length of turnaround, as to the production of shipping, and as to the possible losses. If we did not do this we would be clearly incompetent to raise, train, and manage an Army.

In addition, we have had to consider the factor of production with relation to strength and one section of the War Department is devoted exclusively to that consideration, under Judge Patterson,[25] the Under Secretary of War.

We obtain much information relating to our estimates as to manpower

---

[25]The Honorable Robert P. Patterson, Under Secretary of War.

through General Hershey's office.[26] This is studied and analyzed at great length.

I could be much more convincing if I could talk with complete frankness, but to do so would probably endanger the lives of American soldiers as well as jeopardize the success of operations.

* * *

GENERAL MARSHALL: We have calculated with extreme care what we must have and the greatest speed with which we can get to it by the end of December 1943. But it should be perfectly clear in your minds that what we turn out in January 1943, is not available until January 1944, and the men whom it is proposed to induct under this estimate in December 1943, will not be available in newly trained units until January 1945.

This planning must be made far in advance and we must have a long period of training before units can be used in combat. New organizations must be created—they must make their own history, their own traditions, and be trained to operate as complete teams.

Our preparation must be based on obtaining the highest degree of skill because these soldiers will have to make their first appearance on the battlefield to meet a highly trained, veteran foe of many campaigns. They will have to compete on the battlefield with men who have encountered and emerged from every phase of modern warfare.

That requires a very high degree of training, and it requires a very elaborate logistical set-up. Every military factor involved is of vast importance to us not only in the successful accomplishment of our purpose, but in order to insure a moderate cost in life, and with as little loss of time as possible.

To come to the immediate purpose of this hearing, the 18- to 19-year-old clause, all of the details of this can be gone into by those who follow me, but the situation in brief is this: ·

Under the present system, the law and the manner of induction, the age of the combat army has risen to a point which is not acceptable to the War Department. For example, consider the newly organized divisions; these have been activated on a normal wartime basis and were not subjected to the emasculations and transfers that the original divisions had to endure. While the training of these new divisions has been conducted on a uniform basis and has produced amazing results, the age bracket has gone up and has reached the point where it is changing month by month. My staff can give you the exact figures, but I think

[26]Major General Lewis B. Hershey, Director, Selective Service System.

the average age of men in a new division in February was under twenty-five years; by July it had increased to just under twenty-nine.

I went through a three-thousand-five-hundred-bed hospital at Fort Bragg, North Carolina, last Sunday a week ago, and I was shocked at what I found in both the surgical and medical wards. They seemed to be filled with old men. I say that with apologies because they were much younger than I am but the point is I was looking for field soldiers and found men who seemed to be much older than I. Most of them had only been in the service a few weeks, some of them had been at Bragg only three or four days; and already they were in the hospital.

Inducting these men does not increase the Army; in fact it reduces the Army, because a bed, a nurse, an attendant and a doctor were necessary where each man was involved. And what made it worse, in questioning a specific individual I would find a man who had just been taken off a machine-tool job in a plant at Detroit. Instead of being on that important work he finds himself in the hospital with several different complaints, including an operation for hernia. Such a man is a burden to the Army, yet he was a very valuable person where he came from. He was forty-three years of age.

Alongside of him in the next bed was another man, an expert rigger or driller—another case of several complaints and an age beyond forty.

They were scheduled for limited service, but nevertheless even for limited service we have to give them hospitalization. The Medical Corps is checking the matter. We may have to enlarge our hospitals because the rate is going to be higher and all of this occurs before these men have entered an active theater.

In amphibious divisions involving the most strenuous service, we find privates closely approaching their fortieth year. That is not a practical proposition toward a successful war, and is a great injustice to the individual involved.

The effect of this program on production has been discussed. These older men ought to be in defense plants with their machines and these younger men—who I am reasonably certain, judging from my own reactions as a younger man, and the few I see, all want to go into the Army. They bring the age down to that point where we can have combat units of vigorous aggressive soldiers and can endure for long periods the pressure of active field service. They must have the stamina to go on. In this war you don't fight a battle today and rest tomorrow.

Everything we did in the World War was more or less on a stabilized basis, at least up to the last week or ten days. Then our troops deployed in delimited sectors and in trenches, with a degree of training that was lamentable.

We can't take such risks in this war. Everything must be a highly geared, a highly trained machine, everything about which is exceedingly complicated. Youth is required.

These young men in this war have to be trained. I have previously referred to how long this takes; they have to be trained, they have to be hardened, they must be highly disciplined.

I think I have covered the general situation. I will now be happy to try to answer your questions.

THE CHAIRMAN: Senator Gurney [Senator Chan Gurney of South Dakota], you are the author of the bill and I think you are entitled to lead off with anything you want to on general questions, after which we will give an opportunity to the members of the committee to ask such questions as they may desire, bearing on the pending bill.

SENATOR GURNEY: General, I have no specific questions to ask except this: The Army wants this bill passed as quickly as possible, does it not?

GENERAL MARSHALL: Yes, sir.

SENATOR GURNEY: Do you want it passed about as is, without any restrictions?

GENERAL MARSHALL: That is right.

SENATOR GURNEY: There is a definite need for it, by the Army, is there?

GENERAL MARSHALL: Very definite. As a matter of fact, to use Mr. Stimson's phrase, it is imperative.

THE CHAIRMAN: Senator Hill?

SENATOR LISTER HILL OF ALABAMA: Of course, General, we all know that in all past wars young men have excelled as soldiers. Isn't it true that in this present war, with our air and parachute troops and our many new forms of fighting, young men are needed far more today than they were in the old-style warfare?

GENERAL MARSHALL: Much more urgently. You mentioned two or three types of troops. Probably the greatest endurance test is in the Armored Force owing to the close confinement in tanks with temperatures up to 130 degrees. Others might feel that the heaviest task of endurance is that of the infantry divisions that have to march on foot, because it isn't all truck by any manner of means.

The main complication of the modern problem is not only that soldiers must know so much more in order to coördinate the large number of weapons, but they have to stand the pressure of a rapidly moving battle, for long periods of time. They have to go ahead, go ahead and keep on going ahead, far beyond what the average man thinks he is capable of enduring.

The limited food, the limited water involved, the very sketchy services of supply that is possible, and the rapidity of movement, combine to produce a tremendous strain on the individual soldier.

SENATOR HILL: General, don't you think that the sooner we take this step the sooner we can hope for the end of the war, which means a saving in lives?

GENERAL MARSHALL: Yes, sir; this proposal makes for efficiency—

SENATOR HILL [interposing]: And efficiency makes for saving in lives?

GENERAL MARSHALL: Yes, sir. I would amplify that still further. There isn't any question at all about what the sick rate will be with the induction of these older men, and that means an added burden because other military personnel must look after the sick.

*   *   *

THE CHAIRMAN: There is one question that I wanted to ask you that I have had many letters about, and I have been unable to answer them. The American public is extremely desirous of knowing as to who sets the number of men that will constitute the Army of the United States. I make that inquiry because you mentioned a moment ago that the public itself was confused because some people had said we would have an Army of thirteen million men and some people had said we would have an Army of ten million men, and you tell us this morning that you expect to have seven million five hundred thousand by December 31, 1943.

Who is responsible for setting the figure of the maximum of our armed forces?

GENERAL MARSHALL: I am, sir, but we go about it in this way. It is a long, complicated procedure and takes many months. We have, first of all, our theaters to consider, actual as well as prospective. We have, as to a theater, the turn-around involved in cargo, in what we call troop-lift, and in varieties of cargo. We have the possible attrition rate on those turn-arounds. We have the production of shipping, both existent and anticipated; we have the availability of matériel, of planes, of weapons, tanks, and everything of that sort.

We consider the type of organization that we feel is best suited for each theater, having in mind what the enemies' prospective force will be at this future date, and his character of fighting, and what he is using, and what can best be employed in the particular theater.

We must consider the various portions of the Army, the air, the ground forces, the tank forces, get all of their views, which are often conflicting. All of these factors have to be balanced.

There is the supply phase under General Somervell.[27] To give you an example, I remember when we were working on this particular matter, last April I believe, on this figure of seven and a half million, General Somervell went over with me his difficulties in meeting the supply requirements. He talked about shelter in the United States while we were training units. He discussed matériel and labor requirements to construct the necessary shelter in this country; he talked about the advisability or inadvisability of building more camps—we try to avoid so far as we can, new installations. He discussed the use of resort hotels instead of new construction, which would require more material and more labor and cost more money, and then be torn down when the war is over. He talked of the health rate as to air space, the matter of using double-deck bunks.

He was involved in the question of the military matériel, its rate of delivery, our commitments to Russia, to China, and to the British; when it would be available for our troops and we could give new divisions their portion.

Next I talked with General McNair.[28] He came in with relation to matériel—how many divisions could he train with efficiency; how much must a division have for training; what substitute weapons could be used for training; and would the most modern matériel be available long enough in advance of the prospective sailing date for the men to be experienced in its use. Just the SOS factor is extremely complicated. The tonnage factor I have already discussed.

General Somervell is related to Judge Patterson's office as to what the production is going to be, and through the air forces as to what the air schedule is going to be.

That has to be tied in with the Operations Division as to what the necessities of our various deployments are going to be. We then get into troop organization, which is General Edwards' responsibility, as to how these things form up in units, and what particular type of units come out of this.

Then we get to the individual as to replacements in the great training centers, and I talked to the people responsible for that as to how many more training centers there shall be. For example, when this thing was first being formulated last February we were trying to arrive at a trial figure which has come out now as this seven-million-odd. Another factor was the question of these new divisions. Normally the man would come to the division with that three months' training I am talking about, even though the division is newly formed. However, I made a departure from

[27]General Brehon B. Somervell, Commanding General, Army Service Forces.
[28]Lieutenant General Lesley J. McNair, Commanding General, Army Ground Forces.

the policy and required the new divisions to be prepared themselves in a period of three months to give the basic training to the fourteen thousand men who would arrive untrained, in order to avoid the building of these additional centers for the individual training of men before they join a unit. That order saved the construction of some three hundred fifty million dollars worth of camps. That delayed the development of divisions, of course, and there was great opposition. However, it seemed to me that a compromise was necessary and it turned out very well.

Then we were involved in the training centers for all of these supporting troops for the Air Corps, their antiaircraft, their engineers, their signal quartermaster, their medical—which have to be trained and disciplined. In some respects they have to be disciplined earlier in their career than others because they are sent overseas earlier than divisions and they are so scattered in their employment that they are more apt to get into loose habits. We had to go into the matter of where they would be trained—because the Air Corps can't train them. They need them, have to have them, but somebody else has to organize them so that when a unit sails from the United States it is a dependable, organized, disciplined American outfit.

That meant more training centers, which we established in the SOS, under a very able line officer, to coördinate the training of all these people.

Our main problem was the amount of construction that could be avoided. All these various factors were considered.

Finally General Somervell informed me, "We can manage this, from the construction point, from the matériel point, from the medical point, the hospital point—all of those things—we can do it. The figure is practicable from the SOS viewpoint."

The departments were compromised as to who got more of this or less than he wanted. And finally out of all this came this total of seven million five hundred thousand.

That then had to be related to the requirements of the Navy and what the country could accommodate.

Our trial figure was then submitted for approval to the Secretary of War, the Bureau of the Budget, and the President.

THE CHAIRMAN: Having set your figure of seven million five hundred thousand for December 31, 1943, of course that is as far as you can see, and the future might demand that we have an army larger than that, even?

GENERAL MARSHALL: The future might demand that. We couldn't settle on that, I would say, before the late summer. Meanwhile we must go ahead with plans, we mustn't be caught without them; but I would say that we couldn't approximate a decision until along about August. Of course there is going to be a point where we either feel we don't need any more divisions, or we cannot afford to organize any more divisions. As I said before, when we come to that point then we can reduce our overhead, can contract, because many of the men and installations necessary to the expansion program, which is so difficult, would no longer be required. All we would then have to do is turn out replacements. I imagine that all the Germans are doing now is turning out replacements, or reorganizing existing divisions, and things of that sort—not creating new units.

The British are turning out replacements, and as to the Japanese I don't know, but I presume they are similarly engaged.

But we are developing entirely new units, we are still making an army and when you look at the number of enemy divisions with which we are confronted, our figures are very modest. We must make up in quality, in the air, in the Navy, the superiority we hope to develop, and in the selection of the theaters.

*   *   *

39
The United Nations

An Address Before the American Academy of Political
Science, New York City, November 10, 1942

*The first step taken by the Chiefs of Staff of Great Britain
and the United States at the initial meeting in Washington in December 1941, was to establish a basis of procedure to secure coördinate action. . . . The framework
and details . . . established at that time have furnished
a foundation for all combined action between Great
Britain and the United States since that date.*

WHILE it has been advisable for me to refrain from public discussion or speeches, I was glad to accept the invitation of Mr.
Lewis Douglas[29] to talk to you gentlemen because of a certain
similarity in our problems, particularly during times of peace.

We both are concerned with a large number of imponderables. On
your side you have to deal with the uncertainties of public reactions and
the complications of international relationships. On the military side we
have even more of imponderables which often decide the fate of an
operation, or of a war, or even of a nation. And always the enemy endeavors to upset our plans. In the field of political science the public
reactions or the international complications may upset your best-laid
plans but not with the ruthless methods of a desperate enemy.

In contrast to this the engineer, for example, who designs a bridge
can calculate to the fourth decimal point the stress and strain to be imposed on each member. He can be certain that it will carry the load for
which it is designed unless an act of God beyond the anticipation of
mere man should intervene. We, however, encounter unpredictable difficulties. For example: during the recent Dieppe raid, despite all the
secrecy precautions, the success of the raid was seriously affected by the
chance encounter with a German guard ship convoying some barges
along the French Coast. The African operation now in progress involved innumerable imponderables and hazards. Certainly ours are not
exact sciences and for that reason are all the more difficult of application.

I believe the subject for tonight's discussion is the United Nations.
The question of unity of command among allied nations is therefore

---

[29]Mr. Lewis Douglas, President, American Academy of Political Science.

pertinent to the occasion. It is a dominating factor in the problem of the United Nations at the present time. Of all the military lessons which could have been learned from the last war, the question of unity of command is probably the most outstanding; personally I learned my lesson in observing the problems of General Pershing in France and the reluctance of our allies to meet the issue until almost overwhelmed by the great German offensive of March 1918.

For that reason the first step taken by the Chiefs of Staff of Great Britain and the United States at the initial meeting in Washington in December 1941, was to establish a basis of procedure to secure co-ordinated action. The first move, which had to be made immediately, was to establish a basis for unity of command in the Southwest Pacific—to gather together in the quickest possible time our scanty forces to meet the carefully prepared Japanese onslaught. The framework and the details of procedure established at that time have furnished a foundation for all combined action between Great Britain and the United States since that date. In other words, within three weeks after our entry into this war we had organized a system which would provide a working basis for the strategical direction of our war efforts, the allocations of forces and of material, and the coördination of production of munitions. It has of necessity been a vastly complicated problem. The interests of many nations are involved. Take for example, the initial problem of establishing unity of command in the Southwest Pacific under General Wavell. The interests, the aspirations, the military forces and the people of the United States, of Great Britain, of the Dutch, the Chinese, the Burmese, the Australians, and the New Zealanders, all had to be considered, and it must be remembered that you cannot reach decisions through a Congress of Nations that will furnish unlimited debates but rarely timely decisions to meet a pressing situation.

In the Southwest Pacific were factors involving the isolation of an American command in the Philippines, the approaching isolation of a British Empire command in Malaya, the threat to the Burma Road, China's sole line of communications to the outside friendly world, the destruction of the Government of the Netherlands East Indies, the threatened invasion of Australia, Portuguese interests in Timor, and our communications with the Far East through the islands of the South Pacific. The distances were tremendous, the racial groups numerous, and the political interests often diverse. In addition, the matter was complicated by problems of shipping, the vital factor of time, and the vast logistical requirements. So, while it is an easy matter to talk of unity of command, it is an extremely difficult matter to arrange an effective basis.

Despite all of these difficulties the most heartening factor of the war to date, in my opinion, is the remarkable success which has thus far been achieved in coördinating and directing the military and allied interests of the United Nations.

In the past two days we have had a most impressive example of the practicable application of unity of command, an American Expeditionary Force, soldiers, sailors, and aviators, supported by the British fleet, by British flyers and by a British army, all controlled by an American commander in chief, General Eisenhower, with a deputy commander also an American Army officer, General Clark [Major General (later General) Mark W. Clark]. They are served by a combined staff of British and American officers, of soldiers and sailors and aviators. Officers of the British Army and Navy senior to General Eisenhower, men of great distinction and long experience, have, with complete loyalty, subordinated themselves to his leadership. The instructions of the British Cabinet to guide their Army commander serving under General Eisenhower furnish a model of readiness of a great nation to coöperate in every practicable manner. I go into detail because this should not be a secret. It will be most depressing news to our enemies. It is the declaration of their doom.

My particular interest at this time in your affairs rests on the fact that after a war a democracy like ours usually throws to the winds whatever scientific approach has been developed in the conduct of the war. This is an historical fact. It is the result of the immediate postwar aversion of the people to everything military, and of the imperative demand of the taxpayer for relief from the burden imposed by the huge war debt. Incidentally, I do not think it is an overstatement to assert that if our government had followed through with the system of National Defense laid down in specific terms by the Act of June 4, 1920, Germany would not have dared to involve herself in a war that would draw the United States into the conflict. In other words the present dreadful situation with the colossal debts to follow might quite possibly have been avoided by a scientific approach on our part to the matter of National Defense in accordance with the terms laid down in the carefully drafted military policy of the Act of twenty-two years ago.

We are in a terrible war and our every interest should be devoted to winning the war in the shortest possible time. However, in view of your interest in the science of government and the intimate relationship that it bears to military requirements, I would ask your very careful consideration of these related military factors in whatever studies you make regarding the readjustments which must follow this war. The theories on the subject will have to be compressed into the realities. The attitude of the taxpayer is human and inevitable. The differing reactions of the people in the center of the country, of those along the coasts, of the people who face the Pacific and the people who face the Atlantic, must be considered. The extreme distaste for things military to which I have already referred and which always follows an exhausting war will have to be taken into account. Then with all of these reactions, how can we so establish ourselves that we will not be doomed to a repetition of the succession of tragedies of the past thirty years? We must take the nations of the world as they are, the human passions and prejudices of peoples as they exist, and find some way to secure for us a free America in a peaceful world.

40
We Know What We Are Doing

An Address before the National Association of Manufacturers,
New York City, December 4, 1942

~~~~~~

*We must have your confidence, since we cannot spread our
cards on the table without hazarding a massacre and possible
loss of the war. We are just starting to lead trumps in a desperately hard game. Let's not start trumping our own tricks.*

SOME weeks ago I came to New York at the request of Mr. Lewis
Douglas, President of the Academy of Political Science, to talk
before a meeting of that society, in company with Admiral King.[30]
With great respect for the distinguished character of the gathering, I
was reluctant to accept the invitation because this is not the time for
men in my position to be making speeches. We should be otherwise occupied. It developed that through pressure on me because of Admiral
King's tentative acceptance and pressure on him because of my probable acceptance, we both were committed to that occasion.

I was even more reluctant to accept Mr. Witherow's[31] invitation for
this evening, but under the circumstances I felt that I must find the opportunity to talk to you gentlemen of the Manufacturers' Association
who are doing such vital things for the Army in this war.

The machines which you have built are now being tested in battle
around the world—planes, tanks, guns, vehicles, ships, and a world of
electrical and similar devices. They are meeting the test. Our munitions
are as good as the best of the enemy's, usually better. This was to be
expected. Our problem, however, was to get them in quantity, in time,
to the various theaters. That has been our desperate struggle of the past
year while your equally desperate struggle has been to produce at a more
rapid rate than was previously believed possible.

I am familiar with some of your difficulties—shortages in raw materials,
loss of skilled manpower, changes or conversions in design. You have
been asked to change overnight from established practices for manufacturing equipment designed to increase the efficiency and comfort of
your fellow man, to weapons purposely designed to destroy him. You
have had to scrap or store your stocks of machine tools or other equip-

---

[30]Fleet Admiral Ernest J. King, Commander in Chief, U. S. Fleet and Chief of Naval
Operations.
[31]Mr. William Porter Witherow, President, National Association of Manufacturers, 1942.

ment and completely reorient your entire program. The speed with which you have made these changes is a convincing demonstration of the flexibility of the American system.

The news from the various fronts in the past few weeks has been encouraging but I am disturbed by the rapidity of the change from a speculative pessimism to undue optimism regarding the course of the war. Nothing could be more dangerous to the success of our arms than the development of a national attitude that the victory is about to be won. We are faced with a long ordeal and it is imperative that we devote every resource we possess to the relentless crusade which has just been started. The situation requires confidence and determination far beyond that ever before demanded of the American people.

Carefully though we may prepare our plans, warfare involves many imponderables and the world-wide character of the present struggle is literally filled with uncertainties. Allow me to cite an example: to all intents and purposes, the initial phase of the North African operation developed with clock-like precision. One of our greatest concerns had been the problem of landing men, tanks and guns from small boats on the west coast of Morocco. At this period of the year the winds over the Atlantic drive huge swells onto the exposed beaches of Northwest Africa. Normally only on seven days out of thirty are landings possible. Yet we were faced with the fact that great convoys cannot loiter; they must not turn back; their fuel is soon expended.

On the night of the actual landing, the date of which had to be set months before, weather reports indicated that two storms were approaching the coast, creating a surf that would make landings utterly impracticable. But the hand of the Lord was over us. The storms appeared to neutralize each other. An old Frenchman in Casablanca reported that the sea was calmer on that particular night than he had seen it in sixty-eight years.

Every manufacturer present tonight has been involved in planning. It is indispensable to your business, as it is to ours. But that word "planning" suggests a public reaction which gives me considerable concern. That is, a feeling in some quarters that we are building too large an army —that we could not transport it to active theaters even if we had it—in short, the belief that we do not know what we are doing or where we are going. I realize that in a few quarters this reaction may be stimulated by an ulterior motive, a willingness to wave the flag but a reluctance to accept the hardships when the shoe pinches.

Plans proposed by the War Department represent months, sometimes a year or more, on intensified study and research. They are based on a mass of factual statistics unavailable to the civilian. The Army has only one concern—one purpose—the destruction of German and Japanese military power. The assumption that we have not even calculated our ways and means necessarily implies a serious doubt as to our competence to direct military operations. In fact, it challenges the integrity of the War Department General Staff, a staff which labors day and night and whose accomplishments will always go unsung. Its problem has been colossal, to raise and train a vast army in record time, and at the same time to direct its progressive employment on every continent of this earth. Bases and lines of communication have been established on a scale undreamed of in the previous history of the world.

Officers of the War Department General Staff are always en route between Washington and the various theaters. In a single morning a few days ago, I interviewed two General Staff officers just in from Kokoda Pass and Milne Bay in New Guinea and from Guadalcanal; another from Chungking, China, and New Delhi in India; and still another from Moscow, Basra, and way points. London, Iceland, Greenland, Labrador and Alaska are frequently visited by officers of the War Department.

A democracy demands effective military leadership, which is a good guarantee for efficiency. The trouble arises, not from the condemnation of leaders, but from the effort to dictate or influence the strategical employment of our forces without knowledge of the logistical requirements or of the various military situations and the world of international relationships involved. So much of this appears in the papers and magazines, regarding matters of which I am in possession of the facts—I am not talking about judgments—that at times it is very discouraging.

What do you suppose would have been the reaction of the American public had our convoys for North Africa been subjected to a mass air and naval attack, the bulk of the transports sunk, thousands of soldiers drowned and the entire expedition forced to turn back—mutilated and defeated? Exactly such major disasters struck the Japanese on at least three occasions, in the Coral Sea, at Midway, and again in the Solomons. They suffered heavily in Macassar Strait and their smaller landings have been beaten off time after time with heavy losses in both the Solomons and in New Guinea. Possibly the Japanese people have been kept somewhat in the dark regarding these losses, but their determined persistence in offensive action regardless of losses makes them an extremely dangerous enemy.

I mention these factors to remind you of the hazards of war, also of the necessity for secrecy—if the lives of our young men are not to be wasted at sea, or on some foreign beach. We must have your confidence since we cannot spread our cards on the able without hazarding a massacre and the possible loss of the war. We are just starting to lead trumps in a desperately hard and deadly game. Let's not start trumping our own tricks.

Finally I wish to emphasize one point. It is a comparatively simple thing to cut a program, to check the development of the Army, if the happy day comes when that is found permissible, but I assure you that it is utterly impossible to improvise military organizations, and it requires more than a year to build them. Therefore, it is our opinion that no more tragic mistake could be made than to ignore the great mass of enemy divisions and expect us to win this war on a shoestring or by some specialized process. If there is a demand at some later date for us to correct such an error of public judgment when the necessity for these troops finally becomes apparent to the layman, it would be demanding the impossible. The most disheartening influence we can impose upon our enemies is the vision of a rapidly growing storm of legions of virile young Americans organizing to destroy their military power.

In the summer of 1941 when I was struggling for the support of the proposal to extend the service of the men then about to leave the ranks of the Army, Hitler in Berlin charged me with making fantastic misrepresentations regarding the dangers of the situation to this country. I beg of you gentlemen not to allow his hidden emissaries to repeat the process of confusing the American public and interfering with our plans. We know what we are doing. And God willing we are going to do it.

41
Report to the Nation

An Address before the Conference of State Governors,
Columbus, Ohio, June 21, 1943

The pattern of victory is clear.

IT has seemed advisable as the war develops that public statements by the Chief of Staff of the Army should be restricted to a few special occasions. A conference of the governors, the leaders of the various States, is such an occasion. Furthermore, this is a most critical summer both for us and in the history of the world. We have passed through the period of military adolescence, our initial deployments have been completed and lines of communications solidly established. Quantity production of both men and matériel, the former in as exact a pattern as the latter, is now in full blast, the enemy's initial advantage in men and guns, and in ships and planes, has been overcome. We have seized the initiative, the most vital factor in war.

The past two years of preparation have been a trying period, especially the prolonged strain of German and Japanese successes during which we struggled to meet the surge of power which they had carefully accumulated during the past decade. The change in the attitude of the public essential to the furtherance of the necessary legislation and appropriations presented many complications. The establishment of our industries on a full war basis had its multiplicity of troubles, and the building of the full war military machine entailed a stupendous task of a wide variety of problems, invariably arousing pronounced individual reactions of our people.

Today we stand squarely on our feet in all these respects. Initial strategic problems involving hectic application of piecemeal tactical actions—anathema to a soldier—are things of the past.

Furthermore, and probably most important of all, we have secured a basis for unity of action as to strategy, operations, shipping, matériel, and virtually every phase of this warfare, in a manner without precedent in history.

The pattern for victory is clear. If we had set the stage we could not have provided a more sharply defined picture than that offered by the battle of Tunisia. There we had:

A perfect example of coördinated leadership for Allied action.

An assemblage of overwhelming military power, air, land, and sea. The explosive effect of the skillful application of that power.

Incidentally, the psychological by-products of that battle are proving of immense importance. There has been a rebirth of the French Army with a splendid example of courageous and aggressive fighting power. The observing nations have seen selected Germans troops humbled by an extension and improvement of the technique that brought about the downfall of France. The Allies have gained great confidence in each other, and in the Allied fighting men, and the scales have so tipped that those nations who have been maneuvering merely to be on the winning side can no longer escape the conclusion that there is no victory in prospect for Germany. The Superman has had his day. The democracies have called his bluff.

Tunisia gave us an invaluable pattern for the future. But the tasks will be increasingly difficult, usually with the great hazard of an over-water approach and a heavy battle to be maintained beyond the beaches. The way will be far from easy, the losses heavy, but the victory certain.

The recent battle in Attu has special significance. There we encountered probably the most difficult of fighting conditions. An amphibious operation in uncharted waters over a stormy sea, deep snow and high mountains, with a complete absence of roads and trails; an enemy dug in with complete cover and communications and our own troops transferred through necessity directly from the pleasant climate of California to a battle with the elements over extremely difficult terrain, against a desperate enemy. It was a severe test of the American soldier, but today we hold Attu, with more than one thousand nine hundred Japanese graves as a memento of their previous occupation. More than three Japs were killed for each American soldier lost.

The fighting in the tropics of the South and Southwest Pacific has also presented great difficulties of climate and terrain. It has been vicious throughout but we have been successful in each operation since the initial offensive move into the Solomons.

One of our great puzzles is how the Japanese can stand the beating they are taking in the air—no other word adequately describes the situation in this respect. Judging from our own reactions, particularly those of the press men when we have a moderately heavy loss in planes, it is hard to visualize the state of mind of the Japanese command when their ordinary air losses run from thirty per cent to seventy-five per cent, with very moderate losses on the part of the American pilots. In the recent air battle in the Solomons we destroyed ninety-four out of one hundred twenty planes and lost but six. Furthermore, the Japanese suffer continuous losses of planes on the ground. We find the usual average is one destroyed on the ground for every one lost in the air, and in addition probably a training or operational loss outside of combat at the same rate. Evidently our equipment is excellent, and our pilots, gunners, bombardiers and navigators are superb.

The daylight precision bombing out of England has had a tremendous effect on the air operations of the German Army. The losses inflicted on German fighter planes during these daylight bombing expeditions had a direct and important bearing on the victory in Tunisia and a similar bearing on the German air power on the Russian front. The fact of the matter is, the Germans must check this precision bombing and they have assembled their best pilots in large numbers in an endeavor to halt these staggering blows at vital installations, delivered with constantly increasing frequency and mass.

Measured by the losses in planes and installations suffered by the enemy our own losses have been surprisingly small.

While on this subject I think it proper to express a word of caution against hasty conclusions or impromptu conceptions regarding the utilization of air power or any special weapon in the conduct of this war. I am convinced more and more each day that only by a proper combination of warmaking means can we achieve victory in the shortest possible time and with the greatest economy in life. Pantelleria was an experiment, for which there appeared to be, and proved to be, a sound logical basis. However, the situation there was unique as to the character of the island, the quality of the garrison, the complete naval control of the surrounding waters and the proximity of Allied airfields. The victory of Tunisia was favored by overwhelming air power, but the result would have been a stalemate without aggressive ground and naval action.

Your adversary may be hammered to his knees by bombing but he will recover unless the knockout blow is delivered by the ground army, with infantry and artillery as important as tanks and antiaircraft, and engineer and signal troops vital to the whole.

The encouraging aspect of the situation today is the fact that we have the men trained, the guns and tanks, the ships and planes in constantly increasing numbers; that the Russian forces grow steadily more formidable and present a constant and terrible threat to the bulk of the German Army; and that there is a steady improvement in the equipment and training of the Chinese forces to sustain them in their fixed determination to expel the Japs from China. There can be but one result unless the enemy succeeds in creating internal frictions among the Allies, divisions of one against the other and misrepresentations leading to public loss of confidence in our war effort.

We are engaged in this war to maintain the democratic form of government. We fight to destroy dictatorships, to guarantee freedom of speech and of the press. Yet sometimes I am discouraged by the democratic processes in a great and critical emergency like that of today.

For example, I returned from Africa two weeks ago to find the most atrocious, if not subversive, attack being directed against an organization of the Army, one of the finest we have ever created. I refer to the Women's Army Auxiliary Corps. There was no foundation for the vicious slander, though it was given wide publicity.[32] Some seem to be intent on the suicide of our own war effort, not to mention the defamation of as fine an organization of women as I have ever seen assembled. Such a procedure to me appears inexcusable. If we can't be decent in such matters we at least should not be naïve enough to destroy ourselves. I very much hope you gentlemen will take the lead in building up a public opinion which will suppress actions of individuals who abuse our liberties by propagating such outrages.

There is another phase of the present situation for which I would solicit your strong support, and that is a check against sudden waves of optimism leading the public to feel that we have made our great effort and the end is in sight. This is far from the case. We are just getting well started. The great battles lie ahead. We have yet to be proven in the agony of enduring heavy casualties, as well as the reverses which are inevitable in war. What we need now is a stoic determination to do everything in our power to overwhelm the enemy, cost what it may, to reduce him to a supplicant under the impact of aroused and determined democracies.

The failure today to surge forward with every ounce of power and effort we possess would be to write a tragic page for history. The temptation to ease up after initial and relatively minor successes seems difficult to resist. The Axis nations probably count on this as a weak element of Allied psychology. Their opinion has been contemptuous of our soft way of living, of our toughness and our military stamina. The most forbidding prospect with which we can now confront the enemy is the continuation in full measure of methodical, ruthless preparations to overwhelm them in the same manner that the army of Von Arnim was eliminated in Tunisia. The Allies have unified their military effort. We must all do the same at home.

Two things we must guard against:

There must be no divisions among the Allies.
There must be no let-up in our preparations.

----

[32]On June 9, 1943, several metropolitan newspapers carried a column in which the following sentence appeared: "Contraceptives and prophylactic equipment will be furnished to the members of the WAACs according to a super-secret agreement reached by high-ranking officers of the War Department and the WAAC chieftain."

42
Pre-Pearl Harbor Fathers

Statements Before the Senate Committee on Military Affairs, on Consideration of S. 763, Exempting Certain Married Men Who Have Children from Liability under the Selective Training and Service Act of 1940, as Amended, 78th Congress, 1st Session, September 20, 1943

Certainly if you cut us now you inflict a much heavier loss than we anticipated suffering from the Germans or Japanese, because that is right at the source. . . . My emotions, so far as I am permitted to have them, relate to the soldiers, relate to those fathers that are already in the Army, what happens to them in this affair, to what extent they are backed up. . . .

THE CHAIRMAN [SENATOR ROBERT R. REYNOLDS OF NORTH CAROLINA]: General Marshall, as you no doubt have been advised, we have under consideration a bill by Senator Wheeler [Burton K. Wheeler of Montana] that was introduced before the recess of Congress in relation to the deferring of induction of pre-Pearl Harbor fathers. For the past several days we have had some officers of the Army and Navy, as well as Mr. [Paul V.] McNutt of the War Manpower Commission, to testify before us.

Have you a prepared statement?

GENERAL MARSHALL: No, sir.

THE CHAIRMAN: You have not?

GENERAL MARSHALL: No, sir.

THE CHAIRMAN: We would be very glad if you would make a statement as to what your views are pertaining to this subject before us.

GENERAL MARSHALL: Is this [indicating microphone] to be used here?

THE CHAIRMAN: I think that is for your benefit and for the benefit of those who would be glad to hear what you have to say in regard to the matter.

GENERAL MARSHALL: Mr. Chairman and gentlemen: I have read General McNarney's[33] statement, and of course I was familiar, roughly, with all the facts that he dealt with there; so, you already have a great many of the details. I might summarize some by stating that we have

---

[33]Lieutenant General Joseph T. McNarney, Deputy Chief of Staff; later General, commanding Mediterranean Theater of Operations.

[226]

planned, both in the War Department and in keeping with the decisions, approved decisions of the Combined Chiefs of Staff, to build up the military forces of the Army to a figure of 7,700,000 by the end of this calendar year, and that we have at the present time about 7,300,000 including officers and Wacs, as well as soldiers.

As General McNarney stated in some detail we have to have approximately seventy-five thousand a month in any event, merely to keep in being what we already have. It has always been difficult to estimate the maintenance requirements because we cannot tell exactly what the casualties may be. For example, we do not yet know what casualties have been suffered in the Salerno fighting. It will be some little time before we can obtain that information because they are busy fighting. Tabulating will come a little later. So, we have a going requirement of maintenance.

I might amplify that a little bit by stating to you gentlemen that at the present time we have, for example, four divisions which we have not yet been able to carry into the cadre basis of one thousand five hundred men per division. We had hoped we would have them filled up in August, but they still remain to be filled, and that requires some four times fourteen thousand men.

We have at the present moment I believe approximately one hundred thousand vacancies in other units to add to the daily shortages that develop through sickness, through battle casualties and through discharges for one reason or another.

I should also mention, I believe, the fact when you have a man pass out of active combat and put him in the hospital, he may be on the rolls of the Army but he is no longer effective, he is a charge and one that we must be very careful to do everything possible for, and he requires other people to do that in the way of doctors, medical attendants, nurses, and so forth.

Our plans involve us in the creation of additional units during the remainder of this calendar year. I am giving you approximate figures. We are planning some four hundred or four hundred forty additional battalions other than purely our troops, which amount to some two hundred twenty-five thousand.

Now, I had probably better comment on that for a moment. These troops are all on demand for certain times at certain places. I know of no group that would object more strenuously than you gentlemen to sending hastily gathered people into this war. It is the most expensive and dangerous practice we can be involved in. We had to do that in the early part of the war, but at the present time, thank God, we will not have to do it if we are allowed to go ahead with businesslike planning and arrangements to produce men that are required at the proper time and place. I am talking about antiaircraft troops, I am talking about engineers, signal troops; I am talking about port battalions, because you must understand, with each advance that we have, we have a new requirement, additional antiaircraft, and so forth. We are moving in now with men to man the port of Salerno. We hope shortly to move in the men to operate the port of Naples. At the same time we are not abandoning the port of Bizerte, or Tunis or Algiers. They all have to be operated. At the same time we must move in the antiaircraft to cover them, and all these are additional commitments because we cannot abandon installations in the chain of supply. However, at times we must reduce the installations in the rear and move up toward the front. That has notably been the case in the Pacific when our first deployments were very few and as we moved along—Admiral King, I might say, will corroborate this—we more or less emasculated or abandoned installations that we had to put in, in the January-to-June period of 1942.

These men are all on demand. We are pressed heavily daily by General Eisenhower, we are pressed by General Devers,[34] we are pressed by General MacArthur, by the commanders of the Navy in the Pacific region, where we have a large group of Army troops, for the special organization that I am now talking about. They must be created, they must be trained, disciplined and prepared to do efficiently their job in those places.

If we do not do it now we cannot do it at the time that the planned operations are set up for it.

Let me illustrate a little further. I am possibly getting into the dangerous ground of publicizing information, but maybe the end justifies the means. At the present time we are shipping to England, this month, some fifty thousand special troops, engineers, mechanics, signal troops, and so on, to keep that place operating. We are sending over some six hundred bomber crews, not to increase the bombers we have in England but to maintain the bombers we have in England, and we are being pressed very heavily to send them as rapidly as possible, to keep that great operation going. There is a constant drain, and we must have the people in time, trained and ready to sail when they are required.

We are behind in the bomber-crew operation, because the conditions have been such that the demands were more heavy than we anticipated eight months to twelve months ago. Regardless of this, we must provide them, and they are now en route in the numbers I have just mentioned. The same is going on in the Mediterranean but the attrition there is caused by a totally different set of factors. The enemy reactions to the

---

[34] Lieutenant General Jacob L. Devers, Commanding General, United States Forces in the United Kingdom; later General, commanding 6th Army Group.

Mediterranean air operations are much less effective than they are in Germany or northwestern France. It is quite natural that this should be the case. The weather permits many more frequent missions, which means a much heavier task for the flyers. In addition to that, we have had a number of ground operations, starting amphibiously but ending up on the ground, all of which require a continuous and exhaustive effort on the part of the Air Forces. They have to fly many more missions than would normally be required of them, but they must do it, and they have been doing it in the most remarkable manner during the past two weeks in connection with the operation at Salerno.

Now, all that makes heavy demands on us. The fatigue of pilots in the Mediterranean area rather than the casualties in pilots, because they proportionately do not suffer at all the casualties that are suffered in the north, must be met by trained troops. We have men, therefore, going overseas in planes, and going overseas more slowly in ships, a matter which is opposed by the overseas commanders because they think it is too much delayed. However, we cannot help that.

We have men who are evacuated, who are sent home to stimulate training, to give them rest while they are out. All of those men are in action while they are en route. You cannot conduct a war all over the world and not consider the temporary loss of the troops going and coming. The pipeline must be kept filled toward the theater, but there are also necessary certain withdrawals that I have just mentioned here, particularly of officers.

Now, frankly, I am puzzled by the reactions at the present time. I most sincerely turned over in my mind what is wanted, what the understanding is in regard to the desire, and have tried to figure out what it is desired that we should do.

Under the circumstances, it seems to me all we could do is reduce our program and change our strategy, unless you feel we are unduly extravagant somewhere, which is quite another matter. I will refer to that later.

Certainly, if you cut us now you inflict a much heavier loss than we anticipate suffering from the Germans or Japanese, because that cut would be right at the source of the power we are trying to inflict on the enemy. We have been a long time—a long, long time acquiring momentum, and I personally think it would be most unfortunate if we kill the momentum at this moment. Specifically, if we reduce the number of divisions.

Why, gentlemen, we are just getting ready for our deployment. By "deployment," I mean putting soldiers in action. Up to the present time we have had rather small ground forces of the Army in action. We have been involved in establishing bases all over the world and in getting our air force in action just as quickly as we possibly could, but up to the present time there have been, comparatively speaking with relation to all the forces, a very small ground force complement involved.

We have now, in general, set up our bases, we have all of the operative personnel, except as I mentioned in relation to the African theater and European-United Kingdom theater a few moments ago. The basic establishments are going. It is a matter of maintenance now with regard to those factors. Our shipping can now be largely turned to the deployment of our ground army.

We have the troops trained. This is the first time in our history, this is the first time in this war that we really had the men trained before they sailed, because we have been forced to complete training abroad. It has been very well done, but it means a very large overhead requirement.

While the Tunisian battle was going on, for example, General Clark with the Fifth Army established in North Africa one of the most remarkable training schools I had ever seen. It took in everything. It trained men in amphibious operations, mountain operations, village fighting, and everything else in the most practical fashion. But the uneconomical feature was that we had to do that overseas. We had to set up the overhead over there, which is bad business because it uses water transportation. In short, we want to do as much here as we can rather than in the war theater, except the actual fighting. We started, as I say, while the Tunisian operation was still under way. Then, as rapidly as the divisions completed their training in Tunisia they were removed from there and given this additional training. Prior to that time, due to lack of ammunition they had not been able to get the target practice that every American soldier feels he should have, and which from our standpoint is desirable. All of that had to be made available over there.

The same thing took place in Australia, in New Caledonia, and also of course in Hawaii which have made a training center for deployments into the Pacific. So my comments do not quite apply to that locality.

Now, we have been able to develop in this country the great ground force that is essential to the winning of this war. We are now, for the first time, ready for that deployment.

I have mentioned some of the shortages that occur in the rear units of that deployment. Do you wish to cut that? Do you wish to cut down on the special troops that I referred to, some four hundred battalions that are to be in being and starting their training during the remainder of this calendar year? What is the effect of that going to be? Well, from a business point of view, as a military business as well as a civil business, I think that would be most unfortunate. Certainly, you would not wish to cut down the program of air development. We have expected a delay in that, but that delay we expected is on the basis of permitting us to develop more crews per plane, because that seemed to be an urgent requirement as the situation developed. If we could have exactly foreseen all the changes of the plot, had the enemy taken us into his confidence, we might have visualized that requirement before this. However, I doubt if we would have been able to obtain the men.

I would like to comment in reference to that remark I just made on the divisions that we landed at Salerno. Now, the first American division to land there had never been in battle before. While in training in the United States, necessary withdrawals had reduced its strength in October 1942 to about nine thousand men. Then we had to build it up, but it took us six months to get the men to build up that division, because we had to divert it into the air program, into this requirement, into the African port battalions, because those requirements were urgent all the way and extended from the British port at Basra, Iraq. The only way we could get them was to take them out of this and other divisions. Consequently this particular division having some trained men was continually weakened and eventually emasculated. After we had necessarily cut it down to nine thousand men, it took us six months to get it up to strength. Then the training started in normal fashion, but not until then. That was the first division to land at Salerno. I think it is reasonable to state that it would have been a better division had it not been ripped to pieces, as we were forced to do, because we could not get the men in time otherwise. We had certain things happening, changes in the requirements. Unpreventable delays, for instance, set us back one hundred seventy-five thousand men in a single month. We had to get the men somewhere. The war goes on. We get no compromises from the Germans or Japanese. We had to meet the issue at each place and in time.

The 45th Infantry Division had had battle experience in Sicily; it had suffered a somewhat similar emasculation but not such long delay in being built up again. It is now back into the battle at Salerno.

It is our urgent desire to avoid any more depletion of organized units, which is a most unfortunate and extravagant procedure. I submit that we have this army organized in a businesslike, efficient basis, and I think it will bear any investigation that you might wish to give it. Considering its mass and speed, I think the various projects have been well planned and very well executed. It is a most complicated procedure, but those complications have been met, and I have no fears as to comments regarding that.

Now, I cannot find just where you would make these adjustments that are now under debate or discussion. Certainly, you would not wish to cut down the war production. That would apparently leave the military effort to be cut.

I have read statements that we have troops hanging around this country. They are being trained for the first time in our history, they are being well trained and given a chance, but even so, nothing like the chance the German divisions are given to prepare for battle. But with our initiative and quality of our people and our great air power, we feel that they can discharge the missions that may be given them.

It may be that some feel that the matter can be settled in another way. I do not agree with that at all. A combination of means will do this in the most rapid fashion, as we see it, and I would deplore anything which would limit that.

If it comes to the emotions, I do not feel that we in the War Department—and I am quite certain Admiral King agrees with me, as to the Navy Department—have any right to emotions. We want it in the divisions where they are fighting, but ours has to be a businesslike approach to this matter.

I might say there, however, in the matter of fathers, which is the matter under discussion at this time, that we already have some seven hundred thousand in the Army. My emotions, so far as I am permitted to have them, relate to the soldiers, relate to those fathers that are in the Army, what happens to them in this affair, to what extent they are backed up.

*   *   *

As to men over thirty-eight, I have already expressed myself in considerable detail. They would be, to my mind, a burden rather than a help, because the number that proved ineffective for our purpose is so large, and the conditions under which we must accept them under the policies of Congress as to hospitalization, and so forth, immediately imposes on us a very heavy burden. I mean by this that a man may never have been in a hospital in his life in his ordinary civil occupation, but when he comes into the Army he gets a certain right and he takes advantage of it. We have him immediately on our hands, and he is operated on for this, operated on for that, and we must do it. So that the men over thirty-eight I would regard as a burden.

We are on the offensive, and I think it would be unfortunate to do anything that would dim the power of that offensive.

*   *   *

We have undoubtedly very heavy fighting before us, and we are now ready to go about it, that is, to deploy our troops, to move them overseas into the theaters, to bring to bear the greatest possible force we can in the shortest possible time.

* * *

SENATOR WHEELER: You said, General Marshall, something about the businesslike way in which the Army is conducting its work. I am afraid from the reports I get—and I know that you cannot keep in touch with all the details—that the great bulk of the people—a great many of them—do not agree with the efficiency in which men are being used in the United States of America in the Army.

Do you have anything to do with what is done in the Pentagon Building at Washington?

GENERAL MARSHALL: Yes, sir, quite a bit.

SENATOR WHEELER: The other day a captain in the Army came and told me that a whole division could be got out of the Pentagon Building without very much difficulty, because of the fact that the men there were falling all over themselves, not only civilian employees, but others as well.

GENERAL MARSHALL: That sounds like the story of the man who gave out the data about Fort Meade the other day.

SENATOR WHEELER: I do not know anything about Fort Meade.

GENERAL MARSHALL: It was an offhand comment, without any foundation.

I am very familiar with the Pentagon Building. I would say that your captain friend is entirely wrong.

SENATOR WHEELER: I have been in the Pentagon Building. I have got reports not only from this captain but also from a great many other people down there to the effect that there are many more employees down there than are needed. We have that condition, likewise, in all the other branches of the Government.

GENERAL MARSHALL: General McNarney, who was before you, goes there once a week. He is the scourge of the place, trying to cut down, but it is a far more complicated matter than it would seem to be offhand.

SENATOR WHEELER: You talked a while ago about bachelors and whether or not the Army should be made up of bachelors. It is not just a question of whether or not the Army should be made up of bachelors. It is a question of the morale of the people back home.

As you have well stated, if a man has a family—if he is the father of children back home—and his wife has got to go to work in a factory in order to support those children, and those children are going to be left running the streets, that man is going to be worrying about those children much more than a single man who does not have any children. Do you not think so?

GENERAL MARSHALL: I would say, in the rough, yes, sir.

SENATOR WHEELER: So, it is not a question of married men or fathers. It is not a question of whether or not you are drafting fathers or bachelors. I think your statement was an unfortunate statement, because you seemed to imply that all everybody wanted was just to take bachelors.

It is a notorious fact, according to the reports of the FBI, that there is an increase of juvenile delinquency in every community throughout the country. This delinquency among children throughout the United States is brought about by mothers working on the outside, who have volunteered to work in the airplane factories, and other factories.

Certainly if that continues and if fathers are taken, it is only going to add to the general delinquency of the children of the United States. While it is your duty to look at the situation from the standpoint of the Army, it is the duty of the Congress of the United States to look at the future of the country from the standpoint of the delinquency of the generation now growing up.

You also made the answer, as I understood you, that fathers, if they were exempted, might be exempted from doing their full duty toward the war.

GENERAL MARSHALL: I do not quite understand that, Senator.

SENATOR WHEELER: I understood you to say that if fathers were drafted they would be exempt from doing their full duty toward the war. A great many of these fathers—a great many of these six million fathers we are talking about here—are now working in industry, are they not?

GENERAL MARSHALL: I presume so.

SENATOR WHEELER: A great many of them are working in the various industries of this country. While they may not be working in war industries, they are working in the transportation industry and in the distributing industry. The distributing industry is an exceedingly important thing for the United States, is it not?

GENERAL MARSHALL: Yes.

SENATOR WHEELER: After all, you have to have laundries, stores, hotels, restaurants, and things of that kind. If you break those down completely and reduce the services that they render you are breaking down the home front, are you not?

GENERAL MARSHALL: If you break them down completely; but I do not admit that you are going to break them down completely. It seems to me that we have not even vaguely approximated what has been done in England up to the present time. They have children and women working in their plants. As far as I have been able to see from all the reports, we have not even vaguely approximated that.

SENATOR WHEELER: That is true, but it is a quite different thing. It is one thing to speak about England, that has been under bombing and threat of attack for a great many years, and is right close to the war front, and it is another thing to compare it with the United States.

GENERAL MARSHALL: That is very true, sir.

SENATOR WHEELER: That is a quite different thing.

GENERAL MARSHALL: That is our great problem.

SENATOR WHEELER: It is quite a different thing to compare Germany and Russia with the United States.

GENERAL MARSHALL: You are talking about the emotional reaction, not talking about the individual facts of the case.

SENATOR WHEELER: I am talking about the emotional reaction, the moral reaction, and the letdown of the morale of the people in a country which is under fire as compared to a country which is three thousand miles away from that. I say there is a vast difference, and you cannot compare them.

It is important to the Army, is it not, that the morale back home should not suffer a breakdown?

GENERAL MARSHALL: I would put it the other way: I would say it is very important to the Army that the people back home understand what is being done.

SENATOR WHEELER: That is one thing that they have not understood —what is being done.

GENERAL MARSHALL: That is quite correct.

SENATOR WHEELER: Because every time we have asked the officials to come and answer questions, the answers have been military secrets and the people back home have not known and do not know today.

GENERAL MARSHALL: I do not think I have kept many secrets from you.

SENATOR WHEELER: I am not complaining about you, but I do say, though, that that has been the fact. We have often had that occur. Before the Committee on Agriculture we have asked for the simple facts on Lend-Lease, such as how many tires were being shipped to a South American country, but we have been told that that is a military secret.

As I understand you, you stated that there are seven million three hundred thousand people in the Army today. That was in your opening statement. You said you expect to ship five million overseas, and that you want to raise the total to seven million seven hundred thousand. That is, you want four hundred thousand more people in the Army than you have at the present time. According to General McNarney, the most you can possibly ship overseas by the end of 1944, and equip, is five million people. That would leave approximately two million seven hundred thousand in the United States. If I remember his testimony correctly, they would be needed for training and other purposes.

GENERAL MARSHALL: They need them for the maintenance of the home bases, for the training of men going overseas, for Panama, Alaska, and the Aleutians, and for certain small detachments up and down the coasts.

One of my greatest difficulties in effecting economies has been in making reductions along our coasts, where I thought we were immobilizing an undue number of men. That has been resented, and very strongly by the civilian interests, and even here in Washington, and, as a matter of fact, up here at Capitol Hill. Everybody is willing to cut as long as it is not in his own backyard.

I am trying to say that we have tried to cut in every way conceivable the number of men in the continental United States.

SENATOR WHEELER: That was some time ago.

GENERAL MARSHALL: I am merely trying to assert that our intentions have not only been good but that our efforts were strenuous.

SENATOR WHEELER: That was some time ago.

GENERAL MARSHALL: Senator, you try to remove some of them right now and listen to the reaction.

SENATOR WHEELER: I have not heard any reaction from the West Coast about the removal of people. There was that fear when the Japs were in the Aleutian Islands, and there was that fear that was largely stirred up, in my judgment, because of the fact that we were told before we got into the war that the Japs and the Germans might come over here almost any time and blow our cities and our country all to pieces. That fear was instilled into the people to such an extent that naturally they did fear that, having these troops along the Pacific Coast, coupled with all the wild stories that were prevalent along the Atlantic Coast, we might be invaded or bombed out of existence overnight.

I do not think that that same situation exists today. I think that the people have come to a realization that that is not entirely true and that the enemy could not capture us overnight. I do not think you will find that same reaction today.

GENERAL MARSHALL: I am struggling right now with a reduction of our coast defenses, and I am in trouble over it at the present moment.

SENATOR WHEELER: I appreciate the fact that every community likes to have some troops. The chamber of commerce of every community likes to have more troops there, because that brings in a little more business to that particular community. But that is not the general feeling of the population of the United States. The people of the United States are not interested in whether some troops are stationed in a particular city for the purpose of helping the business of the local chamber of commerce; they are looking at it more from an over-all picture.

Now, you want five hundred thousand more men?

GENERAL MARSHALL: It does not quite add up that way, because along with that goes replacements.

SENATOR WHEELER: What are the replacements?

GENERAL MARSHALL: The present average is about seventy-five thousand a month.

SENATOR WHEELER: That is the number of present replacements because of what?

GENERAL MARSHALL: Disease, casualties, discharges.

SENATOR WHEELER: You have coming on the boys who are reaching eighteen years of age each month. There are one hundred thousand of them and approximately seventy thousand of those will be physically fit; is that right?

GENERAL MARSHALL: I do not know the figures on that, sir; I do not recall them.

SENATOR WHEELER: So, the four hundred thirty-six thousand are not going into the Army?

GENERAL MARSHALL: Not going into the Army?

SENATOR WHEELER: Four hundred thirty-six thousand of these fathers are not going into the Army entirely, are they?

GENERAL MARSHALL: You mean they will be partly for the Army and partly for the Navy?

SENATOR WHEELER: Yes.

GENERAL MARSHALL: I presume so; I do not know about that, sir.

SENATOR WHEELER: I had forgotten what the figures were that were given me as to the number of men who had to be drafted between now and the end of the year.

General Hershey, what was that figure?

GENERAL HERSHEY: one million two hundred twenty-one thousand for four months—September, October, November and December.

*   *   *

SENATOR WHEELER: You have a lot of men in this country that have been trained for three years.

GENERAL MARSHALL: I would not say a lot. We have quite a number.

SENATOR WHEELER: And a lot for two years?

GENERAL MARSHALL: Yes.

SENATOR WHEELER: And a lot with one year?

GENERAL MARSHALL: Yes, sir.

SENATOR WHEELER: Now, you have made the statement that you couldn't fill up some of the divisions that you had at the present time. Could you fill up those divisions that you have at the present time with the over five million men that you have in the country?

GENERAL MARSHALL: Only by eliminating units.

SENATOR WHEELER: Only by eliminating units?

GENERAL MARSHALL: We have already eliminated certain ones, where we felt we could take the risk, or where the need seemed to be no longer indicated.

SENATOR WHEELER: You don't intend to take the four hundred forty-six thousand fathers, if you get them, to fill up the units that have been trained for two or three years, do you?

GENERAL MARSHALL: I don't know exactly where the fathers will go, but we have to provide men, trained men, to go into those units, to bring them up to their proper strength.

SENATOR WHEELER: When you are taking men for these units, you will take trained men, men that have been trained for two and three years?

GENERAL MARSHALL: It isn't only in the units. We are going to be training men at our training centers to go into those units. We train the men away from the units. That is a single industry in itself. With a new division, we make it do its own training because we set it up as a school; but when we are finished with that, then every man that is given his basic training does it at a station that does nothing but that specialized thing.

SENATOR WHEELER: Then you send him to a unit that has been trained for two or three years?

GENERAL MARSHALL: When he goes into that unit, he is supposed to be able to do his simple soldier duties, squadron duty and his platoon duty.

SENATOR WHEELER: How much training do you give him?

GENERAL MARSHALL: Originally we gave them thirteen weeks. We found it wasn't sufficient and had to increase it to seventeen weeks.

SENATOR WHEELER: Are you sending overseas the men who have been trained three years and two years and one year?

GENERAL MARSHALL: Not unless their unit goes. Otherwise, we would be emasculating the unit.

SENATOR WHEELER: Haven't you got units that have been trained two years?

GENERAL MARSHALL: Yes, sir.

SENATOR WHEELER: And haven't you got units that have been trained for one year?

GENERAL MARSHALL: Yes, sir.

SENATOR WHEELER: And haven't you got units that have been trained three years?

GENERAL MARSHALL: We have no unit that has been trained three years as a unit. However, the 33d Infantry Division, as I mentioned before, was cut down as much as from fifteen thousand to three thousand men.

SENATOR WHEELER: You have taken men out of some of the three-year units and put them into other units, is that correct?

GENERAL MARSHALL: That is correct. There was a demand in Africa and other places for specialized units immediately and we didn't have them.

SENATOR WHEELER: Didn't have the specialized units?

GENERAL MARSHALL: Engineers, troops to operate the ports, signal men, and additional antiaircraft men. Largely engineers, signalmen, quartermaster and mechanic battalions for the aircraft.

SENATOR WHEELER: Then if you deferred four hundred forty-six thousand fathers you wouldn't be able to build up some of these units quite as quickly as you otherwise would?

GENERAL MARSHALL: That is exactly it, sir.

SENATOR WHEELER: By the end of 1944, how many units do you expect to have overseas?

GENERAL MARSHALL: Five million men.

*   *   *

SENATOR WHEELER: The figure of seven million seven hundred thousand was set before the fall of the Axis in Sicily and the fall of Italy?

GENERAL MARSHALL: Yes, sir, but in the light of the planned campaign to accomplish the results that we are now in a fair way to realize—

*   *   *

SENATOR WHEELER: How many troops did the surrender of Italy take out of the enemy's forces?

GENERAL MARSHALL: I don't recall the number of divisions. I can answer it in this way: The Japanese and the Germans between them will have only fourteen less divisions—

SENATOR WHEELER: What do you mean by fourteen less?

GENERAL MARSHALL: Speaking of the general total. A total of fourteen less divisions than was calculated for the entire Axis at the time of the figure of eight million two hundred thousand.

SENATOR WHEELER: Why do you say that?

GENERAL MARSHALL: Because they have created new divisions.

SENATOR WHEELER: They have created new divisions.

GENERAL MARSHALL: After the loss of the Italian divisions the total on the Axis side actively engaged in the war is still within fourteen of the grand total of 1942.

SENATOR WHEELER: Was it the Germans that raised the forty divisions or was it the Japs?

GENERAL MARSHALL: The Germans have replaced some forty divisions and have created some twenty additional ones. They have actually created sixty, but they had to replace those lost at Stalingrad, which I think was about twenty-six, and those lost in Tunisia.

SENATOR WHEELER: How many have the Germans lost on the Eastern Front? Have you any idea what they have lost in this summer's campaign?

GENERAL MARSHALL: I don't know. We know something about the strength of their divisions. We have some data on the number of German divisions that are not now at full strength.

SENATOR WHEELER: Were your losses greater or less than you anticipated in the campaigns in Italy and Tunisia?

GENERAL MARSHALL: I can't speak for Italy yet, we don't know. In the campaign in Tunisia they were very much less than we had calculated. In the campaign in Sicily they were also less. And on the American side, very much less.

SENATOR WHEELER: Now, you have made no changes in your figure since the surrender of Italy, have you?

GENERAL MARSHALL: No, sir.

SENATOR WHEELER: Do you know how many of the Italian—

GENERAL MARSHALL: I might say this, Senator, that during the occupation of Italy we have had a series of messages from General Eisenhower pressing us to speed up the shipment of special units that have to go into the various ports of Italy.

SENATOR WHEELER: That hasn't anything to do with the particular size of the Army; you have got the troops?

GENERAL MARSHALL: It has to do with the additional number of special troops that are being required over and above the original calculation.

SENATOR WHEELER: I mean, he wants more troops than those you now have here in the United States, isn't that right?

GENERAL MARSHALL: We haven't got all he has asked for because they are special units that we do not have enough of. I spoke of the fact that we have to organize between now and December 31 some thirty or forty battalions of special troops in Tunisia, special divisions. In other words, in arriving at our original estimate, we did not allow for a large enough number of these, considering the breadth of the campaign.

SENATOR WHEELER: You can't get those troops out of the fathers that are coming in?

GENERAL MARSHALL: Well, the fathers are related to it, presumably from the man power end, because we need these people here this fall to get these special units ready to sail in early 1944.

*   *   *

SENATOR WHEELER: General, one more observation. During the noon recess a man called me up. I want to call your attention to this because you have talked about the businesslike way in which the Army was conducted.

GENERAL MARSHALL: I might say, Senator, we do not consider ourselves perfect by any manner of means, but we are fairly good.

SENATOR WHEELER: This gentleman was in the Quartermaster Department. He called to say that his division is loaded with young officers under thirty-five. Many civilians, not fathers. He had begged his superiors for assignments as he didn't have anything to do.

GENERAL MARSHALL: Send me his name and I will provide the job.

SENATOR WHEELER: He didn't give his name. He wasn't free from fear.

GENERAL MARSHALL: The minimum we have in Washington is twenty-eight, unless there is a special exception by the Secretary of War.

SENATOR WHEELER: In addition that man called attention to the fact that in the War Department itself, down in the Pentagon Building, you have young men down there, some of them young officers, some who were civilians and had been put in and given a commission in order to have them remain there. I think the War Department ought to go through its own list.

GENERAL MARSHALL: We have done that, Senator. We have some young men. I have one, for example, who had his hand shot off at Hawaii.

SENATOR WHEELER: But these are not men with their hands shot off; these are young men in the departments.

GENERAL MARSHALL: If you give me something a man doesn't put his name to it is difficult for me to deal with it.

SENATOR WHEELER: I can understand why men won't give their names.

GENERAL MARSHALL: We don't run any Gestapo.

SENATOR WHEELER: No, you don't run a Gestapo, but it does seem to me that it is the duty of the War Department to check up.

GENERAL MARSHALL: I agree with you, but we are doing that every day. Every week General McNarney has a meeting and gets a report on that. I can read you from the written record of each month's meeting on the subject you are talking about. I don't think that is ignored.

SENATOR WHEELER: If the Congress depended on those who give names it couldn't get any information from these various departments because they wouldn't dare to give us the information.

GENERAL MARSHALL: I admit a certain amount of that.

SENATOR WHEELER: They would lose their jobs. Take in the Dougherty investigation that I conducted, I got a great deal of information from the department itself, but if I had used the name or exposed the person giving it, he would have been subject to dismissal.

GENERAL MARSHALL: I realize that point.

SENATOR WHEELER: Congress has to rely upon information of that sort. We can't get it from the heads of departments because each and every one of them wants to cover up its own mistakes.

SENATOR ALBEN W. BARKLEY OF KENTUCKY: If those people in the War Department who write anonymous letters, or those who sign their names to letters to members of Congress and ask that their names be not given, if those people would go to the responsible officer of the War Department with that same information wouldn't it be investigated in a fair way by the War Department?

GENERAL MARSHALL: If there was any foundation for what they had to report they would probably get promoted.

* * *

43
Keeping Up the Momentum

An Address before the American Legion, Omaha, Nebraska, September 21, 1943

∽∽∽∽∽∽∽∽∽∽∽∽∽∽∽∽∽∽∽∽∽∽∽∽∽∽∽∽∽∽∽∽∽

I am profoundly grateful that for once in the history of the United States there is suggested the possibility that we have too much of something or other with which to support our armies.

A FEW days ago I submitted a report[85] which pretty well covered the operations of the Army during the past two years, the why and wherefor of our various moves. There is little to add to that statement at this time except that there must be no lessening of the momentum which it has taken us three years to develop. The press and radio are keeping you well informed as to the progress of affairs in the Mediterranean and on the Russian front. You are given most of the details of the heavy bombing we are administering to the industries in Germany and the Axis satellites throughout Europe, as well as the destruction of the enemy fighter planes opposed to these devastating raids. New Guinea, somewhat like the Aleutians, is an unhealthy locality for the enemy and his planes, barges and soldiers. As a matter of fact, the entire western Pacific has become a critical problem for the Japanese. For the first time we are getting under way with the war as we would have it conducted, and I hope that from now on we shall rarely be on the receiving end except as is inevitable when trading punches in battle contacts.

It has seemed to me from reading the papers recently, that there is some misunderstanding as to the degree of success we have attained in the prosecution of the war. One gathers the impression that our various moves of late were the final steps in the conflict.

Perhaps it might be well for me to outline the present state of our deployment. For most of the past year and a half we have been engaged in establishing bases for future operations. Comparatively speaking, large combat forces of the ground army have not yet been engaged. As I endeavored to show diagrammatically in my recent report, our shipping has been largely employed in getting our air forces into action and

[85]*Biennial Report of the Chief of Staff of the United States Army to the Secretary of War, July 1, 1941 to June 30, 1943.* Washington: Government Printing Office, 1943. Also incorporated in *Report on the Army, 1939-1943.* Washington: The Infantry Journal, 1943.

in building up the tremendous installations required all over the world both to maintain the combat forces already moved into the various theaters and to provide for the very much larger forces to come. These preparations have now been practically completed and it is the last-mentioned detail to which I would refer this afternoon.

We have prepared in North Africa and in Sicily, and we are about to prepare in Italy, for the supply and maintenance of heavy air and ground forces. For a long time we have been making similar preparations in the United Kingdom, and throughout the Pacific the same process has been under way since January 1942. Meanwhile there has been built up in this country a formidable force of divisions and army corps with all the supporting troops, disciplined, highly trained, hardened, ready for embarkation for the great and final deployment of our armies against the enemy. Save for assaults in the air, only a small portion of our combat strength has been engaged. Now at last we are ready to carry the war to the enemy, all overseas, thank God, with a power and force that we hope will bring this conflict to an early conclusion. But please remember that this phase is just about to begin, a point which seems not to be understood by our people here at home, possibly because they are far removed from the agonies of war except for those whose sons or husbands have been engaged in the fighting.

Concerning the public reactions of the moment I find myself in a curious state of mind. For three years or more it has been a daily struggle of striving to meet the demands without the available means. There has been the constant problem of weighing the priorities of this theater against that one, of sending men to the front for whom training ammunition had been lacking or similar deficiencies. Now I find myself in the position of being questioned, if not investigated, for having too much of something or other. I don't know yet exactly what this excess is, but I do know that I am profoundly grateful that for once in the history of the United States there is suggested the possibility that we have too much of something or other with which to support our armies. It will require considerable proof to assure me that such an unusual state of affairs actually exists. And I would add this view—my consideration is for the American soldier, to see that he is not limited in ammunition, that he is not limited in equipment, and that he has sufficient training and medical care; in other words, to see that for once in the history of this country he is given a fair break in the terrible business of making war. So I must confess that rather than being disturbed by the doubts that now seem to be arising in the public mind at the present time, I am vastly relieved that they should be of that particular character rather than the usual recriminations over tragic deficiencies of every kind and nature.

There is another phase of the present situation which I believe it will do no harm to refer to publicly and which probably will be of interest, especially to you gentlemen who bore the full burden in France of our unpreparedness for war. We have been engaged for a number of months and very properly so, in plans for the further development of the war in the Pacific with the additional means as they become available from the struggle in the European Theater. The first transfer made possible by our battles in the Mediterranean will result from the elimination of the Axis navy in that region. That means more naval power in the Pacific and that, in turn, means additional bases and equipment which have to be planned and provided for long in advance. We are similarly engaged in planning regarding other forces, particularly air, and it will probably interest you as much as it will discourage the Japanese to learn that our most difficult problem is to find sufficient bases from which to operate the vast forces which are to be poured into the Pacific for the rearrangement of the affairs of the Son of Heaven with his military clique.

Considering the fact that each day of war means both a colossal expenditure of money and a constant expenditure of human life, it is evident that we must not lose an hour in making our transfers from one theater to another. We are proceeding on the basis that nothing is to delay this flood of power to be added to the forces which already outnumber the enemy and are steadily growing stronger day by day. But I would add that these matters are not the affair of a moment, the result of a campaign of propaganda, or of temporary enthusiasms or special interests. We must proceed in the most businesslike manner possible to make this war so terrible to the enemy, so overwhelming in character, that never again can a small group of dictators find a sufficient following to destroy the peaceful security of a civilized world.

44
Responsibilities of the Home Front

Remarks at the American Legion Dinner at the Mayflower
Hotel, Washington, D. C., February 3, 1944

*Our soldiers must be keenly conscious that the full
strength of the nation is behind them; they must
not go into battle puzzled or embittered over disputes at home which adversely affect the war effort.*

IN the few minutes at my disposal tonight my remarks are addressed
to you veterans who are familiar with the demands of battle and
with the reactions of soldiers in campaign. Last fall at Omaha I
spoke to you of the gathering of our great reserves in preparation for a
series of tremendous blows against the enemy all over the world. Today
this is well under way and at the present moment the initial blows are
being struck against Germany from the air, on the beachhead near Rome
where very hard fighting is to be expected, against the Marshall Islands
and in the Western Pacific and out of the air over China. These are but
preliminaries to the general onslaught which will step the Allied effort
into high gear.

For the time being the heaviest concentration of ground and air forces
will be in the European Theater, though a steady stream of reinforcements flows into the Pacific. The great battles which are impending will
decide the course of civilization. The energy and spirit of the assaults will
determine the duration of the war and therefore the ultimate cost in casualties and war expenditures.

In the European Theater American troops will for the first time face
the full power of the German Army. I have no fears whatsoever regarding
the ability of the American soldier to meet the situation. Our men are
well trained. They are now well disciplined. Many of the soldiers are
battle-tested veterans. No army is better equipped. The troops are an
inspiration to their commanders. I do not mean that we will not have
troubles and reverses. These are inevitable in large operations, unless
the hostile forces are disintegrating. We must expect desperate resistance by the German Army up to the moment the German people
throw off the yoke of the Gestapo.

The destruction of German industrial cities is proceeding at a constantly increasing pace despite winter weather and heavy overcasts.
Between the RAF night bombardment and the American daylight pre-

cision bombing the people of Germany are experiencing the horrors of a war, for which they are responsible, to a degree never before approximated in modern times. Berlin, by far their largest city, is now a shambles. The destruction of other smaller targets will require much less time. More than two thousand U. S. heavy bombers are now being directed against the heart of Germany, with appropriate diversions into Austria and the Balkans, and the number will steadily increase.

In the Pacific the Japanese have had unusually heavy air and ship losses during the last six months. In the past few days they have suffered an expert demonstration of the overwhelming air and sea power which is rapidly developing in the Pacific and the perfect teamwork of our landing parties.

The operation in the Marshalls is the first assault on the strongholds which the enemy has been constructing for the past twenty-five years. The fact that the operations have been quickly successful, and were carried out without heavy losses is an indication of what is to come as our forces in the South and Southwest Pacific close in with our fleet on the Jap defenses.

In the United States the combat units have reached a high state of efficiency as they move to the base ports for shipment overseas.

In brief, the Allied avalanche is at last in motion and it will gather headway with each succeeding month. What is now required is the ardent support of our forces by the people at home. I am not referring merely to the production of equipment or to the purchase of bonds, but rather to the need of a stern resolution on the part of the whole people of the United States to make every sacrifice that will contribute to the victory. The soldiers must feel that the home folk—east, west, on the plains and in the mountains—are completely united in their determination to see this thing through to an overwhelming victory in the shortest possible time.

I speak with an emphasis that I believe is pardonable in one who has a terrible responsibility for the lives of many men, because I feel that here at home we are not yet facing the realities of war, the savage, desperate conditions of the battle fronts. Vehement protests I am receiving against our use of flame throwers do not indicate an understanding of the meaning of our dead on the beaches at Tarawa. Objections to this or that restriction are inconsistent with the devoted sacrifices of our troops.

The recent release of the atrocities committed against our prisoners by the Japanese generates a storm of anger and protest. This is a natural reaction. The situation, however, demands a determination which will divorce the individual from his own selfish weaknesses and ulterior motives. Our soldiers must be keenly conscious that the full strength of the nation is behind them; they must not go into battle puzzled or embittered over disputes at home which adversely affect the war effort. Our small sacrifices should be personal even more than financial. They should be proof positive that we never forget for a moment that the soldier has been compelled to leave his family, to give up his business, and to hazard his life in our service.

45
Anglo-American Accord

Remarks on the Award of the Howland Memorial Prize to Field Marshal Sir John Dill of the British Army at Yale University, New Haven, Connecticut, February 16, 1944

∿∿∿∿∿∿∿∿∿∿∿∿∿∿∿∿∿∿∿∿∿

The triumph over Germany in the coming months depends more on a complete accord between the British and American forces than it does on any other single factor. . . . The harmful possibilities . . . of discord have been serious in the past and will continue to be so in the future because of the necessity in the European Theater for combined operations. . . . That we have been able to master these very human difficulties, that in fact we have triumphed over them to the disaster of the enemy, is, in my opinion, the greatest single Allied achievement of this war.

THE award this afternoon of the Howland Memorial Prize to Field Marshal Sir John Dill[36] of the British Army appeals to me as a happy augury for the immediate future. I say this because in my opinion the triumph over Germany in the coming months depends more on a complete accord between the British and American forces than it does on any other single factor, air power, ground power, or naval power. Therefore the recognition today of the contribution of Sir John Dill to such Allied harmony is both timely and prophetic.

Throughout the war we have known that the agents of the enemy have endeavored to stir up ill will and misunderstandings among the Allies. They had worked against our accord with Russia. These attempts were thwarted at the Moscow conference and buried at Teheran. But the Nazi propagandists will be ceaseless in their effort to create dissension between the great English-speaking peoples.

The harmful possibilities of such discord have been serious in the past and will continue to be so in the future because of the necessity in the European Theater for combined operations, even involving on occasions the complete intermingling of troops, as is now the case in the Fifth Army in Italy. Under such circumstances, the possibility that mis-

---

[36]Late Chief, Imperial General Staff, and head of British Military Mission to the United States.

250

understandings may develop into festering sores should be evident to all, not to mention the fatal effect on the power of our blows that would result from any lack of harmony in the command and staff direction of our combined efforts.

That we have been able to master these very human difficulties, that in fact we have triumphed over them to the disaster of the enemy, is in my opinion the greatest single Allied achievement of the war. So I am gratified, I am tremendously encouraged to see Yale University honor the man who, in my opinion has made an outstanding, a unique personal contribution to the coördination of the Allied effort. Little of his great influence on the succession of momentous events in this war will be found of record by the students of history. Therefore it is the more gratifying to see his service to our common cause recognized today in the midst of the conflict.

I might add in conclusion my belief that the hope of a postwar concord which will give us peace and security for the future, will in a large measure depend on the contribution of men like Sir John Dill of whom there are very, very few—men free of prejudice, singleminded in the sincerity of their efforts to promote the unity of our two great nations.

46

The Task Before Us

An Address to the American Legion, Chicago, Illinois, September 18, 1944

~~~~~~

Bickering over postwar rights should not be permitted to delay the Armistice or sully the victory. Let's finish this terrible business as a great team.

LAST September in my talk to the representatives of the American Legion I explained that we had finally reached the point where we could shift our principal efforts from the organization of air and ground armies to the problem of deploying these vast forces overseas and launching a series of great offensive operations. Since then you have followed the prolonged air assault on the continent of Europe, the campaign north through Italy, the landings in France and the forward surge of the Allied armies to the German frontier, coördinated with the massive attacks of the Soviet forces, followed by the collapse of Finland, Rumania and Bulgaria.

You must also have followed our increasingly rapid advances through the Japanese fortified bases in the Central and South and Southwest Pacific areas, until today the enemy admits to his people the precarious nature of the situation. In the Far East we have only had a small, but an extremely potent force of U. S. ground troops. However our campaign in the air in that area has been on a constantly increasing scale, especially notable for the tremendous logistical task involved in the movement of supplies over the Himalayas into China. General Stilwell's[37] development and leadership of a highly effective Chinese striking force were most important factors in the North Burma campaign of the past spring and summer.

During recent months our great advantage over the Germans lay in the quality and training of our men, the abundance and excellence of their equipment and the skill displayed by higher commanders and staffs in the handling of divisions, corps and armies. The fact that the now historic breakthrough to the south and east and finally to the northeast of Patton's Third Army was carried out by three army corps which had never before been engaged in battle is evidence of the quality of our leaders and the soundness of the training given the troops. The large-

---

[37]General Joseph W. Stilwell, Commanding General, U. S. Army Forces in China-Burma-India; later Commanding General, Army Ground Forces.

scale maneuvers in Louisiana and in the desert region of southeastern California, as well as in other parts of the country, declared an amazing dividend in the dramatic liberation of France.

Few people, I am sure, comprehend what is involved in the deployment of our eight-million-man Army. The missions of the Air Forces called for approximately one million men and one thousand squadrons overseas. The deployment of this vast force was completed in May. In addition there are newly formed squadrons for the operation of the already famous B-29 bombers which are carrying the war to the Japanese homeland.

Of the ground army more than sixty divisions have reached the front, thoroughly trained, equipped, and most of them already battle-tested. But an even greater strength in corps and army combat troops as well as service units totaling more than two million one hundred fifty-five thousand officers and men, accompanied these divisions abroad. The movement of additional troops overseas goes forward in a constantly increased flood of both men and matériel. Eight divisions sail this month.

This deployment of our air and ground forces literally around the globe involves a monumental undertaking in transportation and supply. The Air Transport Command alone has more than one hundred ten thousand men engaged in the operation of one hundred thirty-five thousand miles of air supply systems. The Army's Transportation Corps employs one thousand six hundred ships in moving men and supplies overseas. Then there is a continuing and constantly increasing burden for the maintenance of food, clothing, and medical services and for the replacement of battle casualties and the huge matériel wastage inevitable in campaign. It is no simple matter to supply millions of American soldiers on the fighting fronts and keep them fully equipped and provided with every necessity; nevertheless, we are endeavoring to expedite the movement overseas of the remaining combat troops in continental United States.

In planning campaigns we must provide for a myriad of requirements of almost every conceivable description. These greatly influence the timing, the extent, and the character and direction of operations. In a global war of the present stupendous proportions the logistical requirements have ramifications so diverse and so numerous that one has the feeling of picking his way through a veritable maze of obstacles and uncertainties. So far we have been reasonably successful and I believe that we have imposed far greater difficulties upon our enemies. Witness approximately one hundred fifty thousand Japanese troops cut off from their supplies and withering on the vine, with the same fate now in store for even larger garrisons.

It is very important to keep in mind that we have reached a crucial stage of the war. The size and fury of the attacks must constantly increase. The pressure on the enemy must not be eased for a single moment until his last squad is battered into a state of helplessness.

Today and every day thousands of airplanes flash on missions in advance of our armies. Before dawn tomorrow and every morning until the victory has been won, hundreds of thousands of American soldiers will move forward from comfortless foxholes and bivouacs, sweating in the tropics, chilled or freezing in the damp European fall, to press an unrelenting assault against the enemy. They will go about this duty with a courageous determination to get on with the job, without hesitation over the question of personal safety. It is our duty to make sure that the flow of reinforcements and of munitions keeps pace with their advances.

A conspicuous factor in the sustained successes of the past six weeks has been the steady flow of well trained men to replace combat losses. Our divisions are kept at full strength from day to day. The losses suffered by battle casualties are usually made good within twenty-four hours and the missing matériel in trucks, tanks and guns is being replaced at the same rate. On the German side of the line, divisions dwindling in strength and gradually losing the bulk of their heavy equipment, always find themselves beset by full American teams whose strength never seems to vary and whose numbers are constantly increasing. These German deficiencies will bring about their downfall if we on this side of the Atlantic see to it that our forces are maintained day in and day out at full strength, and supplied with every possible need. We have a stern duty here at home if our attacks are to surge forward during what we all hope are the last hours of this great European conflict. We must let nothing divert our efforts from the great purpose of all these sacrifices of life and expenditures of money. We must remember that the individual soldier will place just as much importance on his life in the final week of the victorious advance as he does today. If the protective covering fire of bombs and artillery is curtailed in any degree because of shortages in supply, there will be a bitter resentment. Recently we were forced to inform the commanders in the field we could not give them the quantities of bombs and shells they demand, but I am now able to report that production rates have finally risen somewhat and we hope that the rationing of such necessities will soon be unnecessary.

As our forces have gained positions from which to strike at the heart of Germany and are breaking into the last Japanese outposts, the feeling that an early victory is assured causes certain of our people to relax in the war effort. I have complete confidence in the success of our military efforts provided we can have steady backing on this side of the oceans until the cessation of hostilities.

I am talking very frankly to you veterans of the Legion because your understanding influence has been of great assistance to me in the past and the War Department is depending on your help to weather the gales of the final fighting in Germany and the rapid transfer of our military power to the Pacific. There is also a very special reason why the young armies of this war have a right to your strong support in what is yet to come. They have just delivered from the enemy the cemeteries of your heroic brothers in arms who fell in your war; they have given you back your great war memorials and they have redeemed your battlefields—all of them from Belgium and Le Cateau, through Cantigny, Château-Thierry, Soissons and the Marne salient, across the plains north of Rheims to the awful fields of the Meuse-Argonne and St. Mihiel. And mark this, they did it for you in the best American manner, at top speed and within a few days' time. Not satisfied with that, they are about to introduce the American art of war into Germany so that any doubts the enemy may have had regarding our military competence or willingness to fight will be dispelled in an unmistakable and final manner.

War is the most terrible tragedy of the human race and it should not be prolonged an hour longer than is absolutely necessary. Yet it may have been a good thing for the future that our military forces found the opportunity to develop and display their power on the battlefield, so that the would-be tyrants of the future may realize the power of our great democracy and the willingness of its people to defend the great principles of freedom against wanton destruction at the hands of European dictators or treacherous barbarians of the Pacific.

Finally, I would ask that you keep carefully in mind what I have told you several times in the past and now repeat again, that our power to defeat the enemy with certainty and without the bitter cost of long delays has been largely due to the carefully organized coöperation of the British-American forces under unity of command. This has made possible our great successes, the coördinating of our efforts with the vast campaigns of the Russian armies and the Chinese forces, and has permitted the effective employment of the other Allied forces who bear their portion of the heat of the battle.

For the past year the sole hope of our enemies has been to create dissension in the Allied ranks; and they are still hard at it. Bickering over postwar rights should not be permitted to delay the Armistice or sully the victory. Let's finish this terrible business as a great team, the greatest the world has ever known, and then resolve the conflicting peacetime interests of our countries with something of the orderly procedure which has enabled us to compose our military differences in the much more difficult business of conducting a global war.

47
Army-Navy Cooperation

Remarks at the Navy Day Banquet,
Washington, D. C., October 27, 1944

I do not know another instance in the history of warfare in which an army and a navy, each with its complex organization and system of command, have pulled together so effectively.

I CANNOT imagine a more appropriate moment than this evening for the celebration of Navy Day. Even the destruction of what remains of the Japanese fleet may come somewhat as an anti-climax and I say this with due regard for the inevitable hazards of war.

Exactly two years ago on a similar occasion our then crippled naval forces operating in the Solomons were apparently in sore distress and great peril according to the meager official information of the moment. Three days later, with all the returns in, a fine naval victory was an assured fact. Tonight in contrast we can review a series of remarkably successful operations covering the past two months, culminating in the tremendous blows of the recent naval battle. The Third and Seventh Fleets have made history which will be stimulating reading for young Americans for a hundred years to come. Furthermore, it seems to me that in Admiral Halsey[38] we have found a man with the fighting heart of a Farragut, a Nelson, or a John Paul Jones himself.

The Navy convoyed our armies to Africa, Italy and France. They have now made possible our reëntry into the Philippines. They will support General MacArthur in his campaign for the reconquest of the Islands, an operation which has had a brilliant beginning and will be carried forward with all the skill and daring heretofore demonstrated by MacArthur in his long series of advances from Australia, but fortified today by highly trained and fully equipped ground and air forces and all the vast power of the Navy in the Pacific.

I believe I am expected to make a brief report on the Army, having just returned from France. I visited the commanders along the front, from Field Marshal Montgomery in Holland to General de Lattre de Tassigny, the commander of the French First Army near Belfort. I talked with Bradley, Hodges, Simpson and Patton, with Devers and

---

[38]Admiral William F. Halsey, Jr., Commanding U. S. Third Fleet.

Patch.[39] The local situations were discussed with each of our corps commanders and I visited the leaders of the divisions in the line of battle.

Eisenhower's armies have done amazing things in the past three months but in some respects their present aggressive front, despite limitations in supply, prolonged periods in the line, cold rain and deep mud, surpasses even the spectacular victories of the breakthrough. My admiration for the infantry rifleman who is bearing the hard brunt of the battle increased enormously during this visit to France. The bearing of all of our men, their appearance of professional competence and aggressive spirit, were immensely encouraging. The Air Forces have been magnificent in supporting our ground operation and in the strategic bombing which threatens the collapse of the enemy's economic system and his power for organized resistance.

Everything has been put into the furtherance of the battle, even the shipment of mail has been suspended for considerable periods to permit a greater tonnage of ammunition. As a consequence our soldiers know little of what is happening elsewhere in the world. Incidentally, I hope that while they are in the present bitter grip of battle in the cold and mud, no echoes reach them from home indicating the belief that the war is practically over in Europe and we are free to turn to other interests. I am fearful of the revulsion of feeling that would follow such a disclosure in the midst of the present battle when the greatest concentration of effort is imperative if we are to bring this war to an early conclusion. I may not be expressing myself tactfully but I mean exactly what I am saying, and I am sure that every man and woman in this country would heartily agree with me could they too have visited our divisions in France and Belgium. Let's have no nonsense, no superficial thinking or selfish purposes until we have won this great struggle in which Allied forces on the western front and in Italy are attacking along almost one thousand one hundred miles of a raging battle line.

General Eisenhower has a tremendous task on his hands with inconceivable ramifications, logistical, political, and the purely human difficulties inevitable in the reëstablishment of order in liberated countries of different races with conflicting views on almost every subject, not to mention his far greater responsibilities for the conduct of the battle. I am filled with admiration for the wisdom, the patience, and the military leadership he is displaying in a position almost without precedent.

---

[39]General Omar N. Bradley, Commanding General, 12th Army Group; General Courtney H. Hodges, Commanding General, First Army; Lieutenant General William H. Simpson, Commanding General, Ninth Army; General George S. Patton, Jr., Commanding General, Third Army; General Jacob L. Devers, Commanding General, 6th Army Group; Lieutenant General Alexander M. Patch, Commanding General, Seventh Army.

The troops in Italy under Wilson, Alexander and Clark[40] have been engaged for long, weary weeks in another bitter battle, in the rain and mud of the Apennines. Their steady advances, their fortitude and losses, and the importance of their contribution to the European operations, in the Balkans, in Poland, and on the western front, receive far too little notice.

There are many things of interest that I should have liked to talk about tonight but my thoughts are dominated at the moment by the great naval victory in the Pacific. Admiral King and I have worked side by side since our first meeting at Argentia, the historic conference with the British in Newfoundland three years ago last August. To Lord Halifax I owe my thanks—we all owe our thanks—for his fine understanding and strong influence toward the maintenance of unity in our combined national efforts.

I do not know of another instance in the history of warfare in which an army and a navy, each with its complex organization and system of command, have pulled together so effectively as members of a team. Neither do I recall a similar situation in which allied nations have worked in such intimate coöperation toward a common goal. We know that the soldiers and sailors and airmen can be depended upon to do their full duty. If we foster our unity of purpose, on the farms, in the factories, on Main Street and everywhere, we will not fail them. Let's celebrate the victory in the Pacific with a stern resolution to increase our efforts here at home.

[40]Field Marshal Sir Henry Maitland Wilson, Allied Commander, Middle East; Field Marshal Sir Harold Alexander, Commander in Chief of Allied Forces in Italy; Lieutenant General Mark W. Clark, Commanding General, Fifth Army; later General, commanding 15th Army Group.

48
Universal Military Training and Peace

Statements on Universal Military Training
Before the Select Committee on Postwar Military Policy of the House of Representatives,
79th Congress, 1st Session, June 16, 1945

≈≈≈≈≈≈≈≈≈≈≈≈≈≈≈≈≈≈≈≈≈≈≈≈≈≈≈≈≈

*Whatever the terms of peace, the fundamental basis
of our defense must be universal military training.*

THE problem of the maintenance of the future peace of the world directly involves the problem of the postwar military policy of the United States. The decision regarding the military policy of the United States is directly related to the democratic processes of the Government, really meaning the reactions of the people to the services the individual citizen might be required to render the Government. Another factor is heavily though indirectly involved and that is consideration of the taxes to be imposed on the citizen for the maintenance of the military policy, to which must be added the very positive reaction of the citizen regarding the taxes to which he must submit to meet the huge existing war debt. Any fixed legal demand on the citizen for services to the community, the state, or the federal Government, is quite naturally questioned by the majority and is usually bitterly opposed by at least an articulate minority.

The question of universal military training involves all of the foregoing factors, and the great difficulty as I see it, in reaching a correct decision, will be to avoid details and to get clearly focused in our minds what are the real necessities of the situation, and what will be the best method for meeting them, having in mind our traditions, our national characteristics and the military experience of this Government during its short life of 156 years among the nations of the world.

I think it would be best for me to state in the briefest possible form my own personal conclusions in the matter, which are as follows:

A decision regarding the general military policy of this Government is a matter of urgent necessity at this time.

A large standing Army is not an acceptable solution for three reasons: Its cost would be prohibitive; the necessary men to fill its ranks could not be hired in time of peace; and it would be repugnant to the American people. Therefore some other solution must be found.

To support our determination to maintain the peace, the world must recognize our military power as realistic and not as a remote potential.

Whatever military system we plan we must have a thorough understanding of the practicability of obtaining the annual appropriations necessary.

I know of no system other than universal military training that will meet the requirements I have just outlined, together with an effective program for industrial mobilization and continuous scientific research.

Until the settlement of the terms of the peace it will be impossible to determine the strength of the postwar military forces to be maintained on an active status. We shall not know until then just what our military obligations or requirements are to be. But it is clear to me that whatever the terms of peace, the fundamental basis of our defense must be universal military training. No other practical solution has been offered.

The acceptance at the present time of a general policy recognizing the necessity for universal military training would in my opinion have a far-reaching effect in obtaining a satisfactory international agreement for the terms of peace. It would certainly be in keeping with the tragic lessons of our history. It would be a supremely democratic procedure, and would not involve the individual in military service except by further Act of Congress and approval of the President. It would be far more economical than any other method for maintaining military power. If we are to have an effective and economical transition from our vast war establishment to our peace establishment, we must now decide on the fundamental basis on which we are to proceed.

While I have not been able to read the testimony that has been given before this Committee and have obtained my information largely from the press and by hearsay, it appears to me that those who object to compulsory military training have offered no practical solution for obtaining what is in all our minds today, and that is some guarantee for the future peace of the world.

Whether or not Army training methods would have an unfortunate influence on the individual can be determined I think from the experience of this war. I assert that we have produced a democratic Army, one composed of self-respecting soldiers whose spirit has not been crushed and who have shown splendid evidences of high morale. I submit that the Army has demonstrated that it can efficiently and expeditiously instruct men and that it does this without detriment to the mind and character of the individual, rather the contrary. I firmly believe that universal military training would be a stimulant to education rather than a deterrent. It would be a perfect demonstration of democracy, with rich and poor alike, side by side, rendering a common service.

Index

OUT OF THE FRYING PAN, INTO THE CHOIR

A Ruby, the Rabbi's Wife Mystery

Sharon Kahn

Scribner

New York   London   Toronto   Sydney

SCRIBNER
1230 Avenue of the Americas
New York, NY 10020

SCRIBNER and design are trademarks of
Macmillan Library Reference USA, Inc., used under license by
Simon & Schuster, the publisher of this work.

For information about special discounts for bulk purchases,
please contact Simon & Schuster Special Sales:
1-800-465-6798 or business@simonandschuster.com

Set in Perpetua

Manufactured in the United States of America

1   3   5   7   9   10   8   6   4   2

Library of Congress Control Number: 200604500

ISBN-13: 978-0-7432-4358-2
ISBN-10: 0-7432-4358-7

To my dear Camille,
who will be reading Ruby in the future.
May the stories you're writing continue to bring
the joy to you and to others that they have to me.

OUT OF THE
FRYING PAN,
INTO THE CHOIR

1

TO THE FAVORED FEW FROM ESSIE SUE (and Hal)
ANNUAL CHANUKAH LETTER

To all our family and selected friends:
  It's potato latke time again! Time to consume
(sparingly) those delicious holiday pancakes while reading
my ever-popular review chronicling the achievements and
accolades surrounding the Margolis clan. Be sure to
lubricate your latkes with cooking spray until well done,
top with a dollop of imitation sour cream (20 calories a
tablespoon), add dietetic applesauce (counts as one fruit),
and dig in.
  Note: If you're on Atkins, fry up pure butter with
Breakstone's sour cream into round mounds and skip the

*potatoes and the applesauce. Those celebrating both
Christmas and Chanukah may optionally serve this dish
over Atkins-approved fried pork rinds. Obviously, this does
not include the rest of us.*

*Now for the news. People, this has been another
outstanding year in the annals of our Margolis family
history. In February, Essie Sue and Hal traveled to the
exclusive Strait of Magellan with Hal's alumni group. Essie
Sue was voted Voyager Most Suited for a Desert Island—
quite an honor when one considers that she was disabled for
three days after a regrettable encounter with the wildlife at
mating season—namely, a female elephant seal who
refused to be petted during her reproductive cycle. However,
since the accident took place on an exclusive Added Expense
Optional Trip, Essie Sue used the downtime to research Jews
of the subantarctic forests. Unfortunately, there were none.
(Unless, to be accurate, one counted both Margolises and
Hal's two ZBT fraternity brothers, also on the tour.)*

*It is with great pleasure that Essie Sue and Hal
announce the May graduation from Oxford of Essie Sue's
grandnephew Phil. Since the graduate preferred to be in the
company of family and friends for this Simchas, a facsimile
was held in Oxford, Ohio, so that all could attend. Three
cheers for Phil, and for his proud mother, Sara Lee, who
wore a tiara for the occasion which bore the seal of the
Royal Family.*

*In August, Essie Sue received the Woman of Value award
from our town of Eternal's Chamber of Commerce, for her
prolonged but successful effort to acquire three park benches
from the county. Hindered for five years by County
Commissioner Leroy (Bud) Gantry, Eternal finally secured
the benches on the occasion of the commissioner's last living*

act from his bed in Memorial Hospital. As soon as the order was signed, Gantry received last rites from Father Terry Breen, a close friend of the Margolis family.

And last but not least, in November, Essie Sue was appointed head of Eternal fund-raising for the first Interdenominational ChoirFest in Lake Louise, Canada, in May. Our own choir at Temple Rita has been honored with an invitation to travel by train from Vancouver to Banff, and the tour will be financed by latke promotions to take place from December through April. Custom orders for latkes will make sales possible even after the Chanukah holiday, assuming continuing interest on the part of the public.

Essie Sue and Hal are indeed humbled by the well-deserved honors coming their way. They look forward to bigger and better accomplishments in the year ahead, and will rest assured knowing that you will all be eager to read about them in next year's Annual Chanukah Letter.

As it is written, "Our Cup Runneth Over. Surely goodness and mercy shall follow us all the days of our lives." Book of Psalms. Amended.

> *Happy Chanukah to all,*
> *Essie Sue and Hal Margolis*

2

Email to: Nan
From: Ruby
Subject: A lot on our plates besides
   latkes

What's happening, girl? You left me in
midsentence last night when we'd been on
the phone for only five minutes. I'm assuming your cell phone conked out on you—
surely you can do better in Seattle than
the regional phone company you're using.
I gave up after my third attempt to recon-
nect, and went to bed totally frustrated
that I couldn't whine to you for at least
an hour more.

I'm somewhat sorry I signed up for Essie Sue's trip to Canada, cheap as it is, because this means I have to help with the latke sales to finance it. I thought it was worthwhile because that train trip through the Canadian Rockies is supposed to be spectacular, but who knows if anything she sponsors is worth the aggravation? This comes at a good time, though, when I'm at loose ends.

Ed continues to haunt my dreams, even though it's over, over, over. It's getting better, though—I now spend only the first part of the night feeling wistful over the good bits, while the rest is taken up reliving the yucky parts. This is progress, I suppose, and I do know I did the right thing. The journalist in him overcame the human being just one time too many—and at least I'm not as miserable now that some time has passed.

I'm worried about *you,* though. Don't you think you need to get out of your doldrums and start mixing a little? Come down to Eternal and visit me if you can't find anyone in the big city. I'm advising a computer client in Austin I think you'd find attractive—he has hazel eyes, if you're interested.

Email to: Ruby
From: Nan
Subject: Green-eyed with envy

Yeah, I *am* mired in misery of my own making (no charge for the alliteration) but
I'm getting tired of pushing myself, showing my best side, and pretending I'm having a great time with some guy when I'm
not. I'm taking a vacation from that and
have promised myself I can stay stuck for
six more months before they cart me off.
   BUT, you lucky dog, I don't see why
you're whining at all . . . you might have
ended it with Ed, but now you have Lieutenant Paul at your doorstep, don't you?
And talk about sexy—he's definitely my
type, even if he is a cop. Care to offer
him up, or do I only get a crack at the
computer client?

Email to: Nan
From: Ruby
Subject: RE Green-eyed with envy

Things are getting warmer with Paul, but
I'm taking it easy. As for his being your
type, you've known him for years, and he
still praises you to the rafters for helping solve the bagel killing a few years ago.
You're welcome to throw your hat (or in your
case, barrister's wig) into the ring.

Email to: Ruby
From: Nan
Subject: Right

You're just saying that because you know
you have the home-court advantage. I say
go for it.

I'm taking some time off, even though
I do have the hots for Paul. Which is why
I shouldn't admit this, but you two do
make an awfully cute couple with your
matching green eyes and cat-swallowed-
the-canary grins. I like the way your head
just reaches to his shoulders, too.

And don't turn down that Canadian trip,
either, Ruby—you never know.

3

"My podiatrist's sister-in-law Bitsy is a party planner, Rabbi.
I think we should hire her to do the Chanukah latke event at
temple. She's also a grief counselor."

Kevin Kapstein, the one and only rabbi in Eternal, Texas,
looks at me for any cue as to how to respond to Essie Sue
Margolis, lifetime chairwoman of the temple board. Essie
Sue claims to revere his opinion as her spiritual leader, but
also cosigns his contracts—a potent combination that usually paralyzes him into silence on these nonliturgical occasions.

Not me. "How much does she charge?" I ask.

"I wasn't talking to you, Ruby. I was telling the rabbi
about someone who might be of service to us."

"Speaking of service," my partner Milt Aboud interrupts,

"how many of you want cinnamon bagels with cream cheese, and how many choose sesame with lox?"

Milt owns the majority interest in The Hot Bagel, a venture I bought into several years ago after my husband and Kevin's predecessor, Rabbi Stu Rothman, was killed. While Milt runs the bakery, I keep our finances intact, a task made easier by my freelance work as a computer consultant for small businesses.

The six of us sitting at the round table by the window split evenly on the bagel choices—we should only be so accommodating on the subject at hand.

"You have to spend money to make money, Ruby," Essie Sue reminds me. "And the woman's a grief counselor, too. We'll be getting a twofer—it's a bargain."

"How much?" I ask again.

"Only two thousand dollars. And she'll throw in three sessions for any congregants who happen to be grieving during the time she's planning the party."

"But I thought I was the grief counselor," Kevin says in my ear. He's nervous about any preemptions, and understandably so.

"For less than that, I'll plan the party," I say.

"You're only an amateur, Ruby," Essie Sue says. "This woman is a professional. She planned for the sheriff's swearing-in ceremony before he was caught with the teenager. Tell Ruby how lovely that event would have been, Hal."

Hal Margolis, unlike his wife, is a man of few words, not all of them devoted to her support.

"You're asking me?" he says, sharing our common disbelief. "I think Ruby's right—the party planner's too expensive. Why don't you handle it? You'll end up telling her what to do anyway."

"Maybe you can get her to volunteer her services," I say. "After all, the congregational functions could be a gold mine for her once she's established. Maybe she'll do it for expenses."

"I'll work on her," Essie Sue says. I'm not sure if this instant agreement on her part is shock at Hal's independence or pure practicality, but we're going with it.

"All in favor of trying for a freebie, raise your hands," I say. It's unanimous, and that includes Rose Baker, the late Herman Geunther's daughter, who's looking great in one of her usual long skirts. She never adopted pants when the rest of us did. Rose has been a good friend of mine ever since we worked together to discover her father's killer a few years ago. She's the temple choir representative for this planning session, and Essie Sue's already loaded her with responsibilities. I just hope we can help her.

"Rose, you're in charge of the program for the latke event," Essie Sue says. "The choir should recruit its best voices for our entertainment."

"The choir only has ten members, Essie Sue," Rose says, "and two of them don't sing, remember?"

"Don't sing?" Milt tries unsuccessfully to hide his snort. As the one serving the bagels and the only person present who's not a temple member, his self-appointed function at these meetings is to *ootz* Essie Sue.

"Keep your sarcasm to yourself, Milt," she says. "There's a good reason for it. Tell him, Rabbi."

"Essie Sue thinks it's more aesthetically balanced to have ten people than eight," he says. "And after Mel and Reneé Rafer moved away, we had two extra choir robes going to waste."

"I don't want to hear any more," Milt says, filling my cup with the mocha java he knows I love.

I give Milt a quick look over my shoulder as he pours. "You don't want to know what the two extras do?" I ask.

Kevin beats me to it. "They mouth the words. It's harder than it looks—I had to help them practice their Hebrew."

"It bulks up the presentation," Essie Sue says. "You'd be surprised how good it looks."

"I'm more concerned with how it sounds," Rose says, "but we'll take care of it. I'm enlisting the help of my good friend Serena to whip the program into shape. She's our top soprano, in my opinion. If you want our cooperation, just don't lean on us, Essie Sue."

"Your cooperation? This whole fund-raising event is for your benefit—it shouldn't cost you a penny to take this trip of a lifetime."

"I'll believe that when I see it," Rose says. "We haven't raised the money yet."

"I was going to use André Korman to be our driving influence for the choir," Essie Sue says, "not Serena Salit—she's such a health nut, whereas he's a forceful baritone."

"What's health got to do with leading the quartet?" Rose says. "I thought you said I was running the program, Essie Sue. If I am, then Serena's my choice, forceful or otherwise. And speaking of health nuts, André owns a health store—have you forgotten? He already thinks he's the choir director, which he's not, even though Serena seems to think he's something special. We all take turns directing, like the rabbi advised."

Sounds like Kevin's idea, although I've never heard of a choir without a director. André's forceful, all right—obnoxiously so, I'd say. I can't imagine his accepting any advice Kevin had to give. And I didn't know he was on Essie Sue's favorites list, either.

"So what are you envisioning?" I ask Rose. "A couple of songs?"

"Maybe more than that," she says. "Our best voices—Serena, André, Irene Cohn, and Serena's ex-husband Bart Goldman make up a quartet within the choir. They'll have to perform at least two selections, with the choir following up with a couple of others."

"That's not long enough," Essie Sue says. "We need a more complete program to entertain everyone."

"No." Rose and I react together, with Hal nodding his support.

"We'll put them to sleep with a long vocal program," Rose says. "Just let us take care of it, Essie Sue."

I suggest we adjourn the meeting before they come to blows. I should be so lucky.

"Hold on," Essie Sue says. "First we have to figure out how to get the carbohydrates out of the latkes. Rabbi, I'm appointing you to research this. Maybe the scholar Maimonides had something to say about it—I understand he was interested in weight loss."

"Huh? You mean from the fourteenth century?"

"Well, he *was* a doctor," Essie Sue says. "See if he was a cardiologist like the South Beach guy."

Kevin does what he usually does in these situations—he scribbles notes furiously. I shamelessly look under his bent arm to see what he's writing, but think better of it when I see that he's written the word *Google* over and over.

"Don't bother, Kevin," I whisper in his ear. "You know she forgets half the stuff she tells you to do."

"Easy for you to say, Ruby. I'm staying on her good side."

Well, I tried.

I get up to leave—definitely the only way to bring meetings with Essie Sue to an end—when she raises a magenta-taloned hand to my arm and pulls me back down.

"Ruby, I don't think you're seeing the selfish possibilities in this grief-counseling operation."

"Huh? I don't know from selfish, Essie Sue. Can you explain this in under two minutes?"

Since I can't begin to fathom how this woman's mind works, I usually find it best to give her a time limit for her revelations. I roll my eyes in Rose's direction for a reality check and notice that Rose is already biting her lip.

"I guess I'll have to spell it out for you," Essie Sue says. "You're a natural for Bitsy's first class."

"I still can't believe she calls herself *Bitsy*," Hal says. "That's a name for a grief counselor? A party planner, maybe."

"Not now, Hal. I'm telling Ruby about Bitsy's grief-counseling skills. Picture this, Ruby. You're sitting in the grief-counseling orientation session, trying to get over Stu's death."

"Whoa," I say. "He was killed years ago, and although I can't say I'll ever be over him, it's pretty clear I have moved on."

"So you need a little help, not a lot. But remember, Ruby, these sessions are coed. Some nice widower or divorced man—Bitsy does divorce grief, too—might have lost his loved one a short time ago. Before some pushy neighbor with a bowl of chicken soup can get her claws into him, you'll have the edge from the class. Look at the possibilities."

Rose chokes up her last swallow of coffee. "So you're saying we'll get a threefer, not a twofer?" she asks. "A grief counselor, a party planner, *and* a matchmaker?"

"See, Ruby—Rose gets it, and she's not even single. If you'd learned to be smart for yourself, you'd be married by now. You lost the journalist already, not that he was any great catch."

"Ruby's interested in someone else," Kevin says. "Lieutenant Paul Lundy—he always liked her."

"Do I look like I'm wearing Harry Potter's Cloak of Invisibility?" I ask as I stand up for a second time. "Lay off, everybody."

Milt tries to put his arm around me, a gesture I'd appreciate more if he wasn't cracking up at my expense.

Essie Sue's not finished, unfortunately. "Lundy the policeman? She'd be robbing the cradle, for starters."

"At least it's better than robbing the grave."

4

"Either your hair's gone curly or you've never let it grow long enough for me to tell," I say, reaching to tuck a dark lock of Paul's hair behind his ear. A very cute, nicely shaped ear, I might add—with a lobe that fits the tip of my thumb perfectly.

I'm relaxed just being out to dinner with him, not that the soothing Beefeater martini isn't doing its part.

"You're better now," he says, his smile still slightly dampened by concern. Paul's fussing over me tonight makes up for that dreadful lunch with my "good" friends treating me as though I weren't there.

"They were laughing at Essie Sue, not you," he reminds me.

"I know. I just get tired of being the feisty one who can hold her own no matter what," I say. "Sometimes I'm sick of all of it."

I like that Paul knows exactly when to squeeze my hand and when not to. We've been seated in one of those circular booths for four—it's all they had available. The good news is that we're side by side. The bad news is that we're talking side by side, too. I can't see him without turning.

"So you're robbing the cradle with me, huh?" Now his grin's back full force. "I had no idea five years made such a difference."

"She probably thinks you're younger," I say. "You look it."

"So do you. If you don't know that, you should. I'm glad you told me the whole story, though—lots of women wouldn't, if it emphasizes something they'd rather ignore. Like age."

"Yeah, well, that's me. I'd much prefer my own company to someone I can't be myself with. The added bonus with you is that I can trust you, too."

The waiter puts a piece of aromatic sea bass in front of me—I catch a whiff of ginger in the sauce.

"Couldn't you trust what Ed said?" Paul hides that zinger behind a twirling forkful of linguini.

I put my fork down and he does, too.

"Sorry," he says. "You didn't need that tonight."

"You're still hung up on Ed, aren't you?" I say. "Even now that I'm not."

"I guess I am," he says.

"What am I going to do about it?"

"You don't have to do anything, Ruby. It's my problem. It's just that when you brought up trust, I thought of Ed because that seemed to be a big sticking point with you— the fact that he might have been milking you to get background for his stories."

"That was a problem for me, but it's history. We broke up. Why go over it?"

"You were in love with him. If he hadn't had divided loyalties, maybe you'd still be with him. That was my observation, and I did a lot of observing."

"So you're saying if I hadn't had good reason to break up with Ed, we'd still be together, right? Pardon me if I say *duh* to that one, Paul. Isn't that why anyone ends a relationship? You're too smart for this kind of thinking."

He looks at me in a way that makes me want to backtrack. And I do.

"Okay, I know this has nothing to do with intelligence. It's what you feel. Are you worried that I'm not over him, or are you upset that we were together at all?"

"Both, I guess." He's not reaching for my hand this time, and he's calling for another martini.

"I can reassure you about the first," I say, "but there's not much I can do about the second."

We eat in silence for a while. The sea bass no longer tastes as good.

"So where are we?" he says.

"Honestly, Paul?"

He nods, but not very convincingly. Still, it's enough of an opening to make me know I shouldn't finesse this.

"In answer to your question," I say, "I can't describe where we are. But I can tell you I'm not comfortable with where we are—does that make any sense?"

"Unfortunately, yes," he says. He instinctively offers me a sip of his martini, and I take it. I hate that he's still bothered by Ed. And I especially wish he wouldn't go into freeze mode whenever he's reminded of that relationship.

I guess it's exacerbated because Paul's friendship with me was on the verge of taking a more serious turn just before Ed came along. There's nothing I can do about that interruption. I'm glad the affair is over, but I certainly don't regret it, either.

"Can't we give this some time, Paul?" I say as I try to enjoy the meal. "It'll work itself out."

"I guess I'm the one who needs to work some things out, Ruby."

"I can't argue with you there. Let's take a deep breath, though, and not get so excited over this. Can we maybe talk about something else now?"

The neat part about Paul is that he's so often on my wavelength. Instead of pouting, he smiles at me. Granted, a sad smile, but he's trying, and so am I.

I have a ready-made icebreaker—I give him more details about Essie Sue's party planner and the upcoming latke event.

"Will it be an interminable evening?" he says.

"Is the rabbi Jewish? Of course it'll be long—Essie Sue's in charge of the preparations. Look at it as a test of your devotion."

"Not without some hope of payback," he says. "What's in it for me?"

"I'll owe you big," I say. "Who knows how you might collect?"

"You're wicked when you want something, Ruby."

"So you'll definitely come?"

"I promise I'll be there—I just don't know when. If things are busy, I know I can't get away as early as you might want. But look at it this way—since I'll be there for the last part of the evening, you'll be guaranteed a ride home."

"I'm driving," I say. "So I'll be guaranteed a police escort following me home—that's different. And are you sure you're not wimping out? If so, I'll have no choice but to set my sights on the first grieving widower I can find."

He answers me with a quick kiss, which I'd call delicate if he wasn't still chewing his linguini.

5

To say that our beloved Temple Rita is decked out for the evening would be an understatement. Canadian flags are all over the Blumberg Social Hall, signifying, I presume, the location of the ChoirFest in Lake Louise. Bitsy, the party planner, was apparently at a loss to think of other decorations that might remind us of our neighbor to the north, but she did come up with snow. Lots of snow—the artificial kind, of course.

"Bitsy lucked out," Essie Sue tells me. "Since it's the Christmas season, too, she was able to grab all the snowflakes from the hobby store before the church groups got to them. Now *that's* creative."

"No, that's cruisin' for a bruisin'," I say.

Bitsy herself materializes from a cloud of white—it's my

first glimpse of her. Her administrative style is of the distant variety—she's directed this production by telephone and email as much as possible. Maybe she's smarter than I thought to avoid clashing with Essie Sue in full party mode.

"You're only seeing Bitsy in her planner role, Ruby," Essie Sue says as she throws one of her welcoming headlocks on an unsuspecting Bitsy and draws her close. "I want you to get to know her grief personality, too. This could be to your benefit."

Although Bitsy relaxes as Essie Sue loosens her grip, this is obviously not a woman who lets go easily. Definitely a type A, Bitsy looks more party planner than grief counselor. Tall and blond, she's got to be pushing fifty, but you're not meant to guess it from the ring in her navel, Alice in Wonderland locks to her shoulders, and baby-doll eyes with more blue on the lids than in the iris.

"She's very fashionable with the emphasis on the midriff," Essie Sue faux-whispers to me. I find myself more fascinated with the metal than the midriff—the ring looks tarnished, and I'm sure that's a no-no, hygiene-wise.

I try really hard to pull my eyes away, but don't quite make it.

"Admiring my ring?" Bitsy says. "I can give you the name of the guy who put it in if you want."

"Not this year," I say, unhappy that I have no one nearby to roll my eyes at. "My trainer at the gym made me swear off round objects attached to my organs—I have to stay clean until the scars heal."

"Oh." Bitsy seems unfazed by my revelations, and Essie Sue never listens anyway. She's already switching gears.

"I have to make a surprise announcement," she says, grabbing the nearest glass to tap on. She does it carefully with the insides of her first two fingernails.

"Ladies and gentlemen—I want to report that through some tough negotiations and great generosity, our party planner has produced and directed this event for fifteen hundred dollars less than she charges her real clients. She expects you to repay her by booking her for your own celebrations. Bitsy is available for the usual bar and bat mitzvahs, weddings, and anniversaries. I want a big round of applause before we proceed to the next part of our program."

What a tribute. Even though it's obvious that Bitsy's downsized and cut a few corners, the event is still supposedly a bargain. Aside from the hobby-shop cheapo snowflakes, we've been treated so far to Canadian Iced Decaf, Frozen Tundra Chanukah Latkes (definitely frozen), and multicolor Kool Pops representing nothing that I can see, although I'm sure she had something in mind.

Essie Sue's also insisted on no-fat sour cream to top the potato latkes, which, to my mind, is like making love without sex. And if these are the latkes we're depending on to make money for the trip, we're in deep doo-doo. Not that anyone's eaten enough to get sick—I was pressed into service at the buffet table, and we had orders to serve each person only two thin pancakes.

While Bitsy's talking to a prospective client, I pull on Essie Sue's arm.

"Bitsy who?" I ask. "You forgot to properly introduce her."

"I already did, Ruby."

"What's her name, then?"

"Bitsy."

"That's it?"

"As in *Cher*. And *Barbra*. And *Madonna*."

"Do you like that, Ruby? My stand-alone name?"

Bitsy's back. I hope she's not gonna tell me the name of a guy who can get me one.

"Sure," I say, "I like it if you do."

"It looks great on my business cards, and it leaves room for the logos."

I take the card she hands me. I should have guessed—a happy face and a sad face flanking the stand-alone *Bitsy*.

"I dropped my last name when I dropped my last husband," she says. "It's simpler."

I can't argue with her logic, just her logos. But hey, she's giving us this two-thousand-dollar affair for a mere five hundred dollars, even though she's still making a hundred percent profit, from the looks of things. I'd say this party cost about two fifty.

"Hey, Essie Sue, the choir is ready. When do they go on?" Kevin yells from behind a curtain onstage—his subtle signal that the program is about to begin. I'm relieved to get away from both Essie Sue and the redoubtable Bitsy, and I look around for Rose, who's running the show. I hope. Of course, no show really runs around here without Essie Sue's okay.

"Tell Rose she can start," Essie Sue says.

With a big fanfare from Mr. Wolkin, our new organist, who's at the social hall piano, the curtain opens. The Temple Rita choir, robed in blue, with white cardboard collars in the shape of, right—snowflakes, a Bitsy touch, I'm sure—takes a deep bow. All twelve choir members, including the two fillers, join in the first two songs—rehashed versions from Friday-night services. I'm seriously worried that with these for openers, the crowd won't hold—especially since the Kool Pops seem to have been the last of the refreshments. Make that 150 bucks that Bitsy spent on this extravaganza.

I glimpse Rose directing traffic backstage as the full choir leaves, and run back to check in with her.

"I know," she says. "Don't even tell me—those first two songs weren't even on the list—Essie Sue threw a fit and insisted that we lengthen the program, and the only other songs the group felt comfortable singing were the ones you just heard. I should have put them at the end."

"I know what you're working with," I say, "it's just that I'm afraid it's getting *too* comfortable out there, if you know what I mean."

"It should perk up a little," she says. "I've changed the order and put the quartet in right now."

The four members of the quartet step to the front of the stage, and I plunk myself in the front row beside Kevin.

Serena Salit's my favorite, although most of what I know of her is through Rose. She was married for years to Bart Goldman, baritone in our quartet, and they divorced a year ago. Bart's a doctor—a nice guy but a little uptight. Serena's got a great sense of humor—at least about everything except her vitamin fetish. Rose says she could open her own health food store, so I'm sure she's given André lots of business since he moved here. I think her divorce was pretty stressful, but aren't they all? She and Bart have managed to stay in the choir together despite the split.

The tenor is André Korman. He and his wife, Sara, are relative newcomers—they've been in town three or four years now. I seem to remember that Sara's family is fairly well to do, and once had some dealings with Hal Margolis, which is probably why they're on Essie Sue's favorites list. I can take Sara, but André's so full of himself. I heard *André* used to be *Arnie* before he changed it.

He looks like the Dapper Dan in a Chaplain movie—

sporty little mustache, immaculate shirt collars that look as though they're starched, a year-round tan, and a gold ring on each hand. Even though he owns Eternal's health food store, they live way beyond what that could support—courtesy of the wife's side, I guess.

Irene Cohen, our alto, is part of an old Eternal family— she's a violinist as well as a singer. She's quite attractive, and I know of at least two guys she's gone with—don't know who her current boyfriend is. André seems to have an eye for her, but then, that's his persona—he considers himself irresistible.

Serena Salit signals to the accompanist to begin the intro- ductory passage, but André shakes his head. He leans over to the microphone and says, "Sorry, all, we'll start in a moment." Great, they haven't sung a note, and already he's pulling a power play. I glimpse Rose fuming in the wings.

To no one's great surprise, Serena caves. I feel for her— she's probably trying to avoid a scene in front of all these people. André takes over and the song begins. They're trying something from *Yentl,* which André's arranged for four voices—you can bet without permission from Barbra. Since the piece was written as a solo, it took quite a bit of arrang- ing, none of it successful. Rose peers at me from the wings and shrugs, but before the audience can react one way or the other, Essie Sue jumps up onstage and leads the applause— or should I say, demands it.

Like so many wonders she initiates, it works, and the audience is actually clapping, if in a backhanded sort of way.

I'm beginning to hope they only have two songs for us— this applause on demand can go on only for so long. Essie Sue herself signals the pianist to begin the next selection— a move which even André doesn't dare question. This one's a Yiddish folk song, and they're doing it as a round. Bart Goldman's baritone is crisp and assured—a good start. Irene's next, and sails through the alto part. I see a relieved grin on Rose's face backstage, and I'm almost relaxed enough to go into daydreaming mode, when the sound of silence intervenes. Instead of Serena's soprano, I hear, well, nothing.

I rouse myself fast and refocus my eyes on the stage. Serena's standing there, looking as if singing *should* be coming from her open mouth, but it's not. She seems normal enough, as though she's preparing to get a sound out. It's like a mime has taken over, using gestures instead of words.

Suddenly, normality vanishes and she struggles. Both hands flutter around her chest, and then she clutches harder. She sinks straight down toward the stage floor, her legs giving way under her until she's briefly sitting, then crumpling at the waist and folding over, her arms stretched to one side, like a ballerina taking a bow.

6

It's difficult to focus on the chaos in front of me, and my eyes go straight to Rose, standing backstage. She sees me, too. Her jaw drops and she's frozen for a moment, just before she rushes forward to join what's now a jumble of forms and sounds:

"Get over to her."

"No, stay away, let her have air."

"Looks like she's had a heart attack."

"No, she's just fainted."

Irene and Bart are bending over Serena, and André's pulling them off.

"Unless you're going to give her artificial respiration," he says, "give her some room."

"They say you're not supposed to do that anymore—it

can be harmful to the patient," Essie Sue says from the front row. "Don't touch her until we get a doctor."

She turns to the audience. "Is there a physician in the house?"

"Bart's a doctor, Essie Sue—you know that," someone yells from the back of the room.

Bart's already on the case, and is the only one with the presence of mind to grab his cell. As he calls with one hand, he kneels and touches Serena's neck with the other—I guess he's feeling for a pulse.

I stay put—there are enough people up there as it is. As far as I can tell, Serena's not moving.

Kevin turns and looks at me. His face is pale and miserable—his usual countenance during emergencies like this, when he's wishing he could be anyplace else.

"This isn't the time I'm supposed to do something, is it, Ruby? I mean, this is a medical situation, right? Unless you think I should be counseling the choir members."

"I'd stay put if I were you, Kevin. Let's just hope your services won't be needed."

Essie Sue edges toward me. "Ruby, how long do you think it will take for Bart to get a stretcher here?" she whispers from the side of her mouth.

"I don't know. Sometimes it seems to take ages. Do you think they won't make it in time?"

"That, too, but the audience needs direction. We won't be able to keep them if nothing's happening onstage. And I haven't passed the sign-up sheets for the frozen latke sales. This whole urgent event was to raise their consciousness."

"Well, at the moment we're raising their blood pressure," I say. "They're adults—they don't need direction to see what's happening. There are some situations you can't control, Essie

Sue, and this is one of them. You can at least wait until they take her to the hospital."

"The program?"

"It's over. Do a mailing about the latke sales."

"No way! That costs a fortune."

"Then go consult your grief planner," I say. "I can only deal with one thing at a time, and I'm concerned about Serena, as you should be."

"You're a lifesaver, Ruby. Bitsy's the perfect choice."

Fortunately for Kevin, Essie Sue seems to have forgotten about him. He's shrunk down in his chair to ensure things stay that way. I'm headed over to get a better view of the stage and maybe speak to Bart, when I hear Essie Sue tinkling on a glass. Actually, she's not tinkling, she's banging on it, and I'm expecting a shatter of shards any minute now. Bitsy's in tow, looking slightly shell-shocked.

"More help will come soon, ladies and gentlemen," Essie Sue says. "Meanwhile, remain in your seats while Bitsy passes out the sign-up sheet we've prepared for volunteer latke salespeople."

She couldn't have thought of a faster way to empty the house if she'd arranged it. As if on cue, everyone makes for the exits, most of them remaining outside to wait for the ambulance. Only a few die-hards choose to wait inside on pain of being accosted by our new party planner.

Bitsy, caught between looking cheerily upbeat to encourage signatures, and appropriately downcast to reflect current circumstances, is no doubt wishing she'd never volunteered, either. I just hope the grief part of her job won't materialize concurrently with the party part, and that Serena gets to the hospital fast.

I'm wondering whether it even makes sense to approach

Rose while she's keeping her vigil beside Serena, when I hear a buzzing among the few audience members in their seats.

"Why are the police here?" I hear someone say.

I look around, see Paul in the back of the room, and wave him over. Since he's in a suit, and drives an unmarked car, I'm wondering how the busybodies identified him, but then remember that this is a small town. Plus, he's had plenty of experience with Temple Rita, unfortunately.

"What's up?" he says in a low voice as he comes over to me.

"Why did the police get called?" I say, realizing I've just echoed everyone else.

"You're not surprised to see me, are you, hon?" he says. "You invited me, remember?"

"I did forget," I say, pointing toward the stage. "We've got an emergency here. Serena, one of our singers——"

"She's down?"

Paul takes off like a jaguar and springs onstage with that lithe grace that always amazes me when he's working. I hear André ask if he's another doctor, and some of the choir members look alarmed and a bit confused when he says he's police.

"You're here to help?" Bart says. "I'm her ex-husband."

I see Paul crouch down and use his cell while he looks at Serena—maybe he can get faster action than Bart did. Before he can do anything else, though, the EMT people arrive, thank goodness.

Two guys come in, lay down a stretcher right onstage, and start doing their thing, under Bart's direction. I see Paul talking to the one taking Serena's pulse while the other unwinds some equipment, and then Paul helps clear the area. He blocks our view, deliberately, I'm sure, and asks those onstage to step down. I'm anxious to talk to Rose, who comes and sits by me.

"Can I get you some water or coffee?" I say, putting my arm around her.

She shakes her head no. "She's just so . . . so quiet," she says. "I know she was in pain because I saw her grab her chest, but it all happened so fast she never even cried out. Now she won't respond at all."

"Maybe she's in shock," I say. "Is there someone else we should call to meet her at the hospital?"

"Aside from Bart, she has no family here. She and Bart are on speaking terms, but I wouldn't exactly call them friends now, but he's a good doctor, thank heavens. I can't think of anyone else who's a relation. She has a sister in Ohio she's very close to, though."

"Okay, then I guess everything's covered."

"Will you go to the hospital with me?" Rose says. She seems shaky. "I've called home and told Ray and Jackie to go to bed if I'm out late."

"I don't think you need to be driving," I say. "I'll take you, and we can pick up your car after we go to the hospital. Maybe Paul will take both of us."

Paul and I had been hoping to spend a little time together tonight, but that's not going to happen. I know he'll be glad to take us over. Now that I think of it, though, he might not want to hang out at the hospital, so maybe I'd better drive my own car.

I talk Rose into having a little tea, and wait for Paul to do his work with the medics.

"What happened to the choir?" I say. "I don't see many of them up there."

The place has emptied out fast—I don't even see the

other members of the quartet, except for Bart. Now more people are outside than in.

"Bart told us we should go home and check on Serena later when she gets to the hospital," Rose said.

"Rose, do you feel comfortable being around Serena when Bart's here?" I ask.

"You and your instincts, Ruby. No, frankly I don't. I just heard too much during the divorce trauma for me to be friendly with Bart. But in an emergency, I guess the rules don't apply. I'm definitely staying with her, though."

"You'd think the rest of the quartet would be here at the very least," I say, "not to mention the choir."

"Until a few minutes ago I couldn't keep them all out of her face," Rose says. "Now I don't know where they are. It's probably for the best, though, that the crowd has cleared."

I see some stirring among the medics, and wonder if that's a good or bad sign.

It appears to be a good one. Paul comes down from the stage and puts his arms around the two of us.

"They found a pulse," he says.

7

As Rose and I walk down the hospital corridor to get some coffee, I'm sorry Paul and I had no time to talk. Not that he wouldn't have come with us, but I knew it would be pointless for him to stay, so I discouraged him, saying I'd call when I heard something. Paul had only showed up at temple because I'd invited him, and he'd never laid eyes on Serena until tonight. I don't know her that well myself, but if I can help Rose by being here, I will.

The crowd at temple may have diminished, but here at the hospital, Serena's friends seem to have multiplied. Essie Sue and Hal are here, plus Kevin, and two or three choir members. Serena's internist is here, and Bart's conferring with him. Hal's tired and is trying to persuade Essie Sue to go home, but she's undoubtedly afraid she'll miss something.

"They're sure taking a lot of time," Rose says as we walk away from the group.

"Maybe you should call Serena's sister," I say.

"My gut tells me to wait at least until her internist comes out," Rose says. "I need to have *something* concrete to tell the woman. Unless you think I'm just procrastinating because I don't want to be the bearer of bad news."

"No, you're probably right, and a few minutes aren't going to make any difference—it's not as if she lives here in town and can rush right over."

Rose pours something molasses-like into two Styrofoam cups. "I think this is supposed to be coffee," she says. We both stare into our cups, waiting for the other to taste first.

"Bart had Serena's sister's number in his Palm Pilot," Rose says. "The sister's name is Joellyn Frank, and she lives in Cincinnati. She's married with a couple of kids, I think. Serena and Bart didn't have any children."

"So why do you think Serena and Bart stayed in the quartet together after the divorce?" I ask as we head back to the waiting room.

"Frankly? Pure stubbornness, I suspect. They both liked to sing, and neither of them was about to be pushed out of the quartet by the other. And who knows—maybe it showed that they were still tied to one another in some weird way. Maybe, given enough time, they might have gotten back together. I doubt it, but stranger things have happened."

"Where were you for so long?" Essie Sue says to me as we join the others. "I was about to send the rabbi after you."

"Any word?" I say.

"None," Kevin says. He looks upset, and knowing Kevin, it's probably not just about Serena.

"Don't worry," I lean over and say to him, "you're not supposed to be doing anything. Just relax."

"Did anyone notice something unusual just before she keeled over?" Essie Sue asks.

She draws blanks from all of us.

"Was she healthy, Rose?"

"Nothing wrong with her at all," Rose says.

This is making me nervous, and I'm about to go find the water fountain when the doctor comes out.

Rose stands up. "How is she?" she says.

"We lost her," he says, taking Rose's hand. "I'm very sorry."

We're stunned. I think we all assumed that when the EMT people found her pulse and started working on her back at the temple, she was, well, not out of danger, but definitely in the land of the living.

Rose sits down with the rest of us, and nobody says anything.

Her doctor seems uncomfortable with the silence. "Is there anything you want to ask?" he says. "Is there a next of kin present besides Dr. Goldman?"

We all look at each other, and then shake our heads no.

"I guess I'm actually the closest in town," Bart says. "We've been divorced about a year."

Rose is crying and clearly in shock, so I try to take her place. I tell the doctor about Serena's sister in Ohio and then ask what we're all wondering.

"What happened to her?" I say.

"Cardiac arrest—her heart stopped again when they were taking her out of the ambulance. When we put her on the table in the emergency room, we hoped to get her started again, but nothing worked. We were too late."

"She never even saw you, except for annual checkups," Bart says to the other doctor. "At least while we were married." He's trying to keep it together, but I can see his hand shake.

"We should have had her flown to Houston instead of to the hospital," Essie Sue says. "They can work miracles with heart transplants."

This is the doctor's cue to give us his card for later review and excuse himself for other emergencies—smart man.

Bart, who's held up until now, suddenly folds and says he wants to go home.

"Maybe the rabbi can take care of the preparations," he says.

Now I *know* he's not thinking clearly. Since Rose appears to be in no condition to do anything, and I wouldn't trust Essie Sue to impart bad news to anyone, I attempt to clear the room. I ask Hal to persuade Essie Sue to go home, ask Kevin and Rose to stay for a bit, and ease everyone else back to their cars.

Rose's functioning doesn't improve when the others leave.

"Ruby," she says, "could you make the arrangements here? And if I give you the number, would you call Joellyn in Cincinnati? Maybe Rabbi Kapstein could drive me home—I need to be with my family."

"Sure," I say.

"I'm sorry. I know I shouldn't fink out like this, for Serena's sake."

Kevin seems glad to have something to do that doesn't involve making arrangements, and although he might be helpful later, I send him along with Rose.

When they've all gone, a nurse comes out and asks if I'm in charge of the deceased.

Apparently, I am. I was fairly effective during these moments when I was a rabbi's wife, but since Stu was killed, I don't do death well at all. Too many memories, too many churning emotions.

There are only two other people here—a mother with a crying baby and a man with what appears to be a sprained ankle. I wish Bart had stayed, but maybe the fact that he's an ex complicates things for him.

I want to go in and see Serena, and I need to call her sister.

I do neither. I just wait. This is a waiting room, and I wait.

Finally, I ask to look at her. Serena's lying peacefully on the gurney, tubes removed, her longish brown hair spread out on the pillow and her face turned to one side. I take her hand and hold it. It's still warm.

A loved one should be here for you, I think.

And for me. I most definitely need a loved one.

A few minutes pass, and as if in answer to my thoughts, Paul walks through the door I've left ajar.

"You didn't call," he says quietly. "I thought of phoning, but I decided to come over."

I can't say anything back right now, but he doesn't seem to expect it. We stand by Serena for quite a long time, his arm around my waist and mine around his.

8

The Temple Rita sanctuary is strangely silent this afternoon as we wait for Serena's memorial tribute to begin. It's so quiet in here you can hear a prayer book drop—emphasizing for me once again the contrast between sudden death and any other. Our congregants are not exactly known for their decorum—there's always a buzz in the temple before a service, even a funeral service. Last week when ninety-year-old Harry Bloch was laid to rest, the rabbi had to shush the crowd twice just to be heard.

Granted, Kevin's not at his best on these occasions, and today is no exception. He's having trouble herding the choir onto the platform along with the temple executive board. Essie Sue's insisted that they all take part in the ceremony. Since Serena's family is out of town and planning to have their own burial service when the body is flown to Ohio, Essie Sue has no opposition—certainly not from Kevin.

I'm sitting with Rose and her family while Kevin begins a lumbering attempt to introduce all those on the program.

"How long is he going to take, Ruby?" Rose asks me. She was supposed to sing with the choir, but wasn't up to it. I don't blame her—of all the people here, she was closest to Serena, and she's taking her death hard.

"I like the old-style funerals," she whispers, "where the mourners could grieve in silence while the rabbi took charge of the service and gave the eulogy. Now everyone has to get their two cents in, you know? I've even seen people that the deceased couldn't stand get up there and intone as if they were best friends."

"I have to admit this has aspects of a city council meeting," I say, "although I like hearing mourners speak when they have something to say and can do it with some taste. Just relax and think your own thoughts—that's what I'm doing." I don't add that going into my head is my chief coping strategy with *anything* that happens at the temple these days. And that anything is better than Kevin's eulogies.

After the choir has performed too many numbers and the board members have made their speeches, the three remaining members of Serena's quartet take their turns.

André Korman goes first. Although he seems genuinely moved by Serena's death—his hands are shaking a bit as he holds his notes—what he has to say seems vaguely out of key with the occasion. The subject is Serena, but it's all about him. He drones on about how he solicited her for the choir, how he needed a specific combination of voices and she completed the blend, and how she always answered the call of duty when he commanded. Kind of like an Essie Sue in male clothing. He makes a big deal about how he and his wife were so close to Serena.

Rose is rolling her eyes. "Serena never even mentioned André's wife to me," she says. "She never shows up at anything."

"Yeah, I know her," I say. I'm happy to see that Rose's husband, Ray, who's sitting on the other side of her, has grabbed her hand for support. I can see how difficult this is for her.

André ends by saying that "Serena, under my guidance, was beginning to understand what lies beneath the layers of our Jewish lives."

That one gets a collective eyebrow lift from the congregation, not to mention our little group in the first row.

If André's remarks are odd, those of the next speaker, Irene Cohn, are even more so. She continues where André left off. After delivering the requisite litany of Serena's virtues of dedication and diligence—none of which reveals in the slightest what kind of person she was—Irene tells us that "Serena Salit was a promising initiate into depths unknown to ordinary plodders."

"Huh?" I say, nudging Rose. "Did I miss something?"

André is either congratulating Irene on her presentation or conferring with her—I can't tell which. She makes a couple of bland concluding remarks and sits down. I see Kevin looking at his watch. He's probably wondering if he can skip his eulogy, considering the length of the program so far.

The third quartet member, Serena's ex-husband, Bart Goldman, gets up and spends most of his allotted time on how uncomfortable he is in speaking about Serena when they've been divorced for so little time.

"This is a fiasco," Rose says. "The rabbi ought to do something about it."

That'll be the day. Mercifully, though, Essie Sue takes over, apparently deciding that the eulogizing needs to end. I see Kevin eagerly nodding his head at that—he's off the hook. For a change, even *I'm* glad she's taking charge.

"People," she says, "thus endeth the life of Serena Salit. The rabbi tells me that there will be no continuation of the service at the cemetery since the deceased will be buried at another ceremony in Ohio at the home of her sister."

Kevin stands up, apparently feeling the need to say *something* in clarification. Big mistake.

"I think Essie Sue means buried at the *cemetery* of her sister, not her home," he says. "Or maybe the cemetery in her sister's hometown." He looks to Essie Sue for confirmation, but doesn't receive it, now that he's not only corrected her in public, but also put the final stamp of confusion on a most forgettable day. Serena deserved better.

9

Email to: Nan
From: Ruby
Subject: Stuff

No, I'm actually not that excited about
the choir trip yet—Serena's death has us
all reeling here. I knew you'd be nauseous
over the funeral details at the temple.
I hear through the grapevine that the
service and burial in Ohio went well (or
as well as a funeral can)—she had lots of
friends there.

Paul was beyond wonderful through all
this, Nan—he becomes more endearing each
time I see him. It's not just that he seems

to know who I really am—he also supports
me in a way no one has since my marriage.
But I have a horror of falling too far too
fast, when I'm barely over the fiasco with
Ed. I know Paul senses this, too . . . hell,
he doesn't just sense it, he's usually fix-
ated on it. Which is one of our problems.

Email to: Ruby
From: Nan
Subject: Relax

Ha . . . I guess you're laughing at my
telling you to relax when I'm usually
advising you to get a grip, but this time
I think you need to enjoy some of what's
going on in your life. Do you realize that
people wait years to find someone like this
guy? Okay, I know I'm pushing, but at
least don't take him for granted.
    And I do get it about the trip. Another
thing . . . although the scenery in the
Canadian Rockies is fabulous, the idea
that this is a choir trip is a bit dreary,
isn't it?

Email to: Nan
From: Ruby
Subject: Trip

Yes and no. I know what you mean by *dull*,
but this might not be. I've told you about
the new emphasis on the Kabbalah and some
of the more expressive elements in
Judaism these days. True, you got as
excited about it as I thought you might,
knowing your preference for the rational,
but since I'm always open to new stuff on
the Jewish horizon, I'd like to see what's
out there. And what's out there is definitely nothing Kevin knows about or will
ever bring to our little outpost in Eternal. Some of the people exploring this
sort of thing will be at this choir conference. Music's a big part of it, and
who knows—I might learn something.

Email to: Ruby
From: Nan
Subject: Pu-leese

Remember that old song, Ruby—"Accentuate
the positive, eliminate the negative, and
don't mess with Mr. In Between"? I don't
want to hear that you, of all people, are
going Woo Woo on me. It doesn't suit you.

Email to: Nan
From: Ruby
Subject: Woo Woo

It's just a point of interest, babe.

Email to: Ruby
From: Nan
Subject: RE Woo Woo

Yeah. I've heard *that* before.

Email to: Nan
From: Ruby
Subject: P.S.

Forgot to tell you I think Kevin has a
crush on Bitsy, the new grief counselor.
This can only come to grief (you'll pardon the expression).

10

Kevin's car wouldn't start, so I'm picking him up tonight for Essie Sue's emergency meeting at Temple Rita. I'm looking forward to it, for a change, since it'll give me a chance to pump him about his new love interest. First, though, we have to make a stop at the vet's. She's working evening hours tonight and is giving my own personal adoring couple their shots while I'm at temple.

Oy Vey, my three-legged retriever, gives a low growl as Kevin backs his way into the front seat. She's usually placid, but she's never taken to Kevin.

"Why's she in the cage?" he asks, adding, "Not that I'm unhappy about it."

"I admit you're not on her top-ten list, but she certainly wouldn't hurt you, Kevin. I used her old crate to transport

Chutzpah, the cat I was keeping for Joshie. When Oy Vey saw Chutzpah in the dog carrier, she crawled in after him and wouldn't get out."

"Aren't they supposed to hate one another? As in 'fighting like cats and dogs'? I'm not a pet person, but even I know that."

"They're in love. As in 'wild about each other.' Chutzpah even sleeps on Oy Vey's back at night. When Joshie brought the cat home on his last visit, I thought for a while that they'd be enemies, but they've done a complete turnaround. Now I can't separate them."

"So you're keeping him? I thought Josh was just bringing him home to Momma temporarily because he didn't have room for him in his girlfriend's apartment."

"It's permanent now—they're a pair. And speaking of couples, what's up with you and little miss one-name? I hear you have the hots for Bitsy. Planning any private parties?"

Kevin doesn't blush—he does the reverse. His face loses all color when he's teased.

"Quit it, Ruby—she's just a friend."

"I've heard that before, and said it a few times, too."

"But it's true. We haven't even had a date."

"Well, if you ask me, the party planning and grief counseling would look pretty good on her *rebbetzin* résumé."

"They didn't look so good on yours."

"Touché. You're getting a lot looser these days, Kevin."

"That's because I know you're not out to get me, Ruby."

"Come on, you've got to drop some of that paranoia. If Stu and I hadn't developed a thick skin early on, we'd have been long gone. You have to give it back to them in kind when people start pressuring you."

"Easy for you to say—you're not doing this job anymore.

I have to watch my every move." He's biting his nails again, but I try not to notice.

"Then it's even more important to have some fun on your off hours. Who started this flirtation, you or Bitsy? As if I have to ask."

"I guess she did. She called and asked me out."

"And you said no to a date?"

"Well, I said I'd think about it. She wanted to know how many days I had to have before I accepted."

"Just the kind of girl you need, Kevin."

"You mean you're encouraging this? I thought you said she was trivial."

"Trivial's good at this stage. What do you have to lose? Bitsy's even cute, in a . . ."

"Trivial sort of way?"

"Maybe she'll be able to get you out of those black wing-tipped shoes and into something more twenty-first century. Somebody needs to grab you, boy. You're already way smarter than she is." I reach over and pat his knee. Bad idea.

"How about you?" he says.

"We've covered this territory before, Kevin. After all these years, I feel closer to you than I ever thought I would, but this is not a romance. Remember when I went to that temple dance with you and you told everyone we were dating? I'm not going through that again."

Fortunately, we're pulling up to the vet's and I'm off the hook until the next time.

I open the door to the crate and we have to bribe Oy Vey with a dog cookie to get him out. Chutzpah immediately goes into a shrill whine, which doesn't let up the whole time we're at the front desk. The vet promises me she'll keep them together for the staff's sake as well as for theirs.

Bitsy's car pulls up to the temple just as we do, and Kevin's face loses color again. She gets out to walk in with us, doing a kissy kissy in the air by my cheek, and giving him a real one on the lips. A quick one, though—she obviously doesn't want him to freak in front of me.

"So how are you?" she says to him, twirling his index finger while she gazes at him. "I didn't know you and Ruby were good friends."

Kevin and I look at each other—this is one of those questions with no answer, under the circumstances. We don't want to say we are, and we don't want to say we aren't. It didn't even occur to me until now that she might consider me, of all people, a rival.

"We're old friends," I say, "sometimes good, sometimes not so good, huh, Kevin?"

Not a great line on my part, and it leaves him looking utterly bewildered as to how to reply.

"I guess so," he says finally. "Aren't we late?"

We *are* late, so we avoid further awkwardness and head inside, where we're ushered to the front row of a darkened Blumberg Social Hall.

"I saved you seats," Essie Sue says, interrupting her slide presentation and turning on the lights. "I need you on the front row. Why are you late, Rabbi?"

"It was Ruby's fault," Kevin says.

This, in essence, is why our relationship will forever remain at arm's length. The boundaries of Kevin's support extend only as far as his narcissism will permit. To put it even more bluntly, he'll drop me faster than a hot latke to save his own skin.

"Ruby had to go to the vet with the dog and cat," he says. "If I'd thought we would be late, I'd have stopped her."

"You should have reminded her this is why Jews and animals don't mix," Essie Sue announces. "And as I've told you many times, Ruby, wild creatures in rabbinical families are especially ludicrous. It's like making a ham sandwich on challah bread."

"Unfortunately for you, Essie Sue, I'm not in a rabbinical family anymore, and if you don't get off my back in sixty seconds, I'll illustrate that."

The lights go down in ten, and we're treated to a history of the latke, illuminated with hand drawings by Essie Sue's niece Sherry, age six.

"Chanukah's over," Kevin faux-whispers to me. "Why does she think we can take fund-raising orders for these in January?"

Apparently, he doesn't realize I'm not speaking to him after the blame game I just witnessed. I close my eyes and hope for a few more minutes of blessed darkness before some sort of surreal discussion begins.

I don't have long to wait.

"Have I put you all in the mood now? Are you latke-motivated?"

Essie Sue turns off the projector and points to Bitsy, her newly appointed shill, who jumps up and raises both fists in the air with a *yay*. I think that's supposed to rouse us, but it's about as effective as the Dallas cheerleaders are when the Cowboys are losing. And a lot less sexy.

Not that this daunts Essie Sue.

"I want to tell you about something that's just come into my life, people," she says. "I've now become a with-it member of the computer generation."

"Just in case you don't know, it's the second generation already," Bubba Copeland shouts from the back of the room.

"This is like saying you're with it because you have a telephone instead of a tin can and a string. Are you gonna wow us with the fact you're doing email now?"

"That and more," she says, ignoring the sarcasm. "My darling Hal gave me an iMac for my birthday. As you all must know, the new Macintosh is not a computer, it's a work of art. It's so stylish I'm displaying it on my coffee table in the living room. In its own way, it's as slim as I am."

"You're using it on the table, or just looking at it?" I ask.

"I sit on the sofa and lean forward, Ruby."

I can picture her aiming long fingernails at the stylish keys.

"We Mac owners are a special breed—surely in your business, you've noticed that."

"A breed apart, I hope," Bubba says.

"Enough, Bubba. I've decided we should have a website promoting our latkes. We can send orders all over the country."

"Let me get this straight," I say. "Are we selling advance orders for next Chanukah, or leftover orders from this one?"

"The latke, being a pancake, is as timeless as the potato," she says.

"And as boring. When do we get to vote on this loser?" Bubba says.

"There's always a market for Jewish culture, Bubba, and if you were more sophisticated you'd see that. We have to think big here. I can certainly tell you're not an Apple computer user."

"I get my electronics from Radio Shack, with the rest of the peons," he says. "And we don't eat latkes in January, either."

I guess Essie Sue gets the hint from the cheers Bubba receives. She switches gears fast, using her executive prerogative.

"I'm putting my cousin Zelda in charge of a committee to

explore the website idea," she says. "I don't need a vote for that. Zelda's a computer person. She works at Circuit City."

"She works the switchboard," Kevin says in my ear.

I hate getting publicly involved in Essie Sue's messes, but there's a point that needs making fast.

"Look," I say, "this fund-raising project was supposed to help pay for the choir trip this spring. If it's not going to work, I think we should drop it and think of some other ways to finance the conference expenses."

"You're a spoilsport, Ruby," she says. "I will not have you coming in here after this stunning slide presentation and demoralizing the congregation."

She glares at Bitsy, who seizes the moment and goes into meditation mode in the wink of a false eyelash.

"Let's all close our baby blues," she says. "Picture a white beach with lapping waves washing over you. I want you to think of that diastolic blood pressure number going down, down, down as you take yourself from this place and transport your psyche to Bermuda."

"What's wrong with the Dead Sea?" Bubba Copeland says. "You can float there, too. Israel needs the tourism."

"Okay, imagine whatever you like." Bitsy's no fool. "This is what I tell my grief-counseling clients, and it'll work for our dear distressed Ruby Rothman, too. Ruby, pretend you're melting into the pool of life, and that you've lost all boundaries between yourself and the universe. You can get this effect quicker with Prozac, but this is an emergency."

Essie Sue seconds that. "A definite emergency," she says. "You're a genius, Bitsy—worth every penny of what we're paying you. Get us back on track for the latke sales."

"How do you feel now, Ruby?" Bitsy asks, stretching a hand toward me.

"Like calling for a vote," I say. "Who'll second trashing the latke sales?"

"You mean all this counseling has been for nothing?" Essie Sue says. "You're hopelessly confused, Ruby. The meeting's adjourned. We'll discuss the sale another time."

Forget the Robert's Rules—Essie Sue knows what to do when she's outnumbered. I can't say the same for Bitsy— she gives a helpless glance at Essie Sue to make sure she's not being blamed for my failure to melt into the universe. The jury's out on that one, though—Essie Sue's headed out the door, leaving no clue as to what she's thinking about the results of the evening's boundary therapy.

Now that Essie Sue's out of here, the peace and love have departed from Bitsy's eyes, leaving cold appraisal in their wake as she glares at me.

"I guarantee you Prozac would do it," she says.

11

I've invited Rose to meet me at The Hot Bagel for lunch today—I have to be here anyway this afternoon to do the books. Since the business end of the bakery is my territory, with Milt handling the day-to-day operations, I'm able to set my own schedule most of the time. This has been an easy month so far, leaving me whole days free for my computer consulting.

"You don't look so hassled today, Ruby," Rose says as we sip some hot Lapsang Souchong tea. Neither of us is very hungry, and we're skipping bagel sandwiches to share a whitefish salad Milt's made for us.

I'm glad I appear calmer than usual, but I'm not about to tell Rose she's taken on all my agitation and more. She's drumming two broken nails on the table in a *pitty-pat* that's driving me crazy, and when she's not eating, she's twisting a strand of hair with her other hand. She's also doing that humming thing under her breath that she does unconsciously when she's stressed. I try to approach the situation in a more roundabout way—which is not my style, and I'm never successful at it.

"And you?" I say.

"And me *what*?"

"Are you hassled?"

Well, there goes that subtlety.

"I guess my nervousness shows, huh?" she says.

"Oh, I don't know. I just sense you're on edge."

"Well, I am."

She dives into her salad so hard that the tines of her fork scrape through the lettuce to the bottom of her plate, screeching like a blackboard eraser.

"Okay, stop," I say. "Why don't you put down your fork and just tell me what's going on?"

"I've been thinking about Serena a lot since last week."

"After that weird memorial service, I'm not surprised. We never did get a good chance to talk about it."

"It left me feeling that I didn't know Serena as well as I thought I did. To tell you the truth, I always enjoyed making private fun of the other three quartet members when I was with Serena. Bart was a special case, since they were in the throes of a divorce—not much fun to be made there, I admit. But André and Irene were so full of themselves and so humorless about life in general that they were just asking to be taken down. I always thought Serena shared my view that they were both so serious they were comical, you know?"

"And she didn't share that?"

"I'm not certain now. They both sounded a lot closer to her than I thought they were."

"You can't be sure of that—they were probably trying to appear important at the memorial service. And since the dead can't respond, they felt safe in hinting at secrets with Serena that weren't there."

"Do you think?"

"I do. I wouldn't put any stock into what was said at that service."

"Okay, forget my doubts about them, Ruby. Aside from that, I don't understand about the heart thing, or problem, or whatever it was supposed to be. Serena had absolutely no history of heart disease, and her age and general state of health made it unlikely she'd drop dead like that. That happens more with middle-aged men, doesn't it? And she wasn't a smoker, and wasn't in the midst of violent exercise when she died."

"She was performing, Rose. That's a stressor of sorts."

"Before that crowd? They can't tell an alto from an Altoid. It's not as though her singing was being critiqued."

"Cardiac arrest does happen, Rose. And we checked with her internist—remember? He confirmed the diagnosis."

"Right. But you did want to know what was going on, and I took that to mean you were asking why I was on edge. That's why."

I don't think this lunch is helping her state of mind.

"What do you think could make you feel better about this, hon? It's over, and I hate to see you stuck in this emotional state. Mourning the loss of her friendship is one thing, but honestly, what else can you do?"

"It's too quick, Ruby. It's just too soon."

"Have you spoken with Serena's sister, Joellyn?"

"Several times. I finally got myself together enough to call her and offer my condolences last week. She was as shocked as I was. I called her again after the services here, just to tell her the nice things people said. She was very appreciative, and invited me to visit if I was ever in the area. She's called me twice since."

"That's unusual, isn't it? You've never met her?"

"No, but they didn't have much family, and she knows Serena was my friend. I think she just wants to talk with someone who knew Serena in her current life, if you know what I mean. She keeps asking me to visit. She can't bring herself to go through the belongings that were shipped to her."

"I know this seems off the wall, but have you considered going for a day or so? You could visit the cemetery together— maybe you'd feel some closure."

"It's expensive."

"Not if you get a weekend special off the Internet. I've seen fares as low as a hundred fifty round-trip, but you have to decide on the spot. And you wouldn't have expenses once you got there—she'll put you up, right?"

"Oh, yeah, no problem about that. She said she has a guest room and everything, and would pick me up at the airport."

"So she's really pushing for it, right?"

"Apparently."

"Want me to do the Net shopping for you? I'm on the email list for bargains from Austin to wherever."

"Let me call Joellyn and see how receptive she'd be to a spur-of-the-moment visitor, and then we'll see. Ray and Jackie could do without me for two days."

I have no idea if this is a good plan or not, but I do know that Rose's fingers aren't drumming the table anymore.

12

"We're like those couples with a double sink," I say. Paul and I are standing in front of my gas stove, each cooking on a different burner.

"Only this is sexier than brushing our teeth together," he says.

"I didn't know you thought of cooking as sexy," I say.

"With you it is." By way of illustration, he plucks a fat mushroom from his sauté pan, cools it in the air so it won't burn me, and plops it into my mouth.

"Umm . . . I can taste the garlic and ginger . . . that's positively orgasmic, now that I think of it."

I'm poaching the salmon in my pan, and he's sautéing the most luscious vegetables in his.

"Soon they'll be nestling together over here," he says,

bending toward me to try the salmon I'm offering. I kiss him before letting him taste if the fish is done.

"So which is better," I say, "me or the salmon?"

"Right now? You," he says, "but remember, we haven't put it in my delicious sauce yet. Ask me later."

I only have the Key West souvenir pot holder to throw at him at the moment. It displays the recipe for the Key Lime pie I've made for our dessert.

"Keep that up and there'll be no later," I say.

I forget that Oy Vey's waiting by the stove for any goodies that might drop from our cooking pots. The poor thing makes a lunge for the pot holder because it's carrying such delicious odors, and gets nothing but a mouthful of cloth. Which she promptly shares with Chutzpah, and they go off into the living room to make a game of it.

"They've eaten the pie on the pot holder," Paul says, "so you'll have to give me the real thing."

He's wearing a new gray sweatshirt with old gray sweatpants that would match if they weren't so faded, his beard is a day old, and he's without a doubt the sexiest man I've seen in this town. Between the workouts he does to keep in shape as a cop, and the fact that he's naturally lean and lithe, Paul's a hottie. I can hardly keep my hands off him, but they're occupied culinarily at the moment, which I'm telling myself is a good thing. We're still taking things easy.

"Are we going to set the table with the watermelon place mats I brought you?" he says.

We have a *tacky* thing going—whenever either of us sees something especially outrageous, we buy it as a gift for the other. Until tonight, he hadn't been able to top the Elvis-Pelvis salt-and-pepper shakers I gave him. But his plastic place mats cut in the shape of watermelons—a tribute to my house on Watermelon Lane—may have tipped the balance.

"I was thinking of candlelight and white linen," I say, "but since I don't want to hurt your feelings, I'll forgo the romance and use the plastic."

"No, maybe we should save the watermelon mats for breakfast and go for your choice—especially with this great dinner."

"How do you know you'll be here for breakfast?" I can't resist saying.

"I don't know, maybe it's in the stars. The receptionist at the station house told us the planets were aligned in love mode this month. I wanted to be sure and remember to tell you that."

"Because you're so into that, right? Admit it, the only signs you care about are the thirty-five-mile-per-hour speed trap signs all over Eternal."

"Rats. I told her the horoscope shit wouldn't work with you."

"Wrong. It's all working, sweetie, can't you tell that? I think you're adorable tonight."

"Only tonight? Not all the time?"

Just as I'm thinking we should get the salad out of the refrigerator, the phone rings. I look quickly at the caller ID and see that it's a call from Ohio.

"Should I answer it?" I say, after telling Paul it must be Rose phoning from Joellyn's house.

"Wonder what she wants?" he says.

"Your call," I say. "What should I do?"

"Answer it and I'll put the fish in the sauce for a few minutes."

"Okay, but remember that salmon can overcook fast."

I pick up the phone on the last ring before the machine answers.

"Hi, Rose," I say.

"Oh, you know it's me already."

"Miracles of modern electronics. How's it going there? Is Joellyn with you?"

I'm thinking we might have a more frank conversation if she's by herself. Not that it makes much difference.

"She's right here, and she says hi."

"Are you two having a good visit?"

I'm really torn—this is the worst possible time for a call, and if it were anyone but Rose on the other end, I'd phone back later. But I'm sure she's not calling just for a chat. We're close, but not enough for her to call from Ohio just to say hello.

"What's up?" I say, then instantly regret sounding so businesslike—I don't want to hurry her. I'm just finding myself distracted by the muscles in Paul's back. And he's moving around my kitchen as if he owns it.

In spite of myself, I put my hand over the mouthpiece and ask him if I should tell her I'll call back.

"Better see what she wants," he says.

As if to contradict any sense of urgency, Rose gives me an accounting of the two days she and Joellyn have spent together.

"It's been good for both of us," she says. "Neither of us felt any closure after Serena's death, and we're enjoying remembering her together. Me, especially—I didn't know much about their childhood. And we're looking at old photos, too."

I can see our romantic dinner slipping away as we speak, even though Paul's making good use of the time by setting the table.

"I'm really glad you're enjoying one another," I say. "Paul's here, too—I'll tell him." Maybe that'll get her to the point.

"Uh-oh. Is it dinnertime there? I should have waited an hour."

She should have waited until tomorrow, but that's just me being selfish.

"Lieutenant Lundy's there," I hear Rose tell Joellyn.

There's more murmuring on their end, and then another voice on the phone.

"Ruby, this is Joellyn. I'm wondering if you'd mind if I speak to Paul for a minute?"

"Sure," I say. She doesn't sound in the mood for small talk, so I don't make any. Although I have to admit I'm a bit surprised at how abrupt she is, considering all the futzing around Rose has been doing.

"She wants you," I say, waving the phone in his direction. "It's Joellyn—the sister."

Paul gets on the phone, and I see what I can do to salvage dinner, which has been simmering. I turn off the gas burner, assuming the damage has already been done, and take out a bottle of Pinot Grigio I've been chilling. Then, before I put it on the table, I decide to return it to the refrigerator again. Who knows how long he'll be?

It's a good thing, because he spends the next few minutes in total silence while Joellyn is apparently filling him in on whatever they called about. This is, of course, my tiny version of hell, since not only am I not sharing this candlelight dinner with Paul, but I'm missing out on whatever's going on. And if I hadn't mentioned that Paul was here, they'd have been telling all this to me, not him.

"When is Rose planning on coming home?" I hear him

finally say. "Then why don't you have her bring it on the plane with her. And just for safekeeping, can you put the files on a CD and send it to me by FedEx? Do you know how to burn one? If not, I don't want you to risk losing them altogether."

The answer he gets apparently satisfies him, because he relaxes enough to sit down on one of the kitchen chairs while he talks. Then he stands up again.

"Look, since you're computer savvy, why not do a third thing? Send me the files as an attachment, too. After you burn the CD. Send it tonight to my email address at police headquarters."

As he gives her the particulars, I'm seeing the romance go out the window. Maybe I'm just catastrophizing, but Paul has that all-business look he gets when new information comes in. And then there was that reference to the email tonight.

I'm as nuts as Paul is—now that he's hanging up, I'm as interested in what's going on in Ohio as I am in dinner.

"Let's eat," he says. "I know this came at the wrong time." He brushes my cheek with his lips as he heads for the stove. "Do you think the salmon's still edible?"

I squash my curiosity until we light the candles, pour the wine, sit down, and try the food—which isn't bad, but not what we'd hoped for. Just as I'm about to ask something, he beats me to it.

"Joellyn received Serena's personal effects," he says, "including her laptop. She decided to go through the contents of it with Rose, who's a lot more familiar with Serena's life here in Eternal than Joellyn is. They ran into some disturbing material in several Notes files Serena kept, and they think I should see them."

"Look, hon," I say. "I know this is going to be on your

mind tonight. Why don't we finish dinner and then use my computer to access your email from here? It might not be what we'd planned, but we can at least take a look at the stuff, and maybe afterwards, you can still stay over."

"Thanks for understanding," he says. "Joellyn asked me to keep it to myself for now. I need to look at the material down at headquarters in case I have to access any databases."

"By yourself?"

"Uh-huh."

"No way. Rose called my house, interrupted my dinner date—well, *our* dinner date—and had no idea you'd be here. She would have obviously told me the whole thing."

"Maybe so, but the deceased's blood relation, her own sister, told me unequivocally to keep this confidential until she and I can discuss it. When she found me, she obviously changed her mind about telling you."

I get it, but I don't have to like it.

"That's not fair. You and I talk about things like this all the time—you understand I'm reliable."

"Which is beside the point, and you know it. You're just disappointed, and I don't blame you. I am, too. But what do you expect me to do—betray the woman's confidence?"

I finish my glass of wine. Then Paul does something I *really* hate him for.

"Look," he says. "Why don't I pick up the email tomorrow? We'll have our evening tonight. It won't kill me to wait."

I sit there, twirling the salad greens with my fork, and then I have to crack a smile in spite of myself.

"Yeah, but it'll kill me, and you damn well know it. The sooner you find out what's in that laptop, the sooner I can learn about it. Somehow."

He takes my hands across the table and kisses the inside of each.

"Tell me," I say. "You knew what my reaction would be when you made the offer to wait, didn't you?"

"Let's just say I know who I'm dealing with," he says. "That's why I'm good at what I do."

"Oh, you're good at what you do, all right—you just don't do it with me."

He stands me up and pulls me to him.

"Look at me," he says. "Do you have any doubt whatsoever about how I feel about you? And don't you dare lie for effect."

After he leaves, when I'm eating the cold salmon and finishing the wine, I think to myself that Ed couldn't have pulled this off in a thousand years.

13

"We aren't getting the advance latke orders we need to finance the trip, Ruby—not even with the website."

Essie Sue's waiting for me on my front porch as I drive in from my early morning aerobics class.

"I'm sorry about that, Essie Sue, but why did you hit *me* up at this ungodly hour?"

She's wearing her immaculate winter white pantsuit, and staring at my leotard and the sneakers I untied in the car to give my feet some breathing room.

"Honestly, Ruby, your grooming leaves something to be desired."

Apparently, my appearance is taking precedence over whatever it was she came over here to harass me about.

"If you don't like my grooming, Essie Sue, then why don't

you give me time to groom? I just left the gym to come home and take a shower. And why do I need to give you an explanation anyhow? You're the one barging into my morning, not the other way around."

She follows me into the house, taking great pains to avoid Oy Vey and Chutzpah, who aren't getting near her, anyway. They have long memories.

I lead her onto the deck in back, where she stands up until I find her a towel to put down on the chaise.

"It's cold out here. Why do you use your deck in the winter, anyway?"

"Because we live in the Sunbelt?"

"Don't be cute, Ruby. I wouldn't be over here if I weren't desperate. You're a computer expert, so tell me why our temple website isn't producing a bigger yield?"

"How many orders have come in?"

"Two. And that's worldwide. I want you to fix it."

"I hate to break it to you, but this isn't a computer problem, Essie Sue."

"So *what's wrong?*"

"Like maybe the rest of the world isn't grabbed by the idea of ordering latkes two months after Chanukah? I told you this wouldn't work. You got great response from the congregation, so take it and run."

"I would, but that money's already been spent paying for Bitsy. I had much bigger plans than the local scene."

"You had no plans other than putting this on the website. You could never have filled the orders, even if they had come in—that takes cooking, freezing, mailing—none of which you were prepared for."

"You sound just like the man at the health department— he said he was going to be watching me like a hawk to make sure we were sanitary. Just because we had a few problems with those matzo ball sales a few years ago."

Now I remember why this whole idea had me shuddering—the matzo ball fiasco. I bring us mugs of hot coffee from the kitchen.

"So the health department was on your back, too? You never told me that."

"Forget it, Ruby. Let's have a rummage sale. Otherwise, you people will never have enough to get to Canada."

"The choir has already knocked itself out on this project. Why not use some of that money you've got socked away in that rainy day account? It's earning about one percent interest."

Essie Sue has a habit of squirreling away the proceeds of her fund-raising projects instead of using them for their intended purposes. I have no idea how much she has, but I'm acting on my hunch that there's plenty there.

"You mean my emergency funds?"

"I mean the temple's funds—there's a difference. You can always replenish them later."

"I'll think about it. But only if the participants increase the portion they pay out of pocket for the trip."

I *am* starting to get cold out here.

"I don't mean to be inhospitable, but since you invited yourself over here, are we finished now? I have to get to work soon."

"Just one more thing. The rabbi told me you were still seeing that policeman. I have an idea to get you out of this."

"I don't remember telling anyone I wanted out of it— whatever the meaning of *it* is."

"Don't go Clintonian on me, Ruby. As someone close to you, I have an interest in your welfare. My cousin Claire in

California told me about a fabulous love-connection website full of nice Jewish men. It's called Nu—a Jew for You. Since you're on the computer all the time, I thought of you right away. I got you a guest membership, which allows you to browse the selection of men without giving your real name. They call it *lurking*."

They call it *losers.* Oy.

"No thanks, Essie Sue. I like to look my poison right in the eye from the beginning."

"Oh, they have photos included. You can see the potential partners."

"Don't you remember those stories of the men who sent their mail-order brides pictures of movie stars instead of themselves? This stuff's been going on forever."

"Ruby, you're so naive. It's totally kosher certified. By online rabbis, I think."

"I think not. But, gee, thanks anyway. Let me walk you through the yard to your car."

I usher Essie Sue into her driver's seat, relieved that she at least agreed to leave when I asked her to.

"You'll be getting your first email from these people tomorrow," she yells as she drives off. "Start composing your bio."

14

Email to: Nan
From: Ruby
Subject: Catch-up

I can't remember what I told you on the
phone and what I wrote in email, but here
goes. I don't believe I'm admitting this,
but we only have a few weeks before leaving for Canada, and I still haven't been
able to wrangle any information from Paul
or Rose concerning what was on Serena's
laptop. I do understand that Paul gave his
word, but I don't see why Rose hasn't told
me herself. Paul doesn't want to get in
the middle here, but he thinks Serena's

sister Joellyn wants to keep it quiet, and
must have made Rose promise. At any rate,
it's frustrating, and Rose seems to be
avoiding me.

On the phone you said there might be
nothing much to tell, but I know from
something I overheard this week that
Paul's giving Joellyn advice on how to get
the body exhumed. As you know professionally, permission for exhumation isn't an
easy process, and it certainly isn't a
speedy one. But Joellyn's also a parale-
gal, so she knows her way through the
legal forms involved.

Paul's also asked me not to go on the
Lake Louise trip, which of course makes me
think people from the choir are involved
in all this—not that I have any idea how.
He probably thinks I'll ask a zillion
questions of them once we get out of town.
Which I won't, of course, if he'll just
tell me something.

Email to: Ruby
From: Nan
Subject: Cat and mouse?

So let me see if I've got this straight.
You're trying to use the trip as leverage to get more information out of Paul,
right? You're figuring that if he doesn't
want you to go but refuses to say why,
then you *will* go. And if he's worried

enough, he'll tell you what's going on in
order to keep you home and safe.

You do realize that you could both be
losers here. He's pursuing the one path
which will ensure that you go, because
you're like a two-year-old when someone
says no to you, and you're embarking on
a dangerous journey if you travel with
these people not knowing what you're
doing. In other words, the usual. And now
you've got me worried, too. Maybe I should
call Paul myself and explain the more
unattractive aspects of your character.

Email to: Nan
From: Ruby
Subject: Threats can backfire

Ha . . . if you call Paul, you'll leave
yourself open to charges that you're
interested in him yourself. I distinctly
remember giving you a chance if you wanted
it. Now, of course, I'm so into him that
I couldn't possibly make that offer, but
that won't stop me from using it against
you.

Email to: Ruby
From: Nan
Subject: Not buying it

Good try, but I'm still worried about you.
Keep your man, jealous as I am, and I'll
struggle along in my single state.

Email to: Nan
From: Ruby
Subject: I've got just the thing for
  you

Essie Sue signed me up with a pseudonym
on some dating website called Nu—a Jew for
You. She doesn't think Paul's a suitable
match. I refused to go on there so she's
picking up the responses herself, which
she can do since she's the paying customer
there, not me. I do know that it's trendy
to explore online dating these days and
that they're not all losers, but I'm not
giving her any encouragement. It's still
smoke and mirrors to me.

15

Tonight Kevin's asked me over to his apartment, AKA Gym Central, since the so-called furnishings are leftovers Essie Sue gave him from the health spa she used to own. He never asks me to his place unless he's in trouble, so I'm wary. Just so it won't be a total loss, I figure I can work out on his treadmill while he's filling me in.

"Why are you wearing those spandex bicycle pants?" he asks me as he opens the door.

"Hello to you, too," I say, bumping into the ab machine he uses as a coffee table. "You don't like my exercise outfit?"

"Is that what it is?"

"I thought it would match your equipment," I say.

"Oh, that. I don't even notice it anymore. I just use it to

put things on. And the reclining bike seat is pretty comfort-able next to my reading lamp."

"You realize you could sell this stuff and furnish your whole apartment," I say.

"No, I couldn't. Essie Sue gave it to me, and she thinks I use it. She's the reason I asked you over, Ruby."

I slump down on the bench-press seat and put my feet up on the elliptical trainer. It's not comfortable, but I've plunked myself down in worse places. When Essie Sue's involved, things get complicated fast, so I'm dreading the rest of this.

"Want an energy bar?"

"No, thanks." Kevin's skills as a host are exceeded only by his constant attempts to get rid of the stale supplies Essie Sue unloaded on him from the health spa. These bars have to be years old by now, and I've learned the hard way to avoid them.

"Don't get comfortable," he says. "I want you to come into the bedroom so I can show you something."

Despite the fact that Kevin's had crushes on me in the past, invitations to his bedroom don't faze me. In fact, I wel-come the chance to lie on his bed—the only real piece of furniture he owns.

"My computer's in here," he says, "but I guess you remem-ber that."

And so it is, securely resting on the seat of a biceps builder.

"I can see it here from the bed," I say, deciding that if I'm not going to get a workout, I might as well relax in indo-lence. "It's not broken, is it?"

"No, I didn't ask you over to fix anything."

That's a relief. As a computer consultant, I've had friend-ships ruined by social invitations masking desperation calls for free advice. I don't mind helping friends in the least—

it's their not being honest that bothers me. I hate those "Oh, by the way, can you look at this software?" comments I get as soon as I walk in the door.

"So what's the problem?" I ask Kevin.

"I want you to please go online with me and help me deal with these women who're responding to my ad. I don't know any of them, and already some of them are trying to date me. Or worse."

"You wrote an ad? This is a side of you I don't know, guy."

"That's a side of me I don't know either. Essie Sue did it. And now I have to deal with it."

"Oy. She signed you up on the Nu—a Jew for You site? Just ignore it. She threatened to do it for me, too, but I'm pretending this never happened. Since my name isn't on the bio, I decided to let her handle things. If I don't go on there, it'll all go away sooner or later, and she'll get tired of paying the fees."

"But that's just it—she told me she'd paid a lot to sign me up. She's not your boss, Ruby—I can't ignore her the way you do. Since she has my password, she's seen all the interest in me online, and she wants me to explore some of these contacts."

"She's not entitled to control your personal life, Kevin."

"Yeah, right. She talked me up to Bitsy and now I can't get rid of her. I told Essie Sue I wasn't interested in Bitsy, so she says she's making up for it by fixing me up online."

"Whoa, come sit on the bed, Kevin, where I can see more than your back. I had no idea you had all these relationship problems."

"Yeah, with no relationships. Just tsuris. Trouble plus."

"Okay, first things first. I thought you kind of liked Bitsy. Last I heard, she'd asked you for a date."

"She's too pushy, and she scares me a little. I told her to find somebody else—that I wasn't sure about us."

"So how did that go over?"

"Badly. Now she ignores me."

"Well, what do you expect her to do? You need to fish or cut bait."

"I'm not fishing."

"Okay, so be glad she's ignoring you. Although I'll bet she's just regrouping. But what's the deal with these virtual romances? Are you really just doing what Essie Sue wants, or are you interested?"

"I'm kind of fascinated in one way. And in another, I don't like those women jumping to conclusions about me. Look at my bio and tell me what you think."

"She did the bio, not you?"

"Uh-huh." Kevin's now curled up on the bed in a fetal position. I know from past experience this means he wants me to take over big-time.

He's already logged on, so I go over to the biceps-building machine and take a look.

I skip over the curriculum vitae, which she's apparently taken directly from the form Kevin submitted to the temple. If this doesn't turn anyone off, nothing will. But I'm still curious as to why he's attracted so many women, so I continue with the introductory questions she's answered for him.

Describe Yourself
ANSWER: Somewhere between Brad Pitt and Robert Redford before he got old.

Yep, vintage Essie Sue.

Why You Should Want to Go Out with Me
ANSWER: My exciting sexual nature, my muscular body, my large brain, and my clever repartee.

Where I'd Rather Be Right Now
ANSWER: On a romantic beach with you or in shul.

Last Two Books I've Read
ANSWER: *Life of Maimonides* and *Sex and the Single Man.*

Favorite Songs
ANSWER: "Love Me Tender" and "Hatikvah."

Worldly Goods
ANSWER: Extremely comfortable and willing to share.

Ten Things I Can't Live Without
ANSWER: The Commandments.

Okay, I have to come up for air. I don't know quite what to say as I turn to Kevin on the bed.

"So what do you think, Ruby?" He's uncoiled himself and is now stretched out and leaning on one elbow.

"Let's say it's a perfect illustration of all the things I've ever envisioned about online romance, Kevin."

"Wait until you read the responses," he says. "These women are voracious."

"I must truly say that I cannot begin to imagine what kind of person would be attracted to Essie Sue's creation here."

"Some of them say they're beautiful and wealthy, Ruby. And sexy. And want me."

"If you're thinking of getting involved, why don't you just go on there with your own description of yourself?"

"I thought of that, but it would be a lot more boring than hers."

Hmm. I can't say I disagree with him.

"Why don't I show you a couple of the really good responses," he says.

"Be my guest," I say as I change places with him. "Just read them to me."

"Okay, here's one woman who looks promising. Certainly better than Bitsy. She's more my type—not so *cutesy*."

Describe Yourself
ANSWER: I'm sultry, sensual, and ready to introduce
you to my special brand of love. I've been extremely
lucky so far in my choice of men—the Greek god
type has always been attracted to me, and I'm sure
you will be no exception. I will know your every
need.

"See, Ruby, this woman is a fantasy of mine—someone who'd be all over me and I wouldn't have to do much."

I'm not sure I want to be this close to Kevin's fantasy life, but what the hell. I can't leave him in this wonder world without some healthy hints—kind of like an Héloïse of broadband.

"Uh, Kevin, you should know right off that if all these gods are surrounding this woman, how does she have the time to seduce you?"

"Well, she is a little overt. I don't like women who come on too strong. This is why it's scary. But she's not all about sex—she's very smart. Listen to this:

What More You Should Know About Me
ANSWER: Warning—don't respond to this ad if you're
not willing to ferret out all my brainteasers—this will
indicate whether your level of intelligence matches
mine. Prepare to be bombarded by questions as to
your hopefully esoteric tastes in literature, film, music,
drama, and TV. Can you keep up with me on the
cleverness level?

"See, Ruby? She must have quite an intelligence quotient."
"I'd say she rates pretty high on the dominatrix scale, too.
Do you really want an Essie Sue on hormones?"
"She can't hurt me online. Help me write something
back to her. Who knows—I might be one of those Greek
gods she's talking about."
It's time for me to crawl off Fantasy Island here on
Kevin's mattress and go home to Oy Vey and Chutzpah, who
are suddenly looking healthy, sane, and stable.
"I'm sure you'll come up with something clever, Kevin,"
I say as I avoid the stationary bicycle by the bedroom door
and head back to Watermelon Lane. I think I'll watch a sit-
com Kevin isn't starring in.

16

Carl Harn, my neighbor three doors down, is retrieving his wet morning paper from the grass as Oy Vey and I jog by.

"They didn't double-bag it again, Ruby." He holds up a soggy clump of newsprint, and I try to convey sympathy without having to break my stride. He's used to my multi-tasking, and we both wave as I pass.

"Call Toby," I yell back at him, but I know he won't, which is why our latest news carrier gets away with murder—no one takes the time to complain. I continue my conversation with Oy Vey as we run—since I'm no sprinter, she has no trouble keeping up with me on her three legs.

"This is the day," I tell her. "If Paul won't talk to me about Rose's visit to Ohio, I'm going straight to the source."

Since the look she throws me signals agreement, I speed-dial Rose on my cell phone before I lose my nerve. I'll have a better chance of getting her at the start of the day before we both get busy.

"Hi," I say when she answers, "I hope this isn't too early, but I know it's useless to get you on the phone at night."

"Yeah," she says, "Jackie pretty much takes over with her school friends from the afternoon on. We've thought of getting her an extra line, but it seems indulgent."

"Good luck on holding out," I say, knowing her daughter's powers of persuasion. "I'm calling—"

"I know why, Ruby, and before you start I want to apologize. We were supposed to get together when I came back from visiting Joellyn in Ohio, but I've been so backed up that I knew I couldn't make a definite date with you, and I guess that kept me from calling. Not a pretty picture."

"Look, I don't mind, Rose. I realize what the last few months have been like for you. But how about now? Have you caught up a bit? There are things I need to talk to you about before I leave for Canada."

"Canada? Is the conference coming up already? I can't believe the time's gone by so quickly—thank goodness I backed out early. Another trip is all I need right now. By the way, what's that hissing noise I hear on your end?"

"That's not hissing, it's me panting. I'm trying to talk to you and jog at the same time."

"Do you want to call back?"

Oh, no, you don't. I'm not taking the chance of getting your answering machine one more time.

"No, let's make a date now. Can I come over for a quick cup of coffee later this morning?"

"Everything's a mess here, Ruby. Meet me at Bowery Road Grill."

"What time?"

"Let's make it just before noon—maybe we can get a table then."

"Okay, see you there, Rose. Bye."

Jackpot. I think I caught her by surprise, before she had a chance to make excuses—she's not a morning person, either. And I'll be sure not to answer if she tries to call and cancel. She won't have the nerve to phone the restaurant once I'm there to say she's not coming.

"We did it, Oy Vey," I say as we make it to our front door. "This'll take the pressure off Paul, too."

I'd like to grab another cup of coffee, but I decide to jump in the shower first. I hear the phone ring while I'm still washing my hair, so of course I don't answer it. But then the caller starts the whole ringing cycle again. No one does this but Kevin.

Sure enough, when I check the caller ID later, it displays the Temple Rita number. He can wait until I get my coffee. Kevin's vision of my home life is that I'm never out—that I sit by the phone screening calls, especially his. His response is never to leave a message, but to hang up and dial me again. And again. I guess his theory is that I'll think the call is so urgent I'll pick up.

I settle down in the living room with the morning paper and a mug of Kenya, black. I don't have that much time before meeting Rose for an early lunch, so coffee's all I'm allowing myself. Kevin's at it again, though, and I might as well get this over with.

"Ruby, it's me."

"Yeah, I gathered that. I feel as if we're still having our conversation from last night, Kevin, and that I never went home."

"Well, you could have stayed if you'd wanted."

I'm not about to make the subtle *unsubtle,* so I don't pursue this.

"And this call is about——?"

"There's a complication with my social life, Ruby."

"What's the matter? Is one of your online lovers hopping on a plane for Eternal? Maybe Essie Sue shouldn't make you sound so irresistible, Kevin."

"No, this involves something right here. Remember I told you Bitsy the party planner was ignoring me? Now I find out she still wants to date me."

"Yes, you said you were ambivalent about it, and I was encouraging you. Now that these online women are coming for you out of the ether, I think it's even more important that you do some romancing in real time. Call her for a date."

"That won't be necessary. Adrian, the new temple secretary, tells me Bitsy signed up to be my roommate on the trip to Canada. We're all supposed to double up to save money, and I assumed I'd be rooming with a man."

"I didn't know that—no one's called me about doubling up. But as for Bitsy rooming with you, that's ridiculous. Just call and tell her no. Unless you want to."

"I haven't even gone out with her, Ruby. This is moving too fast."

"Then tell Adrian to take your name off the list as her roommate, and then to call Bitsy and tell her to make other arrangements. Since Bitsy didn't even ask you, you don't owe her a personal call, either. But be sure Adrian lets her know you're not available."

"I knew you'd figure something out, Ruby. Thanks."

"Don't mention it. If that's all you wanted, I have to get off the phone now."

"Uh, Ruby—one more thing you don't seem to know about. I'm not sure how to put this to you."

"Put what?"

"Well, Adrian also said Hal wasn't going along on the Canada trip, and that Essie Sue signed herself up as your roommate."

17

No way am I sleeping in the same room with Essie Sue Margolis. First, I'm shocked that she'd even consider not having a private suite, much less want to room with *moi*. Not that I have much time to obsess about Kevin's call this morning—I'll save that for tonight. At the moment it's all I can do to keep the speedometer down as I try to make it on time to Bowery Road Grill, a favorite of Rose's. The restaurant's located in a small renovated home, and I have to admit it makes up in charm for what it lacks in variety. Of course, I should talk—The Hot Bagel's menu is even more limited, but then, it's a bagelry.

"Ruby, you're the only person who could entice me to lunch in the middle of a week like this," she says as we're led to a table by the window.

"I'm glad I snared you at all," I say. "I thought you'd gone underground."

I'm still somewhat miffed that Rose has ignored me since coming home, busy schedule or not. She was over at my house almost daily after Serena died, and I was glad I could help comfort her. I was the one who gave her the push to visit Serena's sister. Then, after the trip, *nada*. Still, I shouldn't lose patience just yet. She's had a difficult time.

After we order the chef salads they've specialized in since the fifties, I imagine that I'm lighting up a cigarette, and wait for her to say something. It's a trick I learned in my twenties, and it seems to be the precise amount of time needed to give the other person a chance to speak without pressure.

Only she doesn't, and I feel I have to charge in to the rescue.

"So have you felt better or worse since seeing Joellyn?" I say. "I can imagine either."

"I felt better learning more about Serena's life while I was there, but the uncertainty has me on edge now."

"In what way?"

"Well, I guess Paul's told you that the family's having the body exhumed, or trying to."

"I did hear that, but not from Paul, actually."

"I did ask him to keep this quiet, but I suspected he might tell you."

"No, Rose, honey. Anything you decide to share will have to come from you, not Paul—that's just who he is. I was hoping, though, that you *would* want to take me into your confidence. There's no question that the information would be safe with me—I think you know that. On the other hand, if you feel you can't, I'll understand that, too. What I really wanted was for you to tell me directly one way or the other."

"I should have touched base with you, especially after all the help you offered at a time when I needed it. And I do know I can trust you."

"As long as you're sure of that, I'm satisfied."

We eat silently for a minute or two, although I'm mainly just picking at my hard-boiled egg.

"It was just so weird, Ruby. Joellyn and I read Serena's laptop notes together, and it was as if I were eavesdropping on someone I didn't know. It's been embarrassing—I think that's why I found it hard to talk about. But here goes."

"Look, I'm feeling uncomfortable about this, too," I say. "I'm sure the details will all be made public sooner or later, and as long as I know I have your trust, I honestly don't mind not knowing. I feel better just having you explain this much."

"But I don't feel better. I'm feeling frustrated, and I'm beginning to think I really need to tell you everything. Paul suggested that I might want to get your advice because you have this bottom-line way of approaching things. He thought you'd make a good sounding board."

"Really? He didn't say anything to me." That's Paul, of course—he wouldn't. But it would be his way—not only to give Rose an outlet she needed, but to fill me in before the Canada trip.

"So what happened? Were there lots of notes? Emails?"

"You're bottom-lining already, Ruby." Rose is digging into her salad all of a sudden as if she's really enjoying it. Maybe she does need to unload.

"Notes," she says. "Mostly Serena had written notes to herself, like a journal, except that they were written more randomly. She kept them in a file called, of all things, 'Spiritual.' "

"Huh? That doesn't sound like Serena."

"That's what I'm trying to tell you. None of this is like Serena."

"Start from the beginning. These were chronological, I assume. Like a diary?"

"It wasn't a diary. But, yes, we did start reading the earliest notes first, trying to find some unifying factor."

"And did you? Were they especially *spiritual*?"

"They centered around a few subjects—one was a particular person, and the others were about a group and an idea."

"I have the feeling you're dancing around this, Rose. What's the deal?"

"I know I'm not doing a very good job of explaining this. Let me approach it from a different angle."

"That would help," I say. "But get it out."

"Let me put it this way—did you happen to know that Serena was having an affair with André Korman?"

I choke on the anchovies.

"Yeah, I know," Rose says, "it's something of a shock."

"Are you sure?" I say. "She didn't seem the type."

"What's the type when you think about it, Ruby? All kinds of people have affairs, and most of them are big secrets. These files chronicle their meetings, the times she saw him, wanted to see him, didn't see him, didn't want to see him—the whole megillah."

"Do you think Bart knew? Or that it had something to do with their divorcing?"

"I doubt it. Don't forget that André was married at the time and still is—they'd have wanted things private."

"So what *was* the timing, Rose?"

"It didn't happen until after her divorce, although as you say, I guess we can't be absolutely sure that the attraction didn't start while she was still with Bart."

"Bart left Serena, not the other way around, right?"

"Yes, she seemed extremely upset at the time."

"Meaning that this could have been a fling in retaliation, after the fact. Maybe she just wanted Bart to know he didn't wring all the life out of her."

"The reasons don't really matter, though, do they? It happened."

We both take a breather from this shocker—I can hardly eat anything, but Rose is still hungry. Of course, she's used to this news by now and I'm not.

"Hey," I say, giving up on the salad, "tell me what's spiritual about this affair. You did say that's what she named the file, didn't you?"

"That's where it all gets weird. In one of the chapters or sections or whatever they were, Serena talks about the deeper regions of Jewish thought. From what her sister and I could gather, she and André and a couple of other people in the choir had formed a study group."

"You mean Madonna Kaballah or the real thing? Jewish mysticism's also a fad now. Surely it couldn't be the deeper stuff—that's not something to dabble in without direction."

"I have no idea what it was, but I do know André was the initiator and the group was small—all women, I think."

"That figures. Was he sleeping with all of them?"

"I don't get any indication of that. He and Serena were hiding the affair from the group, too, or at least they thought they were."

"I'll bet André would plotz if he knew Serena had written any of this down."

"Yes, his worst nightmare. His wife's inheritance supports their fairly lavish lifestyle, you know—he's certainly not getting rich from the health food store."

"Now I can see why Joellyn's optimistic about getting permission for the exhumation. Although nothing about this file adds up to more than slimy behavior, obviously."

"No, there was one other thing Joellyn and I read that I haven't told you about. It was the last entry Serena made."

We're paying the waiter by this time because I have work to do this afternoon, and Rose waits until he leaves before continuing. Mentally, I'm halfway out the door, so I'm taken totally by surprise.

"She says in this final section, 'They're frightening me.' "

"That's all?"

"Just those words. Maybe someone was threatening her."

"It could be the Kabbalah that was frightening to her, Rose. The mysticism the Kabbalists were exploring was known to be so complex that no one below middle age was allowed to study those subjects. And André isn't exactly a subtle guy. He was probably laying it on just to impress— the scarier the better."

"I hope you're right, Ruby. Because if it wasn't the Kabbalah, then Serena was afraid of something much more concrete."

18

This is my favorite way to talk to Paul when I'm not with him—surrounded by my warm down comforter and three pillows, Oy Vey and Chutzpah sleeping at the foot of the bed. A steaming mug of Constant Comment is on the side table ready for sipping when it cools, and the cordless phone is snuggled under my ear.

"You were a doll to encourage Rose to confide in me," I say.

"I thought it would help her as well as you," he says. "She seemed to be losing her grip for a while after she came back from Ohio. Since I knew it would take time for Joellyn to negotiate her way through the exhumation process, I wasn't sure Rose could hold out."

"I just like the way you do things, honey. You were patient

with both of us and still managed to be professional. I wanted you to know it didn't escape me."

"Thanks. I also had a selfish purpose—now I can kick this back and forth with you. So what did you think?"

"Serena was afraid—there's no doubt about that. And I'm as surprised as Rose was about the affair. Since André's the last person I'd find attractive, I can't be objective about this, but I thought Serena had better taste. On the other hand, he seems pretty confident, so I suppose he must have had some measure of success with women. Do you think he could be that good in bed?"

"I really wouldn't know, honey—I'll leave that speculation to you. I can tell you, though, from years of police experience, that you can never second-guess another person's private obsessions. If Serena was hooked on him, it could have been for reasons only her shrink would understand. Luckily, all we have to do is accept it as fact."

"Well, she makes it perfectly clear, doesn't she? Unless you think there was coercion involved."

"Nope. It was mutual—the notes make that apparent."

"Paul, I have an idea. You probably won't like it."

I taste my tea, and the aroma's fabulous.

"Can you see why you drive me so crazy, Ruby?"

"No."

"It's that way you have of preparing me for something you've already decided to do. If you know I won't like whatever this is, then why not do me a favor and forget it?"

"You mean, not mention it? You said you like me to be up front with you."

"No, I mean forget it, not hide it—you know damn well that's what I meant. Just go my way for once."

"At least listen to my idea, okay? I'm thinking that the

trip will be a great chance for me to get closer to this group. Serena indicated that choir members were involved. We're spending hours on the train trip through the Canadian Rockies, and you know how good I am at this. I promise I'll find out something."

"Yeah, I do know—too good for your *own* good, if past experience is any indicator. This is a closed environment, and it could be dangerous. Serena sensed it, and she was apparently in the in-group. So why would they ever trust you, of all people? You're not even friends with them."

"But I can be. And this isn't the only group on the train. Half the temple leadership is going along, plus others who're headed for the ChoirFest. Hey, did you hear that Essie Sue wants me to room with her? A joke, right?"

"Don't try to distract me. Although if you insist on attending when I'd rather have you stay home, I think it would be perfect to have someone like Essie Sue keeping an eye on you. At least I'd know you couldn't get too far out of her orbit—she wouldn't stand for it."

"You're kidding, right?"

"It depends. Are you determined to go?"

"Yes, and if I'm rooming with the queen of control freaks, how can you expect me to do any infiltrating?"

"That's my bargain. Take it or leave it."

"Or you'll do what?" He's doing a pretty good job of staring me down.

"I'm worried about you. And if you disregard that, then what do I mean to you anyway? I'm going to be seriously pissed, just when I thought we were getting somewhere in this relationship."

"Okay, I hear you. I'll consider it, but only after I set up some house rules with Essie Sue."

"That's your problem—I'm sure you'll deal with it. And I can breathe easier because she's the most intrusive person I've ever met. There's not too much you can do that she won't keep an eye on."

"Yeah, thanks for that."

"Remember this, Ruby—none of these people is guilty of anything. The facts are now that Serena Salit had a heart attack. She could have been frightened for any number of reasons—the notebook doesn't tell us anything concrete. I just have suspicions."

"All the more reason not to be anxious about my traveling with them, honey—they're innocent, at least for now. Who knows? What I find out could ultimately be helpful. And I swear to you I won't cross the line."

"I'm holding you to that promise. And while you're at it, don't cross any train tracks, either."

19

This Canadian vacation is looking more and more unattractive to me, but now I have something besides a pleasure trip to consider. I wonder if anyone other than André knows about the affair with Serena. And if he's successfully hidden all this, what else could he be hiding? I want a good look at him this afternoon when Essie Sue entertains the latke sale committee at her house for the send-off meeting.

For once, I'm glad I promised to come early and help set up. I need more than a few words with my would-be roommate, and I'm still planning what to say as I pull into her circular driveway.

"Wipe your feet, Ruby—the gardener spilled some topsoil he was carrying onto the brickwork."

"I don't see a thing, Essie Sue," I say as I get out of the

car. "I'll bet you cleaned up after him on your hands and knees."

"No, Hal did. I supervised. We decided it wasn't worth a dry-cleaning bill for what I was wearing."

"That's the royal *we* my wife is using," Hal says as he holds the front door open for me.

"What did you have on?" I ask her.

"Oh, just my blue jeans."

"But she doesn't wash her designer jeans," Hal says, "she takes them to the Harry Winston of cleaners, Precious Objects on Oak Street. Their bills have been known to exceed the retail price, so I wasn't taking any chances. What are my knees worth, compared to that?"

"You're the one who's priceless, Hal—I just hope she knows that. So why aren't you joining her for the choir adventure?"

"You mean why are you privileged to take my place? I have a golf tournament at the club and I don't want to miss it."

They lead me into the entryway, where I'm expected to wipe my feet once again on a small Oriental rug.

The objects in the Margolis home sparkle in a way I've never seen duplicated, not even in the best museums. And why not—they don't have the cleaning staff she does.

The house is much too huge for the two of them, or anyone else, for that matter. I'm always curious to see where her partygoers will tuck themselves away. People usually prefer to bunch up at parties, and since this home is so uncozy, the crowd comforts itself by hanging around the breakfast bar while ignoring the enormous baronial space in the living room. Essie Sue calls it the great room, of course—one of those pretentious real estate terms that only serves to make hapless guests feel even more alienated. I never know whether to expect wild boar roasting in the enormous fireplace or Knights Templar jousting on the faux-stone floors.

Needless to say, I can't wait for the arrival of Eternal's answer to a cult, André and company. To my surprise, he's already here, and Essie Sue has him in tow.

"You've shaved off your mustache," I blurt out as I see him. The truth is that he's changed his appearance altogether. He's swapped the Dapper Dan look for New York black, complete with shirttail hanging out and red wristband. No more shirt, tie, and jacket. I'm looking for a tattoo to complete the look, and I find it—a tiny *chai* on his pinkie finger instead of the gold ring he used to wear. Ouch—I can feel how much a tattoo on that finger must have hurt.

"The mustache was getting old," he says, continuing his animated conversation with Essie Sue. André's never had much to say to me, now that I think of it.

"Doesn't he look stylish, Ruby?" Essie Sue says. "He's the essence of a health food store entrepreneur. Ruby's lifestyle's unhealthy, André—tell her what she should be supplementing, now that ephedra's passé."

"No, thanks—I don't supplement, Essie Sue," I say. "I never liked the idea of my bladder being richer than I am."

"That's nonsense." André shoots me a look that could tattoo my retina. "It's so nineties to think a handful of vitamins is going to harm you. I ingest twenty-five pills a day, and I'm bursting with energy."

"Bursting with something," I say. "And besides, you get yours wholesale."

"She has a point there, André," Essie Sue says. She's not coming to my rescue, she's sniffing out a possible discount, having never met a bargain she didn't pursue. "How about ten percent for friendship? After all, I appointed you choir director."

"I'm just acting director, Essie Sue. I've always told you I'm an artist, not an administrator," he says over his shoulder as he makes an escape I need to pay attention to. Anyone who can slip away from Essie Sue that skillfully gets my attention.

"I'll work on his wife, Sara," Essie Sue says. "She's over there talking to Irene Cohn."

Sara looks as happy to be conversing with Irene as I do with Essie Sue—she's perched on one of the mammoth ottomans in the great room while Irene hovers over her. Since her husband has given us the slip, I'm thinking of joining their little twosome as soon as Essie Sue's diverted by new arrivals.

I might as well have a head start on getting to know Serena's colleagues better. I also hate to begin a trip without anyone I'm close to, and these choir members aren't people I can count on as friends. Just my luck Rose isn't going along this time. She says the stay in Ohio was all the vacation she could squeeze in right now.

"Ruby—how's it going?"

Dr. Bart Goldman, Serena's ex, is blocking my path to the ottoman.

"Hi, Bart—I was just going over to talk to Irene and Sara. Want to join me?"

"I didn't know you were friendly with them." He seems surprised.

"I'm not, but I decided I'd better be if we'll be traveling together."

"Well, good luck—I find both of them pretty standoffish. I think I'll pass."

"Hey, I definitely didn't mean to blow you off, Bart—I've known you longer than any of them. Let's go get something to drink on the patio and catch up."

We try sangria from a big pitcher on the umbrella table, and it's not bad for an Essie Sue concoction—at least, if you're not looking for the alcohol. I think she's used a twenty-to-one formula.

"Too bad she decided to go themeless," Bart says. "It's not like her. I was hoping for Canadian Club to go along with the travel topic."

I didn't remember Bart had a sense of humor—maybe he'll be fun to hang out with on the trip. We sit on a stone bench and people-watch.

"How are *you* doing?" I ask. "It must be difficult to have just finished mourning the end of your marriage and then be hit with Serena's unexpected death. Kind of a double grieving process."

"You aren't kidding—it's rough. And none of my friends even *gets* this, Ruby. You're the only person who's been able to articulate it. I feel out in limbo trying to come to grips with everything."

"I'm unfortunately well versed in the variations of grief," I say, "and it's a skill I could have done without. But I know it when I see it."

"If we drink any more of this sangria," he says, "we'll mope our way into a crying jag."

"No way we should let that happen, Bart. I'm glad you're able to get away for the trip. A change of scenery might help."

Oy. I can't get the affair between Serena and André out of my mind, and it's killing me not to have any idea if Bart knew about it. Their being lovers could have occurred after Serena's divorce or been the catalyst for it.

"There's André," I say. "Shall we call him over?"

"Sure."

There's none of the reticence Bart showed with André's wife or with Irene Cohn—maybe he's just more comfortable with another man. It's very weird, though, to think I know a secret Bart could be unaware of. But of course, André knows it all too well.

"Hey, André," I say. "How about joining us?"

He looks over at us and literally recoils. This is very odd, considering how often he must have rehearsed choir programs with Bart over the last few months as Serena's lover. I have no idea what's so different today—he should feel more comfortable with Bart, not less, now that the affair is a thing of the past. But he's definitely nervous, or down, or something.

André's obviously also feeling trapped—there's no reason *not* to talk to us, so he comes over, plastering a politician's smile on his face.

"Hi," he says to us. "I didn't ask you before, Ruby—are you excited about the trip?"

"Once I get out of town I might be. The week before a vacation is hellish—too much doubling up to do at work."

"I know what that's like. How are you, Bart? After everything, I mean."

"You mean Serena's death?" Bart says. "Still trying to work it all out in my head, not to mention my gut."

"If you need building up, drop by the store. We have lots of remedies for stress."

Strange answer, considering that Bart, AKA Dr. Goldman, knows quite a bit about remedies himself. Fortunately for him, he doesn't have to remind André of that, since Kevin suddenly backs into our little group with the subtlety of a Mack truck.

"Somebody pushed me," he says, making a feeble attempt to pick up the chips he made Bart drop on the highly polished floor. "Your wife says she's not going along on the trip, André," he adds.

"Sara's a bit undecided right now, but she'll end up joining us."

"Nope. Sara just told us she won't be there, so she and Essie Sue revised the list." Kevin turns around. "Right, Essie Sue?"

"Absolutely correct, Rabbi." Essie Sue's looming presence is always a bit jarring, and never more so than when she can catch someone off guard.

"Say hello to your new roommate, André," Essie Sue says. "You'll have to be on your best behavior with the rabbi in the next bed."

20

I'm still chuckling over Sara's coup when Kevin picks me up
to go to the airport. Inviting the rabbi to move in when you
can't be there is one way to make sure your philandering
hubby doesn't substitute another woman's nightie for yours
on the other side of the bed. I'm sure Sara goes along on
most of these trips simply to keep André from adding a new
conquest to his list. Not that she's been very successful at it
so far. But I'd call this a very creative attempt.

I don't know who's going to have a more delightful
time—me with Essie Sue, or André with Kevin. I do know
which of our roommates can more easily be given the slip,
though, and I'm sure André's already working on opportunities to practice his seduction techniques away from his
train cabin or hotel room.

My own roommate presents a much more difficult challenge. I went along with this because Paul obviously wants me reined in, and isn't ready to let me be a part of the investigation if I don't allay his fears about my safety. I'll live with Essie Sue because I have to, and because I don't intend to spend any time in the room other than the six or seven hours it takes to sleep. Aside from that, I'll have many opportunities to mix with other people and sniff out what's going on.

"Ruby, do you think I still have a chance with Bitsy now that I'm not rooming with her?" Kevin asks me as he weaves in and out of morning rush hour traffic.

"Depends on what kind of chance you're talking about. Last time we spoke, you were put off by her. Do you want to make a move on her or not? If so, I'm sure you'll have time to do that."

"I don't mean anything specific, Ruby. I just want to get to know her better, and to see what she's like. I don't want her to drop me before we even get started."

"Knowing Bitsy, and seeing her eye you like red meat, I don't think you need to worry that nothing will happen, Kevin. You might end up dealing with too much, not too little."

"How about you, Ruby? Essie Sue will make you her unofficial assistant, whether you want to or not. And I'll bet she'll want to have pajama parties in the room."

"Don't worry—I'm not attending any pajama party with her that doesn't include at least three other people."

"You can't avoid talking in bed at night, or in the morning."

"I don't worry about mornings—I'm a night person, and usually so bleary-eyed when I wake up that I can't see or hear, much less talk. She can ramble on all she wants—it won't get through to me. And as for any chummy late-night conversations, I can pretend with the best of them. So in the morning I'll really sleep, and in the evening, I'll fake it."

"Are you sorry Paul's not coming along with the choir group?"

"Well, we could have fun, and maybe even do some hiking around Banff. But who knows? Maybe I'll meet some sexy Canadian when I'm up there."

"You're kidding, right? I thought you were taken."

Oy. I don't want Kevin to think I'm available to him, but on the other hand, Paul and I have no commitments, and I think I'm too young not to ever indulge my roving eye again. If not now, when? Surely not if Paul and I do become more serious—then it'll be too late.

"Paul's kind of my main man, Kevin, so in that sense, I'm taken."

Hmm . . . I don't like the sound of that. Actually, there's no way to explain my position— especially since I'm not sure what it is myself. I'd better reroute this conversation.

"So let's get back to you, Kevin. Are you going to try to meet any Canadian women, or are you mostly interested in Bitsy?"

Kevin's neck seems to sink down inside his woolen scarf. He's bundled up for Canada in January, not late May.

"Maybe I should be like you, Ruby, and keep my options open. There's one difference between us, though—Paul's back home, and Bitsy's right here."

"And after you in a big way?"

"I think so."

"See where it goes. Bitsy might have her eyes open, too."

Kevin and I take the shuttle from the long-term parking area to the terminal—I'd have liked to be dropped off with the baggage and let him do the parking, but he got nervous at all the security arrangements and was afraid he couldn't find me. I gave in—when Kevin's stressed, it's catching.

We go to our gate and find the usual uproar when Essie Sue's in charge. Hard to believe, but she's trying to separate us into boys' and girls' lines.

"Why?" I ask, wondering why no one else has inquired.

"It's easier to count by gender," she says, "and people are more well behaved."

"If they're in second grade," I say. "Do you see any progress here? No one's paying the least bit of attention."

"It could be worse the other way, Ruby. Help me count heads."

"Let the airline attendants do that. We can't delay the plane for latecomers, anyway."

"The rabbi's here and is going to give a short prayer for a safe trip," she yells over the chatter.

That's obviously news to Kevin, but it does stop the conversation.

He looks at me with the usual deer-in-the-headlights panic.

"How about 'bless you and keep you'—that's short and sweet," I whisper.

It's also something he knows by heart, so we get a quick benediction and Kevin earns a nod from Essie Sue.

"I owe you," he says.

I'd be a rich woman if I had a nickel for every time I've heard that one.

I'm in a window seat beside Kevin, which is fine with me—I don't have to be on with him. I'm wondering who'll take the aisle seat, when Bitsy pops down next to him. Ha— it'd be interesting to know who she had to bribe to get hold of that prized position.

"What a surprise finding you both here," she says sweetly.

"It's a miracle," I whisper to Kevin, and then realize that he actually thinks so.

"Isn't this amazing, Ruby?" he says, apparently extremely happy to help Bitsy hold her armload of Baggies while she fastens her seat belt.

"What are all these?" I ask while she takes them back.

"Two are for my supplements to prevent jet lag, one each with baby carrots, cherry tomatoes, and diet French for dipping, and three more for mascara, liner, and blush. Plus Canadian coins that are too heavy for my wallet, and cotton pads moistened with lotion to rest my eyelids. Plus this teeny copy of the Constitution."

Kevin seems truly fascinated, while I'm only confused, not that it's any of my business.

"Uh—I thought you might have a makeup bag for some of those," I say.

"I sent that along ahead—these are things I'll need on the plane, and they're transparent for the inspectors. I like to be prepared for everything, although they confiscated my fingernail scissors. I'd been told that if they weren't hidden, you could take them on board."

I don't dare ask who told her that one, or more important, why she included the last Baggie. But Kevin does.

"Why that?" he says, pointing at the Baggie containing the Constitution.

"When you're traveling out of the country, who knows when you'll need a copy?" she says. "It could save you from being thrown in jail or something."

I consider reminding her that outside our borders the book means nothing, but I let it go.

"I hear Barbara Jordan always did that," Kevin says. "See,

Ruby?" He gives me a nudge with his elbow. I think he's trying to tell me she's just moved up a notch on the worthiness
scale.

I decide on the spot to give these two a chance to dip
some baby carrots together, so I propel myself across their
laps and take a walk down the aisle for a bathroom break
before the beverage cart blocks the way. Irene is happily
ensconced in a two-seater next to André, with no sign of his
wife, Sara, who must not have changed her mind. Essie Sue's
also in the aisle, keeping several choir members from reading their paperbacks.

"I'm just energizing the group," she tells me. "Maybe I'll
go back and talk to the rabbi."

"He's engrossed in conversation with Bitsy," I say. "Give
them a chance to talk, Essie Sue."

"I thought that might be a good match," she says, "but
now I'm not so sure. Who knows if she's prepared to be a
clergy wife?"

"Who ever is?" I say. "And it's beside the point—let him
have a little fun. Why does everyone have to be a potential
spouse?"

"Because he's a rabbi, Ruby—you know that. They can't
fool around."

"But he gets to date someone without marrying them,
right?"

"Okay, I'll leave them alone. But you're responsible to
see that they don't go too far."

"I have to go to the bathroom now."

I wouldn't give Essie Sue the satisfaction, but I'm leery of
little Bitsy, too. That gleam in her eye is a bit too steely for
me. But that doesn't mean Kevin needs tracking like a
teenager.

I'm waiting at the bathroom door when Bart Goldman comes out and almost slams into me. He takes a step back when he sees me.

"I didn't mean to surprise you," I say. "You look shocked."

"No, no—I'm okay. I mean, I'm just a little spaced out from the trip."

None of what he says makes much sense—especially since the trip's hardly started. But one thing's for sure—Bart's definitely groggy. Wonder what he's on?

21

I crawl back to my window seat, with no help whatsoever from Kevin and Bitsy, who won't even bend their knees sideways to let me pass. I get my revenge, though, when I have to step on their feet in order to wedge my body through. My big hurry is to make sure that I won't miss flying over the snow-topped Mount Ranier on our way to the Seattle-Tacoma airport. I'm barely seated when there it is, peeking out of the clouds like a giant iced doughnut gleaming in the sunlight. I poke at Kevin so that he and Bitsy can see, but their conversation takes precedence.

I've never understood how the flying public could possibly be so blasé about soaring thirty thousand feet above the earth. Forget that my generation's been airborne since childhood—familiarity's no excuse for sticking your nose in a book and ignoring a cotton-cloud carpet stretching beneath you for miles, or the course of a river cutting a state in half, or starlike city lights making it seem as if the plane's flying upside down.

"Can you believe how Ranier is suddenly just *there?*" I say.

"I hope I get my kosher meal," Bitsy answers. "If you're not paying attention, someone else grabs it."

So she *is* paying attention to something.

"I didn't know you kept kosher," Kevin says.

"I don't. My travel agent put me on to it. You get fewer carbs with a kosher meal—they give you a lot of brisket instead of the Mexicali Enchiladas. You should try it, Rabbi."

Odd, but in Bitsy-world it seems perfectly plausible to explain to the rabbi why he should get a kosher plate. Mine is not to reason why, but they've missed Mount Ranier and we're now circling Sea-Tac, so I'm pretty sure this means the kosher meal is out.

We do get fed, for some reason, on the short flight from Seattle to Vancouver. We're treated to a bistro bag containing a dry turkey sandwich and a bottle of water. The flight attendant is also passing around bags of baked chips made specially for the airline. Fortunately, the chips on planes are unknown in real life—they exist only in a rarified atmosphere. Even if I wanted mine, I don't get the chance.

"People, do not eat those chips."

Essie Sue is following the attendant down the aisle, gathering the bags from our collective laps as quickly as they're given to us.

"We need the chips for our cocktail party on the train," she says, forcing us to toss our goodies into a large brown paper Kroger bag. "Remember, we were unable to raise the

funds for this choir trip, and most of you are having to subsidize our efforts."

Not subsidize—*pay for.* And now she can't even throw us
a complimentary party.

"Anyone purchasing those convenient little alcoholic
beverages is asked to either save them or to buy an extra
bottle for our event. It's all for a good cause."

The flight attendant is being a pretty good sport about
this—either that, or she's already been intimidated. She
does draw the line, however, when Essie Sue tries to collect
from the other passengers. Luckily, we're about to land, and
we're all called to our seats.

The Vancouver airport at uninhabited Sea Island looks
like a piece of the planet Mars—it exists only as a recepta-
cle for planes. It is, though, the only uninteresting bit of
scenery in the entire vicinity. To me, Vancouver is a marvel
of the universe, a jewel of a city where beaches and mountains are within walking distance of the world's most diverse
and cosmopolitan population. I adore the place, and I'm just
sorry we're only using it as a stopover.

When we arrive at our hotel in downtown Vancouver,
I'm so glad to stretch my legs and get away from Kevin's and
Bitsy's idea of flirtatious banter that I forget the ordeal to
come. Not for long, though—Essie Sue has already registered for our double room and wrangled an upgrade as the
group leader. I don't remember anyone electing her group
leader, but I'm not about to complain when I hear we're in
a one-bedroom suite.

"I'll take the living room," I say.

"Don't be silly, Ruby—you certainly don't want to give
up one of our two queen-size beds for a pullout sofa in the
living room, do you?"

"Uh-huh. Sure do."

"I'm sure I'll be scheduling important meetings in the living room—after all, that's why I needed the upgrade."

"I can sleep through meetings," I say. "No problem."

She's not kidding—after an unbelievable dinner of broiled halibut in a restaurant next door to the hotel, she's buttonholed me, Kevin, Bitsy, and André for a "strategy" meeting in our suite.

I've had quite enough of Kevin and Bitsy for one day, and I obviously can't get away from my roomie, but I am curious about André Korman. The rest of us are pretty droopy, but the only way I can describe him is that he looks as if he were a woman who just put on fresh makeup. That's as far as the analogy goes, but it's accurate—this is a guy who's always on. It's apparent that he's flattered to be included, which already says a lot about him, in my opinion.

As for me, I'm angling for a quick getaway after a brief period of polite hostessing at the strategy meeting, so I guess I won't have much time to observe André—there'll be other opportunities. Some of us are getting together in an hour for a long walk along Hornby Street, and I don't want to miss that.

"Remember, Essie Sue, I only have an hour for this meeting," I say while we're serving our guests diet sodas from the minibar. "I know how your get-togethers can expand."

"Fine, Ruby, although I don't know why you're so anxious to sightsee tonight. We have plenty of gorgeous scenery to enjoy on the train trip through the Rockies."

"Just because," I say. I don't intend to waste my energy dragging out every discussion with her. Although I'm biting my tongue as I watch her divide each can into two servings.

"We have to conserve, people," she announces to Kevin,

Bitsy, and André. "I haven't had a chance to get to a grocery store yet, and these minibar refreshments are expensive."

"Skip mine," I say. "I'm going out later."

"I already skipped yours, Ruby," she says. "This way there'll only be four of us sharing the two cans."

Why do I bother?

Kevin drinks his glass in one gulp. "Okay, Essie Sue, what do we have to talk about?" he says. He seems emboldened with Bitsy at his side, and I'm thinking maybe I'm not the only one who has plans.

Essie Sue's about to answer Kevin, when André upstages her.

"I'm surprised at you, Rabbi," he says. "Since Essie Sue has been kind enough to come along on the trip to help organize us, it's only natural that she'd have lots of strategy to discuss. We should give her our respect."

Whoa—this guy's just pulled off a triple-header. He's managed to make Kevin look bad, flatter Essie Sue, and give lip service to the respect she never gets, all in one swoop. I think I've observed all I need to.

"Why, aren't you sweet," she says. "How nice to be appreciated for a change, and from a most unlikely source."

Ha—nobody gets a real break with Essie Sue, but André chooses not to notice the small slur amid the faint praise. He manages a look of modest adoration. Yep, he's a player.

Just as the atmosphere is getting a bit too honeyed for my taste, my cell phone rings. I look to see that it's Paul calling. Goody—a call I've wanted, *plus* an excuse to go in the other room.

Essie Sue's way ahead of me.

"Take your call later, Ruby. This is important, and you're leaving early, besides."

"Excuse me, everyone, I'm going in the other room to take this," I say.

"But that's my bedroom," Essie Sue says. "You're sleeping here in the living room, remember?"

"So are you taking them all into your room?" I say, directing a fast "Hi, hold on" into the phone. "Tell me quick, Essie Sue, so I'll know where to go for the phone call."

"Go," she says, waving her hand toward the bedroom.

There's a chair in her bedroom, and it's far away from the door, so I take that for maximum privacy. Besides, I don't dare jump on her bed—too much fallout even for me to handle.

"Hi, babe," I say, "sorry for the wait. I'm so glad you called."

"Me, too," Paul says. "How was the flight?"

"I sat by Kevin and Bitsy," I tell him. "That should say it all."

"My sympathy. Will you be in twin beds with Essie Sue tonight?"

"No, I'm sleeping on the pullout in the living room—we'll be up close and personal on the train far too much as it is. Hey, I miss you. But your call is getting me out of a meeting here in the suite. I'm holed up in Essie Sue's bedroom while she's boring—uh, entertaining—André, Kevin, and Bitsy."

"They're all in the living room?"

"Yeah. Why?"

"Can you talk, honey?"

"Of course. I'm talking now, right? If you mean how private is this, I think it's okay. I'm sitting across the room away from the living area, and I can see the door from here, so no one can surprise me. Don't *you* be surprised, though, if Essie Sue pops in here every five minutes to get me off the phone."

"Ruby, try to keep your voice low, and mostly listen—which means I'll do the talking, okay?"

"Sure. What's the matter? Are you all right?"

"I'm fine except for not liking it that you're in another country."

"A friendly one, though. And adjacent."

"Ha."

"Okay, not funny," I say. "What's up?"

"Right after you flew out of here, I got a call from Serena's sister, Joellyn, in Ohio. Serena's body was reexamined and the lab results just came in. She didn't die of a heart attack."

"You're kidding. Really? So Joellyn's ESP was right on, huh?"

"Dead on, excuse the pun."

"What was—uh-oh—hold on," I say.

If you can slam open a door in the same way you can slam it shut, then Essie Sue does it. I'm glad I warned Paul.

"Ruby, I know you're talking to that policeman—he's the only one who'd keep you this long."

"Believe it or not, I have quite a few other friends who're capable of burning up the wires," I say. "Do I have to give you a list of my incoming calls just because we're rooming together?"

"But we need you in the meeting."

"I'll be there as soon as I can."

"Well, you're not leaving here for that walk with the others," she says. "You owe me some time."

"We'll discuss it later," I say, realizing that she's already yelled out that I'm talking to the policeman.

"Come on, Ruby."

"Out, Essie Sue. And close the door."

"She just flounced out," I tell Paul. "I guess you heard that she told everyone it was you on the phone."

"Yeah, but you didn't confirm it. Good thinking."

"I should have waited to take this call when I was out on my walk later," I say. "It's just that I wanted to talk to you."

"You didn't know the nature of the call, hon. Don't worry about it. No one heard us."

"Thank goodness for cells—I'd never trust her not to pick up the extension if you'd called the room."

"This can wait an hour," Paul says, "but I wanted you to know ASAP. Besides, how do you know you'll have privacy stepping away from a group of people?"

"I don't, except for the fact that those people don't include Essie Sue. Or André, Kevin, or Bitsy, for that matter. But you're not stopping now."

"No, not with your curiosity," he says. "You'd never let me get away with it."

"So what killed her?" I whisper.

"It hasn't been identified yet. But they found a toxic substance in the body, even though it certainly wasn't apparent at first."

"How could someone have poisoned her with so many people around?" I say.

"Well, she probably ate something—all of you were trying out those latkes, right? And she was backstage for a few minutes before the performance. There were opportunities—we just don't know how it was done yet."

"Wow. I'm still floored. Rose must be plotzing. Not to mention Joellyn. Did either of them have any idea what might have happened, or when it happened?"

"No. Joellyn just learned about it a few hours ago, and she called Rose, and then me."

"Did you talk to Rose?"

"No, she wasn't home. Joellyn said they were both upset, of course—this was something they'd dreaded ever since Joellyn decided to have the body exhumed."

"What will you do now?"

"Talk to everyone again in light of what's happened, and hold tight to see what substance is identified."

"I'm assuming you don't want anyone here to know yet," I say.

"True—I don't want you saying anything, for your own safety as well as for other considerations. But I'm not so sure we'll have the luxury of keeping this information confidential. I have no idea if Rose has called anyone there, and Bart keeps in touch with Joellyn—he might have already emailed her from the road. My guess is that people do know about this procedure. And once I start reinterviewing, it's not going to be a secret for long. The papers'll get it, too."

"So what should I do if someone asks me?"

"I'd feign ignorance. They have no way of knowing what I've told you."

"They'll know."

"So what? Pretend you don't know and you won't have to discuss it."

"It'll be interesting, though, to see who does hear about it here."

"Ruby, there's something I haven't said."

"Will I like it?"

"No. I want you to come home. Think of some excuse."

"Don't be silly—I'm in no danger."

"If someone involved decides you might be watching or listening on my behalf, it won't be safe for you."

"You mean spying? Why can't I do that? It's the perfect

time, since you can't be here. And everyone knows I'm a snoop—they'll expect it of me."

"We're in the early stages of this investigation, Ruby, and I don't even know what we're dealing with. I want you home."

"Essie Sue's coming in again," I say. "And I think my battery's running out, too. I'll get back to you later."

Talk about self-sabotage. I didn't even get to hear any sweet nothings from my sweetie. But hey, I had no choice. No way am I leaving now.

22

Before I go back into the living area I make a quick call to my friend Elizabeth's room. She's the one who organized the after-dinner walk tonight.

No answer—I *knew* this would happen. We planned to meet in the lobby and take along anyone who showed up—it's easier not to have to keep up with people. Since they all know I'm rooming with Essie Sue, I guess they figured I got stuck. Or worse, that she'd show up down in the lobby with me. I don't blame them for not waiting. I know I could take off and try to catch up with them, but it's been a while, and they could be blocks away by now.

It was worth skipping the walk to talk to Paul—I miss him. But certainly not enough to go home. He should know me better than that by now. This trip has been planned for months, so I have the perfect excuse to be present, and no one could suspect I'm here for any other purpose than to attend the ChoirFest. What more could I want than to have most of the choir here? People are usually relaxed on a trip, and conversations can flow easily. I'm certainly going to be Miss Congeniality if it'll help get information.

The thought of it is killing me, but I think my best bet is to go back and be a part of the meeting. If Kevin and Bitsy decide to go off by themselves, it'll be a good idea to talk to André with Essie Sue as a buffer. Maybe he'll be so busy impressing *her* that he won't notice I'm paying attention.

Essie Sue opens the bedroom door again and makes things easy for me.

"Ruby, where are you? You promised to meet with us, and now you're taking advantage of my good nature."

"You're absolutely right," I say. "I'm really sorry, folks— I didn't know I'd be on the phone so long. Since I haven't been part of the meeting at all, I'll stay here instead of joining the group downstairs."

Kevin gives me a quick look. If he knew how to raise an eyebrow, I'm sure this would be the time to do it, but that's not part of his repertoire. Fortunately, he's the only one in the group who knows me well enough to question my giving up a good time for an idiotic meeting. I owe him one for not blurting out anything.

André pats the seat beside him on the sofa, and I accept.

"Thanks," I say, smiling in the grateful way he'd expect from any woman who's the recipient of his generosity.

My response hits its mark. "You know, Ruby," he says, "you and I don't know each other very well. We should do something about that."

I give another grateful smile. Wish I could blush, but I'm

as helpless at that as Kevin is with an eyebrow raise. Fortunately, André's the type of guy who automatically fills in the blanks in his favor.

"I understand you're responsible for organizing the Eternal contingent here," I say. "Good job."

I think I'll stop after this—this man's wife isn't here, and he's notorious for hitting on anything that moves. That's not the way I want to extract any goodies from him.

"Okay, you two—make your small talk later," Essie Sue says, seeming not altogether displeased. Since I'm sure she's not interested in fixing me up with a married man, I can only surmise she's just relieved at my sudden compliance tonight.

"We're planning for our hospitality when we meet the other choir organizations," she says. "Everyone thought my plan for a cocktail party on the tour train would be fun."

Ha—no naysayers in this crowd; I'm sure she can get whatever she wants.

"We board in the morning," she says, "so the event could take place halfway through the afternoon. I'm counting on each of you to be a cohost."

"What are we serving besides the drinks and snacks you confiscated from the plane?" I ask. "We'll have to hit a grocery store before we board the train, and that's not always easy in the middle of downtown."

"This was all discussed while you were on the phone, Ruby," Essie Sue says.

"Yeah, who was that you were talking to?" Kevin asks.

He would.

"A couple of people, actually," I say. "Just answering messages and checking in to let people know I'd arrived. I do have business commitments back home."

"But which one called you?" Bitsy says. "Was it the policeman?"

I ignore that, but she's not deterred. "Ruby's been going out with a policeman," she explains to André.

He raises both eyebrows—a move that's definitely in *his* repertoire if not in Kevin's. "A little bit of gossip I'd not heard," he says.

Yuck. Although maybe it'll keep me off his hit list.

"Which policeman?" André says.

"Lieutenant Paul Lundy. I've known him for years." Essie Sue can't stand losing control of the conversation for more than a minute, so I'm not surprised she's plunged in.

"I know him, too," André says. "He's the one who questioned some of us the day Serena had the heart attack."

"Thank goodness they didn't take our prints," Bitsy says. "I was fingerprinted once and they made me cut two of my beautiful long nails—they kept sliding on the ink. Can you believe it?"

"They must have been awfully long," I say, grabbing on to any trivia I can to keep the focus off Paul and me. If André knows about any suspicions of murder, he's certainly not showing it—he's being a regular Mr. Casual. But if I thought he was diverted, I was wrong.

"So, Ruby," André says, "is your relationship with Lieutenant Lundy serious?"

"I'm not serious about anyone," I say, immediately making myself fair game again, I guess.

"Well, I thought it was serious," Kevin says. "He's the only one you've been seeing since you broke up with Ed Levinger."

I can see André's face going into questioning mode already.

"Hey, Essie Sue," I say, "I thought this was supposed to be

such an important meeting. Am I the subject, or do you have other things to deliberate?"

"You're right, Ruby," Essie Sue says, "but we still want to know if it was Paul who called you. If so, then he sounds like a boyfriend to me."

"Okay, I'm dating him and he called," I say. Better to give in on that point than to let them know the call was professional—at least in part. "I'm assuming I'm not required to report our conversation," I say, "and don't you think this is getting a bit intrusive even for you, Essie Sue?"

Never one to apologize, she gives me a nod. "Back to business," she says. "I want our group to wear name tags so that the other choirs can know us immediately. I have the blanks here," she says as she dumps a bagful on the coffee table for us to fill out.

It takes about fifteen minutes for me to do my share, and then I figure the others might be back from their walk and wandering around in the lobby. I'll try to talk to André on the train tomorrow—Bitsy and Kevin don't seem to be leaving, and I could be stuck here all night if I don't make my move now.

"Bye, all," I say, heading for the door, "have to meet some people."

"But we have more to do," Essie Sue says, "and after that I thought you and I could watch TV in our pajamas like I do with Hal."

"Why don't you call him?" I suggest as I leave. Playing Hal to Essie Sue is not my idea of fun on my only night in Vancouver. Maybe she'll be asleep by the time I get back.

23

I see Bart Goldman as I get off the elevator.

"Are you heading upstairs?" I say.

"Yeah. I thought you were going on the walk with us," he says.

"It's a long story," I say. "Where are the others?"

"Most of them were tired and already went up to their rooms. I was thinking of doing something, but most of these people in the lobby are strangers to me."

"Doesn't say much for the party spirit in our group, does it? Let's have a drink on our own," I say.

"Okay, how about one of these sofas right here? You don't even have to go into the cocktail lounge."

"You know, Bart, I hate sticking to the hotel. Let's at least go across the street. I saw lots of places over there this afternoon."

My main worry is that Essie Sue will come down here looking for me, so I hurry us out the revolving doors to safety. Besides, I really do prefer finding nightspots outside the hotel. Dr. Bart Goldman might not be my choice to roam the town with, but we can at least explore something other than the lobby for our drink.

There is indeed a nice pubby place up the block, complete with a French Canadian chanteuse at the piano. To me, any love song in French is ten times more erotic than one in English, regardless of how good the singer is. This one isn't bad at all. And I can see what's up with Bart while I'm at it. Paul would be proud of me—once he got over my listening to love songs over drinks with another man. But come on—it's only Bart. Although we do order some very dusky cognac together.

After I indulge myself for a few minutes pretending Bart is Paul, I get the guilts and try to make conversation.

"How're you doing?" I ask. "I guess this is your first trip in a while."

"Yeah, first since Serena and I divorced, as a matter of fact. I just hadn't felt like going anywhere, and then after she died, I had even less energy for it."

I want to ask if he's been in touch with her sister, but I hold off. Although we really don't have that much in common other than Serena, so I figure he'll get around to it himself if I'm patient. Of course, I'm not even convinced of the cliché that patience is a virtue, and if it is, it's certainly not my virtue.

"Have you thought about dating yet?" I say, and then am instantly sorry. He's going to think *I'm* interested, when I'm really just fishing for conversation. Bart's one of those guys who's not objectionable, but that's the sexiest thing you can say about him. Though I understand he's a busy doctor, his energy level when it comes to anything else has always seemed to me about a zero. And the energy's where it's at in the mating dance, at least in my not-so-humble opinion. It certainly outplays looks, or even personality. No energy, no spark—and I don't mean nervous energy or hyperactivity, but whatever it is the Energizer Bunny has that makes him a proliferating rabbit and not lox. It comes from the core, and if they don't have it, they ain't gonna get it.

"Yes, I've thought a lot about dating," he says in answer to my question. "But it's not so easy in a place like Eternal."

"If you were a woman, I'd agree with you," I say, "but a male on this planet who happens to have a successful medical practice? Don't tell me the girls weren't on your trail the minute they heard about your divorce last year."

"A few were, but they all seemed the same—it's hard to describe them."

"You mean the casserole crowd?" I say. "They *are* kind of interchangeable."

"Yeah, they were at my door at first, but I guess I didn't respond well when people tried to fix me up."

I can sympathize there. "I know what you mean," I say. "The time you're half in shock and least ready to show your best side is the very moment your friends are most interested in shining a light on you. Then, after three or four months, they don't try so hard."

"I was relieved when they quit trying, Ruby. I figured I'd rather get dates on my own. Less pressure."

I can relate, but at the same time, he does sound insecure. Still, the matchmaker in me hopes he doesn't give up. Not everyone's looking for what I'm looking for, and he's a nice guy. Oy—as I say the words *nice guy* to myself, I'm articulating half the problem. On the other hand, my practical side would never underestimate the face value of a nice Jewish doctor whose worst fault is that he's just okay.

"How about you, Ruby? I know you date, but you're not going steady, are you?"

His vocabulary needs an upgrade, but we're part of the same operating system, so I get it.

"I wouldn't say I'm going steady, Bart, but I am seeing someone."

"Does that mean you'd go out with me if we hit it off? You're so easy to talk to, and I feel you understand me."

All too well, and now we're back to the square one I thought I was avoiding.

"I don't think I'm a good bet right now, Bart, but I have paid my dues, and I do understand you. It's not easy to replace someone you've been with for a long time."

I remember that this is a dual-purpose get-together, so I nudge the subject back to Serena.

"Do you think about Serena a lot, or are you just feeling in limbo?" I ask.

He looks uneasy. "I find myself playing what-if," he says.

"That's natural. Do you have anyone to talk to when you get in a funk?"

At first he's quiet, but then says, "I email Joellyn quite a bit."

"Is that helpful?"

"Well, she used to be reticent right after the divorce, since of course she sided with Serena. But now that Serena's gone, we've grown closer."

"Do you phone her, too? I'm thinking of like now, when it's inconvenient to drag a laptop around."

Gotta go easy here—this is obviously none of my business.

"Vancouver has plenty of Internet cafés," he says. "I guess on the road, though, it might be a different matter. And in answer to your question, we mostly email."

I'm dying to ask if there's any news, but I don't dare, and he's not going that way so far.

"How about Rose?" I say. "She visited Joellyn, so I thought maybe that friendship might have brought you two closer together, too."

"Rose took Serena's side completely," he says. "I don't think she's that good for Joellyn—she's not letting her get over her sister's death."

I give him time to say more—I don't want to blow this by asking for specifics. While I wait, the singer is belting out some Josephine Baker, and I'm loving it. But since I'm here by my lonely, it's not going to do me any good. I could tell Paul about it later, but frankly, it's more Ed's thing than his, and that's over. It's obviously off Bart's radar completely— she might as well be calling *sooooie* as crooning a love song.

"I guess Rose is grieving, too," I say, mostly making conversation, but he takes it the wrong way.

"I forgot you're a good friend of Rose's," he says. "I just don't see the point of that trip to Ohio."

Maybe he's just feeling left out that Joellyn didn't ask him to visit.

"I haven't seen a lot of Rose lately," I say. "I've been busy trying to get out of town."

"Wonder why Rose didn't come, too," he says. "She is in the choir."

"I think it was the trip to Ohio—too much travel in a short space of time."

"Another reason she shouldn't have gone there," he says, gulping instead of sipping his current cognac.

Methinks he's making too much of this, and I wonder why he cares one way or the other. And it's certainly interesting that we're both avoiding any mention of the discoveries Rose made in Ohio. He has to know, if he's emailing Joellyn all the time. Unless he's not in the loop. And if not, why not? I'd love to find out whether Bart's keeping secrets from me or they're keeping secrets from him.

24

I get back to our hotel corridor around eleven, hopefully after Essie Sue's bedtime. My real fantasy is to stay out all night and be totally safe from any pillow talk, but that isn't exactly practical—and certainly not with Bart. I slide my key card silently into the slot and hope the heavy door doesn't make any noise. It doesn't open. I try three more times. Nothing. This isn't the first time I've had a key card that was either misprogrammed or not programmed at all.

I go back down to the lobby despite the fact that I'm experiencing a sudden letdown from the long flight and the nonstop activity tonight, but what choice do I have? And maybe the cognac is playing its part, too. I persuade the bell-man to come up with me so he can do some of the legwork if the door still doesn't open. A new card would be ideal, but of course that's not the way it works. First, the guest must always be subjected to instruction as to how to put the card in the slot.

"Upside down with the stripe to the right," the desk clerk reminds me downstairs. "It's really very simple."

He would have made a great kindergarten teacher.

"I did that," I say, earning a look reserved for the legions of dummies who nightly torture the wise ones at the front desk.

"Did you knock?" he adds.

"No, my roommate's asleep by now," I say.

When I'm finally granted leave to bring the bellman to my floor, I realize I'll have to pay for it two ways. Besides the obvious one, he's also noisier than I am. By the third door rattle, I hear Essie Sue yelling from her bed.

"Is that you, Ruby?"

"Sorry, Essie Sue."

"I double-bolted the door," she says. "You can't be too careful."

I'm embarrassed to look at the bellman, who, since he's waiting for my tip, has to hold in his condescension. I guess I *am* dumber than they are.

When I finally get inside the room, I don't have the energy to show my annoyance, aside from asking if she could promise not to bolt the door from now on.

"I wouldn't have to go through this if you didn't stay out so late, Ruby," she says, tying the sash on her three-piece Japanese pajama outfit in jade green satin. "Someone said they saw you in the lobby with Bart Goldman. You aren't thinking of dating him, are you? It would only be on the rebound. He's not over Serena yet."

"We had a drink," I say. "And I'm falling asleep on my feet. Just point me toward the sofa bed."

"But you haven't unpacked yet."

"I'm not unpacking—we leave tomorrow. Hopefully, my flannel PJs aren't too far down in the suitcase."

"I looked at the sofa, and I don't think there are any sheets on it," she says. "They might be in the linen closet with the extra blankets."

I'm so tired I'm ready to cry at this point.

"You can sleep in my room," she says, "in the other bed."

"I'll just flop on the bare sofa."

"There's no way you're sleeping without sheets," she says, taking my hand and leading me to the bedroom. "I have a surprise for you—I found your pajamas for you and laid them out on the bed. Even though you could have dressed up a bit more for the trip—don't you have travel sleepwear?"

All I can manage to mutter is, "Flannel's good for Canada." And I'm doubly thrilled that she went through my suitcase—that, I can't deal with at all in my present stupor. I wash up in the bathroom and literally fall into bed. At this point, I'd sleep with an ax murderer if his bed was as soft as this one is.

I do notice that the lights don't go off, and the TV goes on.

"This is what I've been looking forward to," she says, waving the remote at me, "our pajama party. Hal doesn't like the same shows I do. Let's watch 'Today's Special Value' on QVC—can you imagine that they have this in Canada, too?"

I burrow under the covers.

"I think I should call in for this," she says. "Help me decide."

I feel a tinkle in my ear.

"I poured you half of my Diet Coke," she says, "with ice. It's refreshing."

I'm not sure, but I think she and her remote have moved over to my bed—somewhere near my head.

"Look, Ruby." She's plumping up my pillows and settling in. "This is a knitting machine they're showing on the screen. You weave the yarn in and out of these steel dividers—it's a lot quicker than using knitting needles. I can use it in bed at night. Hurry up before they put something else on—should I buy this?"

"It's probably a taped show in Canada," I say from under my blanket.

"No, it's not."

"Okay, buy it."

"Not until you see it." She turns me over, puts one of the pillows behind my neck, and feeds me a sip of Diet Coke.

"Look at the item. Quick."

Maybe she'll buy it and go to bed. And since I've already opened my mouth, it's not much of a stretch to open my eyes, too.

"Essie Sue, this knitting machine is a three-foot long wooden stick with nails in it. If you maneuver this into bed with you, you could put Hal's eyes out."

"It comes with an instructional video. At fifty-eight dollars, it's a steal. At the end of the day it goes back to its regular price of sixty-eight dollars."

"If you buy it, will you go to sleep? We have an all-day train trip tomorrow."

I warn her not to call from the hotel phone, and it takes thirty minutes to get an 800 number that doesn't produce a busy signal from the switchboard.

"I got through," she says, nudging my elbow in case I'm not thoroughly awake. "But they're not recognizing my account because I'm not calling from my home phone, and

I forgot my password. I need to hang up and call Hal in Texas. I have it written down in a big list on the refrigerator with all my passwords and account numbers."

"Please don't call Hal—it's three in the morning there." Now, of course, I'm thoroughly awake.

Through the indomitable efforts of customer service not to lose a sale, we reach a resolution after she finally finds her credit card.

By now I've had a glass of Diet Coke with caffeine, and we move on to a French Canadian station.

"Just to practice the language," she says, and frankly, anything's better than another shopping struggle.

"Isn't this fun, Ruby?" she says. "I knew we'd love this girl time. But all this French is making me sleepy, so I'm going back to my bed."

The room's finally dark, she snores through her eye mask, her noseguard, and her retainer, and I'm left counting loops of yarn crisscrossing sixty-five rows of nails, in French.

25

I think I slept about an hour—my mind's on the six o'clock wake-up call to meet in the lobby at seven. Essie Sue's still asleep, and I'm not about to wake her with the sound of the shower. I wobble barefoot into the living room—the clock in here says five. Thankfully, my suitcase is in this room, too, hardly disturbed from last night. My favorite dark wine sweater's on top, with a comfortable pair of jeans. I change clothes, use the second bathroom to wash in the sink, and I'm out the door. There's no way I can take her company first thing in the morning, and it's worth anything to make an early exit. I'll have two hours without having to make conversation.

I'm standing by the elevator, glancing idly down one of the corridors, when I see André letting himself into one of the rooms. Wonder where he's been all night? And was his rabbinical roommate out with him, too?

I'm alone in the elevator, as I expected, and no one gets on before the stop in the lobby.

"Ruby, what are you doing here?" It's Kevin, standing right where the door opens to let me out.

"Well, I can certainly ask the same," I say. "You and I aren't exactly morning people."

"Don't forget," he says, "that it's later than this in Eternal."

"I did forget that, but the time change doesn't mean that I got any more sleep last night."

"Did Essie Sue keep you up?"

"That's the least of it," I say. "I just wanted out of there this morning."

Kevin's wearing a gray sweater and his tartan wool scarf—I think the plaid must look Canadian to him. He has his suitcase, too.

"What happened with you last night?" I say.

"Like what?"

I'm not quite ready to say I saw André this morning—I'd rather have Kevin spill a few things first. For all I know, he invited Bitsy to his room and asked André to sleep somewhere else. That's a reach, though.

"Did you and Bitsy go out on the town after the meeting?"

"Well, Bitsy wanted to come back to my room after, to share a fruit platter from room service, but I didn't know what André was going to do, so I didn't think it was a good idea. We turned in early."

"Why didn't you work it out with him?" I say.

"Huh?"

"Guys do these things, Kevin. He'd understand."

"It was too much planning for me," he says.

"Are you still a little bit afraid of Bitsy?" I ask.

"She's kind of unpredictable," he says. "I'd rather just start by taking her out to dinner in Eternal."

"But you thought you might be rooming with her at one point."

"That was more or less a fantasy," he says.

"How about taking her out to dinner here?" I say. "Even if you don't want to room-hop right now, there are times when you can't let a good opportunity go by."

"I'm hungry," he says, blatantly changing the subject. "Let's see if the coffee shop is open."

"Yeah, I need my coffee and a copy of the Vancouver paper," I say.

There's a lone waitress setting up in the coffee shop, and the sign says they're not open until six.

"There's a machine near the side entrance," she tells us, "and they have bottles of Frappuccino."

"Cold coffee?" Kevin says.

"It has caffeine in it," I say. "Let's go for it."

We grab comfortable chairs in a room adjoining the lobby—I'd rather be out of Essie Sue's notice for as long as possible. No newspapers in sight yet, so I take this chance to get more out of Kevin.

"How was André as a sleep-mate?" I say. "Did he talk you to death like Essie Sue did me?"

"Uh, to tell you the truth, Ruby, he hadn't come in yet when I went to sleep last night, and this morning, he must have gone for a jog or something before I got up. His suitcase was still there, but he wasn't."

"So you didn't see him at all last night?"

"Nope."

For Kevin's sake, I hope André didn't connect with Bitsy. Somehow, though, I don't think she'd be interested in a married man. My guess is she has very specific marriage plans of her own, and that they don't include being anyone's mistress first.

I wish Kevin knew more about the latest Serena developments, but I'm afraid to tell him. Since he's such a fixture with our Temple Rita group, he'd be an extra pair of eyes for me and Paul, and wouldn't be likely to be noticed. But he doesn't even know what a poker face *is,* making him totally unreliable undercover. I can just see him giving something away to André or Bitsy, even without meaning to.

It's six, and we both race for the coffee shop. Kevin orders a full breakfast, and I'm happy to get an English muffin and some hot coffee.

"Can I get grits with my eggs?" he asks the waitress. She's clueless.

"Not here," I say. "She doesn't even know what you're talking about."

"We have reindeer jerky," she says. "Out-of-towners like that."

"Just the eggs, then," he says. "And Texas toast."

"Hotel toast," I tell her. "Like mine."

"What are you two doing here so early?" It's Bitsy, followed by half the choir, or at least all those who responded to the wake-up call. "You look awfully cozy."

"We're not cozy," Kevin says. "It's just Ruby."

His attempt to save the day goes down cold with Bitsy, who continues to glare at me. This time, I don't even bother to help him explain—I'm too tired from my all-nighter.

I can see that André's avoiding our table—he's headed to one in the corner with his quartet-mates Irene and Bart, plus a perky newcomer from one of the Canadian choirs who'll be joining us on the train trip.

I'm barely conscious of Kevin's and Bitsy's prattle, just happy to refuel with the coffee and forget that I got no sleep last night. My wake-up ritual would be even better with a newspaper to read, but no luck there.

"Roundup time, people—let's start filling up those buses to the railroad station. As you go through the lobby, bring along any of our group who've strayed from the fold."

Well, at least I managed to avoid Essie Sue for an hour, if not two. She's happily on the rampage, with easy prey so early in the morning—we're all groggy from the plane trip and last night's exploration of the city. I try to get to the lobby ahead of her, but she catches up with me.

"Why didn't you wake me, Ruby? We could have talked over coffee in bed, or watched one of the early morning shows."

I shudder to think what she might have purchased at five in the morning—Irish sweaters for winters in the Sunbelt? Or maybe they feature clearance items at that hour. I run for one of the buses while she's still busy herding.

Too bad it's such a short trip from the hotel to the rail-road station—the bus I've chosen is full of strangers, who're refreshingly different from my hometown crowd. This group is from Washington State—crossing the border into British Columbia is an ordinary occurrence for them.

"Have you made this trip before?" I ask the very cute guy sitting next to me, who has that unusual combination of jet black hair and blue eyes I've always found fascinating. He's in jeans, wearing a brown leather jacket over a heathery blue sweater that just happens to be the color of his eyes, and his boots could have easily come from one of the boot makers in downtown Austin. I tell him that before he can answer my first question.

"Who are you?" he says with a smile that makes me glad I spoke up.

"So which shall we answer," I say, "your one question or my two?"

"No, your *three*," he says. "You just asked another, so I'd better try keeping up with you. I've never made this particular train trip before, but I've been to all these destinations many times—Vancouver, Banff, and Lake Louise. And my boots aren't handmade, but I've always wanted a pair. You're from Austin?"

"A town near Austin," I say. "And in answer to your first question, I'm Ruby Rothman."

He puts his hand out. "Gus Goren."

No wedding ring, I notice.

"Off the bus, all." Whatever version of Essie Sue they have in the state of Washington has just made her wishes known through a bullhorn as we pulled up at the station. "We're boarding by groups," she says, "and each choir's leader has your tickets."

Gus gets off first, and takes my hand as I jump from the high step.

For once, I'm struggling for words—even though I'm suppressing plenty of silent curses for the short length of the bus trip.

"Brief conversation," I finally say.

"To be continued," he says. "I'll just look for the dark red curls."

26

Amazing what a pick-me-up a brief flirtation can be, especially on a trip that's been a big fat zero so far. On second thought, I'd call last night's shopping excursion with Essie Sue a *minus* zero, and cocktails with Bart Goldman not much better.

The first person I see from our group is André.

"Come on, Ruby, they're about to board," he says. Before I know what's happening, he grabs my hand and rushes me around the corner, where Essie Sue is waving her list. He holds my hand a little too long for comfort. Unfortunately, it's the same hand Gus Goren just held, and I'm foolishly annoyed about that, as if André had ruined it.

"You missed my orientation," she says as I shake off André's grip.

"Why don't you and André start off in seats 15A and B," she says, "since you're the only ones not aboard yet. We can all change around at will, once the conductor has passed through."

Well, that's a blessing—I won't be stuck with him. I try to switch gears, though, and go into business mode, since I did promise to see what's up with André. I make a real effort to put the handholding incident out of my mind, and I give him what I hope passes for a smile of contentment at being his temporary seatmate. André's not a pushover by any means—I've known that for a while now. My real job's going to be to find that fine line between being merely an inquisitive friend and another prospective notch in his belt.

As we walk to the red, white, and blue tour train, we run the gauntlet of uniformed greeters lined up by the tour company to give us a proper send-off. André tries to hurry me along again, but I'm savvy this time, and I avoid any offered appendages.

"Sorry you didn't get to sit with your quartet buddies," I say as we find our seats.

He responds with what I've already noticed is a seduction smile—a flash of white teeth that's supposed to mow us ladies down in Latin-lover style.

"Why, Ruby," he says, "I'm surprised you can even think such a thing. I've wanted to get to know you better for a long, long time. I can always see the choir people. You and I have to make a serious effort to go deeper on this trip. We need to share."

"Fair enough," I say. "You know, André, I don't know you or your wife very well, and I'd like to learn more about the Korman family. Where did you meet Sara?"

Ha—silly of me to think that any mention of Sara would

throw a pro like André. He's not that easily discouraged, or distracted. Although on another level, he just seems to be going through the motions for the sake of habit.

"Sara and I grew up together," he says, "but she's home this trip, and I'm sure you and I have other things to talk about."

"Surely not more important things?" I say.

"How about you?" he says, ignoring my goading. "I've heard you've been a widow for quite a while now. Do you like to go out and have a good time? A trip like this is the time to do that."

"Well, now that we're on this train, I doubt we'll be out and about that much—I think it's mostly group activities on the agenda."

Since I'm just stringing out the conversation, I don't expect my remarks to be illustrated so soon in living color, but on cue, Essie Sue comes down the aisle with an announcement.

"Morning service, people. As soon as the conductor takes your tickets, I want you to come to the observation car. One of the British Columbia groups is leading the worship."

Since our tickets have already been punched, I'm the first to jump up and reach for my handbag.

"Coming?" I say.

André flashes me a half-amused, half-smug smile and joins me. He certainly exudes confidence—in a smarmy sort of way, as if to let me know he'll reel me in later.

We make our way to the observation car, where at least fifty people are trying to squeeze into as little space as possible.

"Hey, Ruby, want to sit here?" Kevin and Bitsy are sharing a space for two with one other person already, but Bitsy jumps happily into Kevin's lap and gestures for me to take her seat. I'm sure I've lost André in the melee, but no such luck—I see him picking his way through the car. Since I have no intention of sharing laps with him, of all people, I'm hoping he finds another place to sit. As I thank Bitsy for the seat she's offered me, I look around to see if Gus might be in this car, but no such luck.

I'm glad we're having the service so soon, since from what I've heard, the scenery gets more gorgeous with every mile east through the Canadian Rockies. ChoirFest or not, I don't intend to miss the spectacular scenery because some Essie Sue type is blocking the view as she lectures the group.

A choir from Victoria is in charge of what they're calling a creative service. I hate to say it, but they're not much better than our choir, although with everyone joining in, the total effect isn't bad. I had hoped, though, that we could learn a lot from these groups—maybe the choirs from the larger congregations will provide some inspiration.

I feel a finger touching the back of my neck. This could only be André—anyone else would tap my shoulder.

"Hey," I say, "don't do that."

"Just wanted you to know where I was," he says, "right here behind you."

He's positioned himself next to my ear, and throughout the service, I'm treated to a critique of the proceedings.

"This is their idea of a meditation?" he says after a period of silent prayer. "They have no idea how to reach the meditative state."

I listen to him for a minute or two, trying to get a clue as to where he's coming from, but I can't take it for too long.

"André, I can't concentrate with you talking in my ear," I turn around to tell him. "Can you wait until after the service? I'd like to talk with you about it then." Irene Cohn is beside him.

"André's right, Ruby," she says, "this isn't creative, it's tedious, just like—"

I poke her with my elbow before she can criticize Kevin right to his face. He gives me a grateful look.

"Our choir's better than this," Bitsy says, nestling into Kevin's lap. "Rabbi Kapstein's a genius."

I wouldn't go that far, or even half that far, but Kevin's glowing.

I excuse myself as soon as the service is over, and take off for the next coach car before anyone can realize I'm gone. If André does try to follow me, I'll duck into the nearest bathroom—although I don't want to discourage him completely before I can find out more about the meditations.

I'm encouraged by the fact that quite a few people are using their cell phones. I felt sure that mine wouldn't work out here, but I'll give it a try. With the crazy hours this morning, I haven't been in touch with Paul, and I told him I'd call.

I ring his cell and reach him at the station.

"Hi, hon," he says. "What's up?"

"Just wanted to keep in touch," I say, "nothing really to report. We're on the train already, and I've tried to make some conversation with André Korman. He's criticizing the services, but nothing other than that. I'm hoping he might lead me to something more that might have been spooking Serena."

"Don't be heavy-handed, Ruby, not in that closed-in atmosphere."

"Give me credit for more than that, Paul—it's hard enough just to spend five minutes with him. I'm wasting most of my time trying to avoid the guy, so I'm doing this in small segments."

I don't think it's necessary to mention his coming on to me, but Paul does.

"Remember what a womanizer he is."

"Yeah, I know."

I hope Paul doesn't start with the jealousy bit—we've made no commitments, and yet he's barely gotten over my dating Ed. How he could even think I'd respond to André's pathetic moves, I'll never know.

"What's going on at home?" I ask. It's difficult to hear him, and as usual during the day, he's talking to me at the same time he's being distracted by someone there at the station.

"Aside from finding out Serena was poisoned, not much is happening," he says. "Of course, that's a big deal in itself."

"But who do you think knows that here?" I say. "Anyone?"

"I don't want you finding out," he says. "Bart Goldman's still close to Joellyn, and it's possible she might have told him. But it could be dangerous for you to ask about this."

"I spoke to Bart last night," I say, neglecting to say I had drinks with him. Or that he seemed interested in me. Why get Paul upset about nothing?

"Did he say anything?"

"Nothing about that. I pumped him a bit about Joellyn, and he didn't say he'd been in touch yesterday, which is the only day he could have learned about the poisoning. But he does think Rose should have never gone to Ohio."

"I'm in touch with Joellyn off and on about the case," Paul says. "Maybe I can ask if she's emailed or phoned Bart—or anyone else, for that matter."

"Yeah," I say, "it *would* be nice to find out who knows what—"

"Before you go barging in and put yourself in a dangerous situation," Paul says.

"That wasn't what I was going to say, Paul. You didn't even let me finish my sentence—what's that all about?"

"I'd feel safer if I were up there directing things," he says.

I fight my inclination to chafe at that. It's irritating, but then Paul *is* the professional and I'm not. I still hate it, though, that he's glad to have the extra eyes and ears I can provide, yet he won't give me credit for good judgment. And to make things worse, he's having this conversation while other people there are probably standing around listening.

"Let's hang up before we get into a fight," I say. "I'm doing the best I can."

I guess we're of like mind, because someone says something to him and he's off the phone before I can say a proper good-bye, whatever that would be.

27

At least I'm not missing the scenery—we're passing through the area of the great salmon runs, and I see two gigantic swing span bridges out the window. The steward told me the natives of this region paddled below us centuries ago on their way upstream for the salmon harvest. We can even see Mount Baker in Washington State from here, and I hear we're scheduled to pass through several tunnels along Fraser Canyon.

"Can I sit by you for a few minutes, Ruby? I didn't read the guidebook, and you're always up on these things."

It's Kevin.

"Sure, but where's Bitsy?" I ask.

"Essie Sue needed her for something."

"How's it going?"

"Okay. Bitsy can be a little tiring—she's always so chipper."

"But that's who she is, Kevin. If chipper's not good, you might as well know it now."

"There's one good thing," he says. "When she's around, there's no room for me to think about a lot of other stuff that bothers me."

"That's good?"

"Well, yeah—she's distracting. It's just that I get exhausted from it."

"So mix a little. Try to meet people besides the Eternal contingent. That's what travel's all about."

"I haven't done that yet, but I did hang around Irene Cohn for a while. She's kind of weird, don't you think?"

"In what way?"

"At home, she's always rolling her eyes during services when I preach. I can see her to my left in the choir section."

"Then why would you want to talk to her on vacation?"

"I heard her complaining to André and Bart about how dull the service was, and how it was like ours at home. She said something to André about Serena that I didn't understand, and he seemed to be angry with her. So she went over and sat with me, though I can't imagine why. I thought maybe I could talk to her and she'd like me more."

"Well, it never hurts to go out of your way with congregants if you have a ready-made opportunity. What did she say?"

"Not much. She was still fuming over whatever the argument was with André, and maybe she wanted him to notice that she had someone else to talk to. I was just in a convenient spot. I asked her to tell me why she didn't like the service this morning."

"What did she say?"

"That's the weird part. She asked if I even had a clue about the preparation for real prayer, but then she seemed sorry she said it and backed off."

"What do you mean, backed off?"

"She looked over the aisle at Bart and André and said I shouldn't pay any attention to what she was saying—that she was in a bad mood. But I decided I wouldn't let it go at that. I asked her to get together with me sometime so we could make services better."

"Good for you. Did she respond?"

"She looked at me and said it was probably too late for that. Then she backed off *that* and said maybe we would all meet—that she'd talk to André about it."

"Did you happen to ask her what she said to André about Serena?"

"No, but I did mention Serena. I said their little group must miss Serena, because I'd noticed that the quartet was always very close, and that Serena must have been a big part of that. I told her I was sorry I couldn't have talked with Serena about services, too."

"That's interesting."

"What's so interesting? I was only doing what you just now said I should do, Ruby—trying to go out of my way for her. Serena's dead—my chance to know her better is gone."

I'm in a quandary here—I can't confide too much in Kevin, but if I could encourage him to open up even more to this group, he could be really helpful to me. I'm just not sure how to do that.

"I think you should continue the conversation whenever you can, Kevin. And I can't imagine why the subject of Serena should be off-limits, do you? I wonder what André was so uptight about."

"Ruby, why does everyone always talk around me, as if they're keeping things from me? You're doing it, too. What's up with Serena?"

"I can't say, Kevin. Do you think you could trust me to ask you to keep your ears open when you're talking to what's left of the quartet? I promise you I'll fill you in when I can."

"You're interested in Serena because . . . ?"

"I can't say anything else. Will you go along with me?" I know I'm taking a risk here that he'll tell someone I asked him to eavesdrop, but I decide to do it anyway.

"I guess I'll go along, whatever that means," he says. "You know I'm always the last to find out stuff, so I don't know what help I'm going to be to you."

"I don't either, but let's leave it at that just the same."

They're bringing around a yummy lunch on the train—a big piece of cold poached salmon, lots of salad greens, and some marinated vegetables. I'm remembering the days when we suffered through the all-white airline lunches of taco pie, rice, white rolls, and vanilla pudding—what an improvement. The car steward pours some Chardonnay from a Pacific Northwest winery I'm not familiar with, and it's excellent, not to mention the strawberries topped with powdered sugar.

Lunch is perfect for ten minutes, until Essie Sue finds me.

"Ruby, you know that most of our group is staying at a hotel in Kamloops tonight, don't you?"

"I hadn't thought about it," I say. "Why?"

"Well, you and I have been offered a complimentary roomette on the train, and I think we should take it as a leadership perk. We deserve it."

"If the train's starting out from Kamloops tomorrow, how can we stay aboard tonight when everyone else is at a hotel?" I say. "We'll be way ahead of them."

"The train won't be moving tonight—it will wait for the group. The bedroom's just a bonus."

"Huh? You mean we get to swap a roomy hotel room for a stationary little cabin just because it's on the train? That's a perk?"

"Come see it with me—you'll love it."

I bring along a brownie from my lunch tray and she drags me to one of the roomettes in the bedroom car. As I expected, it's smaller than the cabin on a bargain cruise, and I'm an expert on those.

"You can stand on my bed to get to yours," she says.

"Meaning you get the lower bunk," I say.

"I'm the one they're complimenting by this offer, Ruby, so of course I get the bottom bed."

"So far," I say, "you haven't even been able to close the door behind you. How will you fit your luggage in, much less me?"

Before she's even finished squeezing the door shut, claustrophobia sets in. The thought of Essie Sue's normal intrusive presence bouncing off these walls is enough to set my teeth on edge.

"No, I'm declining," I say. "Thanks, anyway."

"But it will save us the cost of a hotel room," she says. "This is free."

"I'll pay for my hotel room if you stay here," I assure her. "Free's not always what it's cracked up to be."

It's not easy to get out of a room that barely holds both of us, but when my sanity's at stake, I'm pretty efficient.

"I'm outta here," I say. "We'll connect tomorrow."

"No, if you're not staying, I'm not, either—we can keep one another company tonight to keep our spirits up. I'm sure this little pit stop isn't what we're used to in Eternal."

"Kamloops? It's not a pit stop, and it has gorgeous views. There are some great restaurants here, too. Eternal should have so much to offer."

"All right, we'll stay with the rest of the group," she says. I guess I'm not off the hook after all. But just because we're rooming together doesn't mean I have to spend my days with her.

"See you later," I say, heading the other way, through the observation car. The cocktail lounge is in here, too, and the waiters are setting up for business this afternoon, I guess. I'm about to cut through to find our group, when I see André, Irene, and Bart. They're huddled together in a far corner, and they're so intent on whatever they're doing that they don't even see me coming through.

I take the nearest seat so that we're still separated by the length of the car. Irene and André are leading some sort of chant, while swaying with their eyes closed. It'd probably be a good idea to be doing something if they notice me, so I carefully take a paperback out of my leather carryall. Not carefully enough, apparently, because a map I'd put between the book's pages falls into the aisle at the same time, and I instinctively reach down to grab it.

They see me.

28

"Who's that?" André says, looking around.

"It's Ruby over there." Irene, already standing, points my way.

"Hi," I say. "I thought I'd read by these sunny windows for a while. Am I disturbing you? If so, I can move."

When I'm unexpectedly discovered somewhere, I always announce my presence with a question—it's a good distraction.

"No, don't be silly," Irene says. "We're just having a meeting. You can read while we . . ."

It becomes obvious to everyone, though, that they can't, or won't, continue while I'm reading.

"Why don't you join us?" André says. "You might find this interesting."

"I can see I'm intruding—why don't I come back some other time?" I say.

"It's nothing secret," Irene says, to André's obvious annoyance.

"Why would you say that?" he asks her. "Of course it's nothing secret—come on over, Ruby."

"Yeah, come on," Bart says.

I step over to the semicircular booth they're occupying. Irene sits down and lets André take over.

"We're meditating," he says. "A sort of group meditation. We find that these prayers are a way to lead us down to a place of greater spiritual depth."

"Greater than what?" I say.

"Than ordinary modern methods of worship. It's not easy to explain to . . ."

"To someone who's barged in," I say. "I understand— that's why I didn't want to break in on a private meeting."

"André can explain it to you," Irene says. "It's much more than a worship experience. It's his way of giving us directions to the right path."

Bart seems embarrassed for some reason—he can't quite look at me.

"You mean André's directing?" I ask, glancing over at Bart anyway. "Do you all take turns?"

"Not me," Bart finally says. "I don't know much about this."

"Are you using a prayer book?" I say.

"It's not needed," André says. "If you'll stop asking questions and let yourself be a part of the flow, it will come to you."

André pulls me down into the seat beside him—now I'm squeezed between him and Bart, with Irene facing me at the other side of the curved table.

"Can we spread out a bit?" I say. "There's nowhere to put my hands." Or arms, either. And André's sitting too close to me for comfort. I notice that all three of them have their hands on the table—I'm tempted to ask where the Ouija board is, but I hold it in. This is no place for humor—especially not my brand.

Everyone moves over, but apparently not far enough for Irene, who's also noticed André's proximity and is glaring at me.

"I can't stay long," I say. "I really don't want to miss this gorgeous scenery."

"Ruby," André says, "you have no idea what you're missing besides the scenery. Don't you ever think about the unseen?"

"Usually not in a group," I say. "I'm flawed."

"But the group energy is very important. We pray silently—like the Quakers, but our content is biblical."

Biblical? I'm dubious, but I'm not about to interrupt at this point. I want to see what's going on here.

"We can't fully demonstrate it here on the train," Irene says, "but you need to understand that everything we do is connected."

"Like to the universe?" I say.

"No, to Los Angeles."

"That's the corporate headquarters of Jewish Mystic Central," André tells me. "We get praying aids from them, cards printed with the chants, CDs, DVDs, bracelets—you name it, they have it."

"Retail and wholesale," Irene says.

"Wholesale?" I say. "And you've kept this a secret from Essie Sue? She lives for that."

"Essie Sue wouldn't understand," Irene says. "This is a

cutting-edge movement, Ruby. Essie Sue's too mainstream, and besides, she'd want to take it over the way she does everything else around temple."

"We're basically a leaderless operation, Ruby," André says. "That's the way it should be—each finding his or her own right way."

"But I thought Irene said you were the one pointing to the right path," I say.

"I am, but only until everyone catches up with me. I'm on a different spiritual level right now."

"Let me get back to the wholesale-retail level," I say. "Tell me again how you heard about this?"

"Through my business," he says. "You know we carry a lot of wellness material in the health food store. There was an ad about the new spirituality, and about this movement that's attracting as many of those out of the faith as in the faith. It's for everyone—even the movie stars are into it. They buy a lot of the bracelets."

"You mean like Lance Armstrong's yellow bracelets?" I say.

"Yes, but these aren't for charity. They *are* charity."

"I'm getting it," I say. "It's kind of like a franchise?"

"Well, if I launch this correctly, I could be the Central Texas distributor. But that's not the main point—the higher message is to reach the depths of prayer. The stuff they sell only represents the physical manifestation of this—like a study aid."

"And if you introduced this to Temple Rita as an organization, they would be able to use the profits to help the congregation do its work, right?" I say. "Like Essie Sue usually does?"

"That's the last thing I want to do," he says. "She wouldn't

understand. And neither would the rabbi. This is more individual than congregational."

You can say that again.

"So you'd get the profits?" I say.

"To further my work," he says.

I look over at Bart. *"Et tu?"* I say.

"Honestly, Ruby, this is the first time I've ever heard him
talk about profits. It wasn't his emphasis. You really do need
to learn more about this—it's complex."

"Very complex, Ruby," Irene says. "You have no idea how
uplifting these meditations are. If Essie Sue and the temple
board could look beyond what Rabbi Kapstein is doing, they
could see that this represents the future."

"Maybe, but whose?" I say. This sounds all about André's
future.

"I knew you shouldn't have invited Ruby over to our
table, André," Irene says. "She's not the type to understand
deeper spirituality. And now she could ruin everything. Just
like . . ."

"Whoa," I say. "What *everything*? And like who? What kind
of plans do you have? We're talking Eternal, Texas, folks, not
the dawn of a new world."

André takes a deep breath and puts his hand on top of
mine on the seat between us. I instinctively pull it off like a
hot coal, but he's undeterred.

"Ruby, we've always been good friends."

Not.

"This is a very sacred moment," he says. "We think
enough of you to want you to be a part of something trans-
formational and, as Dr. Goldman says, complex. Will you
promise us not to speak to anyone else about these matters
until we've oriented you properly?"

I agree with him that they're a disorienting bunch, but if I'm not careful, I'll make an enemy of these people way before I need to. I think of Paul and back off.

"Sure. Orient me. I'm game."

André and Irene visibly relax. I don't think Bart Goldman is as persuaded, but he's so conflicted about my seeing him in this situation that his embarrassment is calling the shots. He shrugs and looks away.

"Will you come to one of our hotel rooms and hear more?" André says. "Irene and Bart will be there, too," he reassures me. "How about tonight? Or tomorrow morning? We're meeting both times."

"Let's play it by ear tonight," I say. "I'm not even sure where I'm staying yet."

"But you won't say anything?" Irene asks.

"That's taken for granted, Irene," André says. "Ruby said she'll wait."

"No," Irene says, "she said she'll let you orient her."

Orient me? This is beginning to sound pornographic.

"Yeah, yeah," I say to all. "I'll keep your secret."

André flares up again. "It's not—"

"I know," I say. "It's a secret but it's not. Whatever it is, I won't say anything until I understand more.

"How about letting me out?" I push toward Bart as the lesser of the evils. "I'll leave so you can all talk about me."

"Of course we won't discuss you," André says as I get up. "We wouldn't think of it."

"It's a joke," I say.

But I have a feeling it won't be for long.

29

We connected with the Canadian Pacific Railway tracks a while back, and our train roars in and out of the tunnels along Fraser Canyon. I love the sudden blackness followed by the bright flash that means daylight is back again. What a waste to spend time in futile conversation with Mystic Central when I could have been taking pictures like mad with my little Minolta digital, no bigger than a deck of cards. Some of our Eternal group are leaning out between the car couplings to take photos in the fresh air instead of through the glassed-in train windows. I've been thinking of walking up to the engine area to take some shots from the front end of the train, if they'll let me.

There's no way to reach the scenic area we're traveling through except by train or trekking through with a backpack. The highways cut straight through less interesting country for efficiency's sake, while the railroad was planned to take advantage of the spectacular backcountry views. Nan would love this.

Now that I'm cars away from anyone I know, I grab an empty window seat and call Paul. We're not that far from Kamloops, so I'm hoping I'm not too isolated to get through to his cell.

"Hi, hon. It's me."

"Ruby? I can hardly hear you."

"Where are you?"

"I'm in the Starbucks drive-through line," he says, "on my way to check out a crime scene. This is a perfect time to get me."

"I'd be jealous of your latte if I hadn't just feasted on some good Pacific Northwest coffee with country cream."

"What's country about your cream? Aren't all cows rural?"

"I won't answer that, smarty-pants. Miss me?"

"You bet. What's up? I hope you're watching your back."

"Well, since you're not here to watch it, I have to, right? I was wondering if you'd called Joellyn in Ohio. You said you might."

"Yeah, I did. I asked her if she'd contacted anyone since she found out her sister was poisoned. She said she'd emailed Dr. Goldman, as part of a regular email correspondence they have. He must have received the message yesterday, since she said she'd just sent it and hadn't had an answer. I don't think she expects one—she seems to think he won't be able to be in touch that often up there. She just wanted to keep him posted."

"That's interesting. I spent some time chatting with him and he didn't say anything, even though we pretty much covered the waterfront when we talked. He even mentioned Joellyn by name, but didn't tell me that."

I'm still not informing Paul we chatted it up in a cocktail lounge.

"He could have logged on after talking with you, Ruby— maybe at the hotel at night."

"You're right. But I saw him today, too—we're all together here in fairly close quarters."

"Not so odd, I guess," Paul says. "Maybe he just told people he's closer with than you."

"That's a distinct possibility."

We had quite an intimate conversation over cognac last night, but Bart was like an entirely different person today in the observation car. I still can't get over *that* encounter.

"I'm here at the crime scene," Paul says. "Gotta go."

"Can I call you back?"

"I'll try to get you later. I'm still worried, though—have you cut it too close with anyone you're not telling me about? I know how you are when you're hound-dogging something."

"I'm being careful. But after what you've told me about Bart, I'm wondering who's making an end run around whom."

"Later, babe, okay?"

He hangs up before I can answer or say that I miss him. I put my phone in my jacket pocket and stare out the window for a while as we fly by beautiful waterfalls and whitewater rafting spots. I'd love to be photographing this, but instead I'm sitting here wondering if Bart told his friends André and Irene the latest about Serena. And I thought I was so cleverly scoping him out last night. Apparently, he's way ahead of me.

"Hi, Ruby, we're just car-hopping. Can we sit with you?"

Kevin and Bitsy take the two seats facing me.

"I don't like riding backwards," Bitsy says. She moves

over beside me and then asks, "Can you let the rabbi sit by me, too?"

"Huh?" I say.

"You know—like swap with him. So we can be together."

This is vintage Bitsy—the word *passive-aggressive* was invented for people like this. And the reason she's so successful at it is that no one wants to take the trouble to pick it apart. Except me.

"Why didn't you just ask me at the beginning to give up my good seat to the two of you," I say, "instead of trying to extract it by degrees?"

"Would you have?" she says.

"No."

"I don't blame you," she says. "That would have been pushy of us."

"Us? I didn't see Kevin asking."

"It's just that once I got over here in your seat, I started missing him, and I thought you'd understand, being another girl and all."

"I was wondering how long it would take you to blame this on me," I say. "Exactly thirty seconds."

"That's not fair," she says.

"What's not fair?" I ask her. "You've got a fair choice—you can ride backwards and hold hands with Kevin, or sit by me, not get dizzy, and look at Kevin across from you."

She stays put. The only thing wrong with this picture is that she's already won, because at the most I'll only be able to tolerate her for a few minutes before having to move. Which was the point, I guess.

"Hey, Ruby," Kevin says, "remember you asked me to keep my eyes and ears open whenever I was around the quartet?"

The cliché would be that my heart sinks at that, but actually what's sinking is any hope that I'll ever be able to treat this man like a friend who might do a favor for me without blowing it.

I try to ignore this by gathering my backpack off the floor in preparation for leaving the scene, but he doesn't let me.

"Remember?" he says.

I look at Bitsy, there on alert, but he still doesn't get it that this was between the two of us. On the other hand, I don't want Bitsy making too much of this—she could then blab to Essie Sue and company. None of my choices is good, so I plunge in.

"Yeah, I remember. It's not important."

I start to get up.

"Well, I saw them just now before Bitsy ran into me, and we visited for a few minutes."

Bitsy's not missing a word.

"That's nice," I say, standing.

"No, don't go," he says. "I have to tell you what happened."

Now I'm really caught—I want to know, but not in front of Bitsy. And I can't say so without indicating that this might be important to me. Not to mention that if I leave, he's going to tell her anyway.

I sit down.

"Remember that last time I saw Irene, she said she'd speak to André about services at Temple Rita, and that she'd ask him if the quartet would discuss it with me sometime? Well, when I ran into them just now, I asked her in front of André if she'd spoken to him."

"Just temple politics," I say to Bitsy. "I was encouraging Kevin to get to know the congregants more informally on this trip."

"So anyway, Ruby," Kevin continues, "Irene seemed

embarrassed. I thought you'd be interested in that. And André accused her of blabbing to too many people. Namely me, I guess."

I nod, waiting for him to go on. There's nothing I can say to get out of this hole, anyway.

"André said I was the last person Irene needed to talk to. I tried to help out Irene by saying that you'd encouraged me to open up more to the quartet—that it wasn't just Irene's fault."

Oy. This is worse than I thought. Now the quartet won't confide in me at all. André's no fool, and he'll know I wanted Kevin to soak up any information he could. The irony is that I couldn't care less about their secret spiritual quest if I didn't think one of them might be a murderer.

30

Email to: Nan
From: Ruby
Subject: Hi from Kamloops

Hey—found an Internet café here at the train station near Kamloops—odd name, huh? It's an Indian name for "meeting of the waters"—this is the convergence of the North and South Thompson rivers. You'd love it here, babe—we just passed a huge osprey nest on top of a telephone pole near an abandoned mill. I saw one of them swooping straight down to the water, on the lookout for fish. This might even beat what we saw on our trip to Alaska—I think this is a better season for spotting wildlife.

An update to what I told you on the phone—we're pretty sure that Serena's ex, Dr. Bart Goldman, knows that the autopsy showed she'd been poisoned, but he's said nothing to me about it, even though we've talked.

By the way, did I tell you I met a cute guy on our way out of Vancouver the other day? He's one of the Washington contingent, and I hope I'll run into him at the conference.

Email to: Ruby
From: Nan
Subject: How's that again?

What cute guy? I thought your cute guy quotient was filled. Tell all, even if there isn't much. And by the way, are you and Paul getting along on the phone? Remember what I told you about long-distance misunderstandings—things can get twisted on the phone in a way they wouldn't in person. I'm not all that happy to hear that your eye is roving, Ruby.

RE the autopsy information, you might be operating at a disadvantage. One of these characters could be a killer, and if I were you, I'd be glad no one's talked about this. If the wrong person found out you're in possession of damaging information, you could be caught upstream at those rivers of yours without a you-know-what. I'm not there to get your back, and Paul's not, either.

Speaking of loose tongues, Essie Sue hasn't heard the latest about Serena, has she?

Email to: Nan
From: Ruby
Subject: It's all cool

The cute guy is Gus Goren, and we just flirted a bit—and by that I mean for about sixty seconds—honest. But as for my roving eye quotient, or whatever you said, why shouldn't I? I'm not dead yet, and I'm still single, despite your attempts to couple me so soon after the Ed fiasco. I know you like Paul a lot, and he's still the main man, I guess, but this is exactly why I'm not committed, Nan.

Essie Sue doesn't know that Serena was poisoned, but I'm more worried about Kevin. I asked him to keep his ears open when he was around those people in Serena's quartet, and I think he blurted something out to them about my request. This is only going to make it harder for me to get tight with them. They're into some sort of user-friendly version of Kabbalistic practice, and I'm trying to find out what's going on there. I'll keep you updated.

Email to: Ruby
From: Nan
Subject: Uneasy

You're not exactly decreasing my anxiety level. What's keeping you from waiting to explore the circumstances surrounding Serena's death when you get back home to Eternal? You'll have police support and you won't be exposing yourself in unfamiliar territory.

By the way, Ruby, stop confiding in Kevin.

Okay, I accept your single status and your right to connect with a neat guy, but I guess I am prejudiced in Paul's favor. Only be careful—and not just with the romance. Wish I were there with you, because my Ruby antennae (and you *know* they're accurate) are buzzing all over the place.

Email to: Nan
From: Ruby
Subject: I'm perfectly safe

I promise I'll take care of myself. And if I need to make a quick retreat, you're just over the border in Seattle, right?

31

It's a shame to have to look forward to a night as Essie Sue's
roommate after dining at a great restaurant with a spectacular view of Kamloops below us. The two bottles of wine
our table shared are taking their toll, though, and I don't
really have to be persuaded to head home to bed—if sleep
is possible with Essie Sue in the room. I want to get up early
tomorrow morning to catch the meditation service—it's in
Irene's hotel room. The three-legged quartet has reminded
me to drop in before we take the train for the second lap of
our journey.

"No midnight pajama party," I say to Essie Sue in the taxi.
"I need my sleep. You'll have to watch the shopping channels
on your own."

"Oh, they probably don't even have them here," she says,

unwilling to admit that this isn't the boonies. "Besides, I have a surprise for us that doesn't involve television."

I'm too drowsy to take the bait, but I rouse myself when we get back to our room and I discover that my flannel PJs are missing. Essie Sue puts on a three-piece silk lounging ensemble in pale peach.

"Too bad Hal's not here to enjoy this," she says. "I picked it up in Vancouver—they have some very sophisticated boutiques."

I'm amused, though I'm not sure why. "Hal, huh?" I say. "So he's still interested? Good for him."

"Well, I wouldn't say *interested* exactly," she says, "but he says he's always glad when I go to bed happy."

That, I can believe. But since she brought up this topic, I can't quite let it go.

"So do you two still—uh—get it on in the romance department?"

"Hal's past his prime," she says. "I got him samples of Viagra, but he refused to take it, even when we watched the ads together. He said it had side effects. I pointed out to him how self-confident those men on TV looked, with their wives adoringly gazing up at them. Like Nancy Reagan."

"It didn't fly?"

"He said it wouldn't work with him—he was a registered Democrat. I'm not giving up, though. I'm bringing back one of those DVDs of *Massage for Lovers*—even though he's never been very good with his hands. He can't even drive a nail in the wall."

I don't go there.

"Okay, Essie Sue," I say, "where did you hide my pajamas?"

"Not *hide,* dear, *eliminate.* You deserve better, and that's part of my surprise for tonight."

She brings out a plastic shopping bag and pours onto my bed what appears to be an exact replica of her outfit, except for the color. Mine's in slinky black, but it still looks like something Vanity Fair made in 1955.

"Yours isn't silk," she says, "it's rayon, but I knew you'd insist on throwing it into the washing machine, so I didn't waste the money."

"I thought you said I deserved better," I say. "I'll freeze in this. Just tell me where you eliminated my PJs."

"They're gone," she says. "And this surprise isn't just for you, Ruby. It's a step toward your future. Others are involved."

I don't want to know this.

"I'm exhausted, Essie Sue. And this hotel room doesn't even have terry-cloth robes."

At this point, I head for the bathroom. I refuse to waste another hour on this. The outfit turns out to be not only slippery but cold—like I'm wearing someone else's skin. Someone who's not a mammal.

"Beautiful," she says when I come out. "Get used to it— and look what I've collected for you."

She's sitting on my bed with a computer on her lap, plugged in and ready to go.

"I downloaded these five for you from the Internet," she says, "and they're all Jewish. I saved it all on a DVD to show you here."

The Nu—a Jew for You logo comes up, followed by photos and bios. When I take the laptop, the electricity from my faux-sateen outfit almost shorts out the computer, but I'm not so lucky.

"This is Maury Blumenfeld," she says, showing me number one. Maury's seen better days, looking about as confident as I feel in black rayon, and appearing a little Viagra-deprived himself, if I'm any judge.

"His bio's very interesting," Essie Sue says. "He's a doctor."

"No," I point out, "he has a doctorate in lawn improve-ment from University World Online. There's a difference."

Sleepy as I am, I find myself weirdly fascinated by the pickings she's laid out. And besides, she's on my bed.

"Maury Blumenfeld's probably not his real name," Essie Sue tells me.

"Yeah, I'm aware of that," I say. If that's the best pseudo-nym he could come up with, I wonder what the real thing is. Not that I should expect much ingenuity from a doctor of lawn improvement.

"Next is Jerrold Oshman," she says. "He likes his women smart but not too smart, wild, and undemanding. You'd have to work on being undemanding, Ruby."

"Thanks for the two-thirds compliment," I say. "I think. Sounds like every man's fantasy to me. Lots of luck to Jer-rold."

I don't bother to bring up Jerrold's graphic, but then, I'm pretty undemanding when the occasion calls for it. Instead, I flip to number three, Isaac Epps.

"How old are these guys, Essie Sue?" I ask after taking a look.

"I told them you would accept any age," she says.

That explains it. Isaac's photo should be in sepia—he looks like he's fleeing the Russian army. Under the czars.

"Only two more, right?" I say.

"Don't go so fast," she says, "these were the cream of the crop in your category."

"You mean the 'I'll take anything' category?" I say. "I shudder to imagine how you described me."

The competitive part of me is already thinking how a little creativity could bring up a much better rogues' gallery, but right now my goal is to go to bed. Alone.

Theo Tamarkin, number four, is posing with a whip.

"I think this whip still has the price tag on it, Essie Sue," I say. "Is this what they mean by Jewish S-and-M?"

"I thought he seemed a bit more stimulating than some of the others," she says.

Uh-oh. I don't want to go there, either. Poor Hal.

"Now I remember why I picked him," she says. "Theo had an unusual philosophy of life. He said he wanted a generous wife with a good job, and he would only get married in a warm community-property state. Since Texas is a warm community-property state, I thought this would work to your advantage."

"Or most certainly to his," I say. "I think we can safely delete Theo."

I'm about to rush through number five, when I do a double take. On the screen, with captions from the site, in living color, is my ex-boyfriend Ed Levinger. And to add insult to whatever else is injuring me regarding Ed, his quite adorable color photo was taken by *moi*.

"You're kidding," I say, now totally awake. "Where did you get this?"

"Well, I admit it wasn't in your former-rabbi's-wife category," she says, "but I was browsing and ran into it. I wanted to prove to you that you never know who's doing online dating."

"So where's his bio?" I say.

"I only downloaded the photo, since you already know his biographical profile. Shall we go to sleep now?"

32

My attempt to leave without waking Essie Sue doesn't work, so I tell her I have to go to Irene Cohn's room to get a book I'm borrowing.

"I didn't know you two were friends," she says. "She doesn't seem like your type."

"We're not what I'd call *friends*," I say, "she's someone I know from temple. What's the big deal? And while we're at it, what *is* my type?"

"Oh, you know—eccentric. You pick odd people."

Talk about the pot calling the kettle *eccentric*.

"We can talk about my oddball friends some other time," I say, "gotta go. I'll see you on the train."

"But aren't you coming to the box breakfast on the bus

that takes us to the train? We worked so hard on it while the rest of you were out to dinner last night."

"I didn't see any box breakfast on the schedule. What's that?"

"It was an unscheduled opportunity, and I grabbed it. I found out that the hotel had ham roll-ups left over from a big buffet last night that apparently didn't draw as many people as expected. The manager told me we could get them at a bargain price if we wanted them, but of course there was the ham problem. So a few people I organized spent a couple of hours taking the ham out of the roll-ups and replacing it with cottage cheese. We left the celery and the parsley in. I thought cottage cheese roll-ups would be perfect for breakfast as a surprise treat. You won't miss it, will you?"

"'Fraid so," I say. This is one unscheduled opportunity I'm definitely passing up. I just hope no one gets ptomaine from it—that's all we need.

The door to Irene's room has been left ajar, and I slip in just as she, André, and Bart are beginning the service, or whatever they're calling it. The curtains are drawn in the living room and no lights are on, so I'm hoping not to attract any unnecessary attention. The three of them are there, plus two other people I've never seen—other invitees from the train trip, I guess.

I hear familiar Hebrew melodies being played on a portable CD player, and they're all sitting cross-legged in a circle on the floor. Despite my tiptoeing, André notices me and waves me over—the rest of them have their eyes closed.

"We're giving ourselves a buzz before the hectic pace of the day," he whispers.

Nothing wrong with that, although not being a morning person, the last thing I need at this early hour is a buzz, unless it's from coffee, and I don't smell any being made. I guess this group will be ripe for Essie Sue's roll-ups—something tells me there'll be plenty left.

"This is the creative part of the service," André says. "We aim to go down as deep into our consciousness as we can, and when we come up, we'll express it."

Something tells me this isn't what the rabbis had in mind, but it might have been why they didn't encourage novices to delve into this, either.

After a few minutes of silence, Irene, who has yet to nod to me, passes around a set of plastic-coated cards.

"These are for worshippers who might have a hard time expressing themselves," André says.

"Like a study aid?" I say.

"You'll see," he says. "They're part of the meditation pack I'm hoping to introduce to selected people, as soon as I get the licensing franchise."

"And this is why this has to be hush-hush?" I say.

"Of course, Ruby. I don't want others taking over before I've even signed the contract. This is like a beta group—we're the cutting-edgers who are testing the waters."

Got it. I'm so much more comfortable when I understand the mechanics. My card contains homilies about the contemplative life—nothing very cutting-edge that I can see.

André's just asked Bart Goldman to read his card when there's a loud knock at the open door—a redundancy that could only escape someone like Kevin.

"Ruby, are you in here?" he says. "It's so dark I can't see anything. Essie Sue said you were headed for Irene's room, and someone steered me toward this corridor."

Irene jumps up, pulls the curtains, and finally acknowledges my presence.

"Ruby, you mean you didn't even have the courtesy to shut the door behind you?" she says.

"I thought you were leaving it open for other people you'd asked," I say. "How was I supposed to know to close it? There was a book there keeping it open."

"For you," André says.

By this time, I'm up on my feet.

"I'll talk to the rabbi outside," I say.

"No, that won't be necessary," André says, standing and gathering the worship aids from the participants. *Gathering* is hardly the right word, though, to describe his actions—he's practically inhaling those cards. Within a couple of seconds, he's pocketed the pack and jerked the CD out of its player. He obviously doesn't know our rabbi that well—Kevin's not exactly fast on the uptake.

Kevin, not surprisingly, is oblivious to everything but what he's come for. He nudges me into a corner away from the others, half of whom are still sitting on the floor wondering why they're not meditating.

"Ruby, I'm representing Temple Rita tonight when we give our introductions at the ChoirFest. Essie Sue said you'd help me with this speech—she wants it to be extra good. Isn't there a bedroom we can use for a few minutes?"

"Why couldn't you wait until we were on the train?" I say. "I don't think your barging in is exactly welcome."

"Because you're always wanting to watch the scenery or take pictures or something," he says. "I wanted you to help me before everything started. I really, really need this, Ruby."

He's awfully excited, even for Kevin. There's an edge to his voice I don't hear very often, and it doesn't make sense that he'd get this panicked over a speech.

"Why are you so nervous?" I ask him. "Meet me in the lobby in a half hour, and I'll help you."

I try to steer him out the door before André has a fit thinking Kevin will discover something. Between the two of them, I'm wishing I were already on the train.

"No," he says.

"Are you telling me this can't wait?" I say.

"No, it can't."

By this point, André's had time to put Irene in charge of silent meditations, sans CD music and accompanying sales products, and he comes over to us. He's obviously had a chance to compose himself now that he's hidden the goods from Kevin, and he even manages one of those creepy smiles of his.

"Can I help, Rabbi? You seem perturbed. Let's go in the bedroom."

Kevin's now more wild-eyed than ever, but he jumps at the chance to go into another room, even with André along.

"That's what I've been asking Ruby to do," he says.

Well, if André's not worried anymore about his little plot being discovered, why should I be? It could be that he wants to see for himself whether or not Kevin observed anything, but that's not a problem, either. I know Kevin. Maybe we can both help him with the speech and get it over with.

We sit him on Irene's bed and pull up two chairs.

"This is okay for André to hear?" Kevin says.

"Yeah," I say, "we can both help you."

"The rabbi's having a problem with the speech he's giving when the conference convenes," I tell André. "Maybe we can give him some ideas."

"Why not?" André says with a look that might as well be

a wink. I think that in his new role as meditation guru, he's flattered to be helping the clergy.

"Okay," Kevin says, "if you're sure it's all right to talk to both of you."

"It's fine," I say.

"Ruby, I messed up," he says. "With Essie Sue."

"She's just concerned you won't make a good impression," I say. "Once we get this speech nailed down, she'll be fine."

"You don't understand, Ruby—it isn't the speech. That was just an excuse in front of all those people. I wanted to talk to you about something else that just happened— something I really messed up. I should have come to you about it, but Essie Sue was there and you weren't, and I got upset. You know how she always gets things out of me."

"What could she get out of you?" Even with my brain being caffeine deprived so far this morning, I can't think of anything he knows that she shouldn't. Fortunately, I haven't told him anything about my conversations with Paul.

"Well, this morning I got a call from Sara Bernstein, wanting to know if I could conduct a memorial service for her neighbor's mother who died. The neighbor isn't a member of the temple, so he didn't want to call directly. Anyway, we were making the arrangements, and Sara happened to mention . . ."

Kevin looks at André, then at me. "You know," he says, "she happened to mention some gossip that's going around Eternal. I don't usually repeat gossip, but I saw Essie Sue in the lobby right after my phone call, and she said I looked like I was keeping something from her."

"She knows you pretty well," I say, "so I'm not surprised. But hey, what was it? Unless it was some sort of rabbinical confidence. Is that what you're concerned about? If so, we don't want to know. And Essie Sue should be ashamed of herself for pulling it out of you. That's low, even for her."

"No, it wasn't a rabbinical confidence."

"Then tell us," André says.

"Well, Ruby told me a couple of times that there was nothing wrong with bringing up Serena's name in conversation, so I told Essie Sue what I'd heard from Sara Bernstein, and she flipped."

A shot of pure caffeine couldn't do to my system what this does.

"Uh, Kevin, maybe you'd better keep this to yourself." I try to get up from my chair, but Kevin and André stay put. So either I leave the two of them together without me or sit back down and face this.

I sit.

In the few seconds I have to work this out before he says even more, I realize that: one, the secret's out, so I might as well receive the news as anyone else would, and two, I'll at least be witness to André's reaction before he has a chance to get himself together. And, oh, yeah, three, what's up with Essie Sue?

"What did you hear?" André asks again. "We love gossip."

"That Serena Salit may have been poisoned instead of having a heart attack."

André's face freezes halfway between a grin and a grimace. Honestly, I've never seen anyone go so white.

"How was she poisoned?" he says.

I'm not operating on all cylinders yet, but that's a very strange first question.

"They think she may have been injected. That's all Sara said."

Now it's André's idea to run. "I'm sorry," he says, "this is too upsetting. Serena was close to all of us in the quartet, you know. I have to go back to my room."

Kevin and I are left facing each other in the bedroom, and since André hasn't closed the door behind him, I take a quick peek and see that he's slipped out of Irene's suite altogether. Since I don't have the others' reactions to think about, this bedroom is probably the best place to be for a while, but I'll have to work fast.

"Okay, Kevin," I say. "What's this Essie Sue business?"

"She said it would look terrible for our choir at this conference if Serena had been poisoned at our latke party, and that she was sorry I even told her."

"I truly doubt that, Kevin—she lives for this stuff. She probably just wanted to be one of the few people who knew."

"She seemed really mad at me for saying anything. I should have waited and told you first."

"Did you tell me second, at least?"

"Yes—you and André. I wouldn't have told, except you said it was okay to talk to both of you in here."

Yeah, that was definitely brilliant of me. I shouldn't be surprised, though—Paul said this wouldn't remain a secret for long in Eternal. I know Bart Goldman learned about it from Joellyn's email, and now André's aware, too. Only Irene to go, as far as the quartet is concerned.

"André was shocked," Kevin said. "I guess it's pretty devastating news."

André could have been bowled over by the fact that the authorities found out about it, not that it happened. I agree with Kevin that he *was* devastated. But I wonder how shocked.

33

I'm relieved that we're back on track, literally. This is our last chance to see Canada by train, and today we're scheduled to pass through some of the most spectacular scenery on the continent. I'm determined not to miss it, and I know that if I keep ruminating on the events of the early morning, I'll give up any chance of enjoying this unbelievable landscape.

Not that it's easy to make the transition. Once André left the bedroom this morning, I managed to calm Kevin enough to slip us both out of the room while the meditation service was winding up. I'm sure Irene was curious as to why André had left so fast, and she probably wasted no time hunting him down. But we left it to her to deal with—I was personally determined to get my morning coffee or else, and I think Kevin just wanted to get out of there.

I *am* curious to know whether Essie Sue decided to keep the news of Serena to herself—if so, it'll be a first. So now she knows, I do, Kevin does, and André and Bart Goldman do. And whoever else is in contact with friends or family in Eternal—making it just about unanimous, I suppose. Some open secrets, though, are more whispered about than shouted, and I suspect this is one of them. I'm guessing that if the news is being discussed, it's in confidence between one person and another, with each one thinking it's still a secret from everyone else.

I know one thing—I've got to have a break from all this. I want to help Paul despite the fact that he thinks it's too dangerous, but at the same time, I came on this trip to enjoy myself, and I've done bloody little of that. And because I love photography, I've made sure that the batteries in my camera are charged and I have plenty of room on the memory card.

The open spaces between the first few cars are still crowded with photographers from our choir groups, and I can see that if I take too many photos this way, I'm likely to have someone's shoulder or elbow sticking smack in the middle of my picture. There's got to be another option.

My first goal is to avoid a lot of time-wasting conversation while I'm searching out good camera angles, and the best way to do that is not to hang out in cars full of Temple Rita congregants. I head back to the end of the train, many cabins away from our group, with tourists who aren't even a part of the choir convention. It seems to take ages to get back there, but it's worth it. And yay, nobody knows me. There's a big observation car near the end of the train that's perfect—the windows are huge, kept sparkling clean by the maintenance staff.

The best thing about my digital camera is the playback

feature, and I can always see if my photos are correctly exposed and composed before wasting more time and effort. I take several test photos to see if the reflection from the windows will be a problem, but if I angle the shots right and photograph straight through the glass, I'm good to go. And of course, since I'm never more content than when I'm happily snapping pictures of great scenery, I'm in pixel heaven.

I get some great shots as we're crossing Eagle River Bridge, where salmon spawn in the fall. The scenery's marked by milepost signs, so we know how far we've traveled. The Adams River sockeye salmon run is huge, although no one really knows how the fish navigate. The guides tell us it's by smell or magnetic orientation, but whatever, this is where romance among the sockeyes happens. The female opens her mouth and discharges a stream of eggs from her vent, while the male, close to the stream, releases the milt that fertilizes the eggs. Since I consider salmon to be food from the gods, I definitely want to document the breeding grounds.

I'm snapping like mad when I turn too far sideways to avoid the reflection from the window—not good. And I see something I'm not expecting reflected in the glass—it's the face of someone wearing a blue, denimlike baseball cap pulled down over his or her head, with brown hair going down a couple inches from the hat. Not long hair—more like a short haircut that's getting too long and needs a trim.

I immediately try to sit straight ahead and correct my viewing angle through the camera lens so I won't get a reflection, but then I turn—just a reflex action, I think—and look around to see whose face that was. I don't see anyone and I hear people in the observation car *ooh*ing and *aah*ing over a quick view of Kay Falls, a waterfall that runs down Mount Griffin. It's one of those sights you can miss if you're not fast, so I take a few rapid shots in the general direction. I don't have time to zoom, so I'm sure they won't be any good, but with a digital camera, who cares? Later, I can just delete the ones I don't like.

I take a rest when the attendant comes through the car with a basket of fruit for a late-morning treat. I recognize her from yesterday's trip—she's a pleasant person.

"How's it going?" she says. "Are you getting some prizewinning snapshots?"

"Well, you certainly can't beat the subject matter," I say, helping myself to an apple. "Whether my talent can match it is another story. But I'm having fun."

"That's the idea," she says.

She's getting ready to move on when I blurt out something I didn't even know I was going to say.

"Hey," I say, "did you run into someone in the aisle just a couple of minutes ago? Wearing a baseball cap? The face looked vaguely familiar, but then when I looked around, there was no one there."

She shakes her head no, gives me a nice smile, and moves on.

None of this is exactly unusual, except that I didn't realize until I spoke to the attendant that this was a face I knew.

34

Lunch is on the way already, so I go forward several cars—I take a minute to look around for a baseball cap, but people aren't choosing to wear hats of any kind inside the train. I don't waste time on my search—heaven forbid that I should miss a meal, and we have to be in our seats to be served. Today it's smoked salmon salad or turkey sandwiches, and of course I pick the salmon. When in Rome, et cetera, and after all, we're not rolling through turkey-breeding country out these windows. Plum tomatoes and some really good homemade chips are piled on the plate along with the salad greens. I'm glad I didn't finish my apple earlier.

"I'm joining you, Ruby."

It's Essie Sue, of course—she's the only one I know who

wouldn't ask "*May* I join you?" and she plops down beside me with her lunch tray. She's having turkey.

"Too much salmon," she says. "That's all they seem to eat up here, and who knows where it's been? I'm watching my mercury."

Well, we can see where it's been, but I don't bother to point that out, or to mention the questionable poultry processing her sandwich might have gone through on its way here. I use the word *sandwich* loosely—since, of course, she only eats the middle of things. I haven't seen her down a piece of bread since I've known her. I think of asking for her brownie, which I know will remain on her tray, destined for the garbage, but that's only a fleeting, random thought. I haven't lost my mind yet, and I have enough trouble reaching for my own brownie, knowing she'll have something to say about it.

"You're not eating that brownie, are you?" she says.

"Looks like it," I say.

"It has fat calories—the worst kind," she says. "And when fat is married to sugar—"

"I know," I say, "Lucifer's spawn. I'm damned."

"Why do you think they call it devil's food cake?" she says.

I actually don't know the answer to that, but I do know that I'm devoutly wishing she hadn't come along to ruin my delicious lunch. I wish there were a special sort of hell for these people, but they'd probably get off on the deprivation.

She watches me choke down the rest of my lunch, and then leans closer to me.

"Ruby, I have to ask you something," she says.

"Hurry up," I say, "because I'm only staying while lunch is served. When the coffee comes around, I'm outta here."

"Where's to go?" she says. "It's all the same train. Have

you seen André Korman? We were going to have an informal meeting, but I can't find him."

This happens a lot to Essie Sue, I notice—people disappear on her whenever they get the chance.

"I haven't seen him," I say. "Is that what you wanted to ask me?"

"No," she says, "I had something more important to talk about."

"Here's the coffee guy," I say. "You have ten minutes while I drink some."

I would have said five minutes, but I'm thinking she's going to pump me about what Paul's told me regarding Serena Salit's death, and I'm curious to hear her take on all this.

"Did the rabbi say anything to you about a conversation he had with someone back home in Eternal? He heard some gossip."

"You know the rabbi doesn't gossip," I say demurely. I'm going to make her do the gossiping herself.

"Well, they say Serena didn't have a heart attack—she was poisoned."

"Really?"

She cocks her head at me. "You always know everything, Ruby. Don't tell me you weren't aware of this. You said yourself that you speak to Paul on the phone all the time."

"I said nothing of the sort," I say. "He just happened to call the other night when we were together, and you got it out of me that he was the one on the telephone. It wasn't a business call."

"So why aren't you surprised?" she says. "You did know, didn't you?"

"I'd heard some stray remarks, too," I say. "But until we

get back home, you might as well realize that we won't have the whole story. Why waste time with it up here?"

I knew she'd ignore me, and she does. "Who could have done it?" she says.

"I didn't know her that well, Essie Sue," I say truthfully. "How could I even guess? And anyway, isn't that the job of the police?"

"It's a *shandah* for the temple," she says. "A disgrace."

"I don't need a translation," I say. "You mean because she was poisoned at the temple?"

"That, and because all her friends were temple people. That's who probably murdered her."

"Who? Neither of us has any idea who all her friends were, Essie Sue. Is this all you're going on?"

"Not exactly."

I'm drinking my coffee more slowly now. I might as well hear her out.

"So what?" I say. "Get to the point."

"It's just that I heard her divorce wasn't all that kosher," she says. "What I found out at the time was that either she or Bart was carrying on with someone. Or maybe both were."

"Maybe? So you really don't know anything," I say.

"It's something for the police to look into," she says. "And I intend to tell them. Unless you want to tell your boyfriend now instead of waiting until we get back to Eternal."

"If you think it's so important, why don't you tell him?" I say. "But he's certainly going to grill you about what else you might know. From what I can see, this is pure speculation."

"A lot of people thought Bart was running around," she says. "Or that she was."

"So name them," I say. "Let's get to the bottom of it. All I can see now is that you don't even know which of them was cheating on the marriage—that's not exactly cogent documentation."

"I got my information from his receptionist," Essie Sue says. "The one he fired two months ago."

"So much for the temple members," I say. "And a discharged employee—that's a real find. But do pass it along if you want to."

"I want you to do it," she says, "because as I told the rabbi, this could look very bad for Temple Rita—especially at the start of our new building project."

I haven't heard of the umpteenth new building project, and I frankly don't want to know.

"Call Paul if you want to," I say—a throwaway line if I ever heard one. She's going to do exactly what she pleases whether I give her my permission or not, and it's not as though I own Paul Lundy.

I make sure I have my camera with me, and I'm stepping out into the aisle when I glimpse Gus Goren in between cars.

"Gotta go, Essie Sue," I say. "I've got to see some people."

I don't mention Gus—there's no way I want her noodging me about him.

"When will you be back?" she says. "I only see you when you're sleepy."

"Later," I say, making my way through the car as fast as possible without doing anything that might induce her to follow me.

"Hey, Gus," I say when I catch up with him.

"Ruby." He seems genuinely glad to see me, and gives me that smile I haven't forgotten.

"Where have you been, girl?" he says. "I've looked all over for you since our little bus ride."

"Attending too many meetings and dodging too many people," I tell him. "I'm finally taking some time to get more pictures of this gorgeous scenery. Are you a photo bug, too? If so, you're welcome to come with me."

He pulls out a tiny camera similar to my own. "Shirt pocket variety," he says, "but it takes great snapshots."

"Mine's a mini, too," I say, "that way, I always have it with me. No camera bags needed."

"Where are you headed?" he says.

"To the caboose," I say, "if they have one. I want to hang out on the very back end of the train, where I can have swivel room. My only concern is that it might be crowded. Wanna give it a try?"

"Sure. Let's go."

The train's flying as we scoot through the cars, and I have to hold on to keep from being thrown around. Of course, Gus'd be there to catch me, right? But I'm not quite ready to try that approach.

"What's the hurry?" he says. "You're a hard woman to keep up with."

"I just want to make sure the afternoon light's good," I say. "Or maybe I'm so used to being distracted from the things I really want to do on this trip that I don't want to take the chance of being cornered by anyone."

"So that doesn't include me, huh?" he says. "I guess I should be complimented."

"It definitely doesn't include you," I say. "You're fun to be with."

He actually does steady me a couple of times when the train lurches around a curve, and I have to admit, it's nice.

I'm glad I've worn my wool sweater as we approach the outside rails of the last car. There's a brisk breeze out here, and I even have to jam on the stocking cap I knitted last fall so my ears won't get cold.

"Don't cover up all the curls," he says. "I like them."

"Yeah, I can imagine what I look like in this stretchy wool hat," I say, "but nothing keeps me warmer, so that's the way it is."

"I was kidding about the curls," he says. "If it's cold, it's cold. Besides, you look cute in that hat."

"Good," I say. "That's a bonus."

There are a couple of other people out here, but not a crowd. The cold wind has probably scared the hordes away, because this is definitely the best spot on the train for picture taking. With the wind blowing, though, and with the cap over my ears, I can't easily hear what Gus is saying—not great for getting to know him. But he doesn't seem bothered by the lack of conversation, and he's snapping away on his own. I like this guy's style.

And what a time to be out here—we're not too far from the Continental Divide, and we're traveling in and out of the famous Spiral Tunnels. When the railroad was first built in the early 1900s, there was a dangerous grade called the Big Hill by the engineers. Two spiral tunnels were constructed to lower the grade so that a fast-moving train could navigate the terrain safely.

"These things were modeled after gorge tunnels in Switzerland," Gus yells at me through the wind. "It took a thousand men to build them, but they reduced the grade to a safe level."

The Lower Spiral tunnels its way through Mount Ogden, and the Upper travels through Cathedral Mountain. Each tunnel emerges many feet higher than its entrance, so that the railway doubles back on itself twice to cut down the grade—it turns out to be an *amazing* maze.

We're coming out of the Upper Spiral near milepost 1 2 8, and I'm focusing on an especially beautiful spot where we've crossed the river for the second time in that doubling-back process. Because we're the last car of the train, we have a fabulous, unrestricted view.

I have to blink my eyes to make sure they're not blurring, but I distinctly see a human form lying on the riverbank as we pass. I yell, but Gus doesn't hear me, and I pull on his arm.

"Look—over there on the bank."

"An otter?" he asks. He points in that direction so that the other two people on the platform with us can see, too.

"No, a person. I saw a person," I scream at him.

It's obvious that none of the others saw what I saw, and I snap more photos as we roar past the scene. I also make a note of the milepost number I noticed back there—1 2 8.

I pull on Gus again until he comes back inside the last car with me.

"Hey, you're upset," he says. "I didn't realize—I'm sorry. Tell me again what you saw."

We sit down in two empty seats at the end of the car and he gently pulls off my hat for me.

"So you can hear me," he says. "What happened, Ruby?"

35

"There was someone on the curve of the riverbank," I say, "not far from the tunnel we just came through. The person was facedown, with one leg skewed at a peculiar angle."

"Could they have been camping or fishing?" Gus says.

"Maybe to begin with," I say, "but I'm positive that body looked hurt, if not worse."

"Was it a man? Did you see anything alongside it?"

"I have no idea if it was a man or a woman, Gus. I just know I saw it. Let's go back outside and check with the other two people."

"They came in after we did, Ruby, and they left. I have no idea who they were—I was too busy worrying about you. You scared me. But I do know we all shrugged when you said you saw someone—I don't think they caught it any more than I did."

"They didn't," I say. "I could tell. I guess I'm the only one."

"So now what?" he says. "You know what they say about this backcountry that the train cuts through—it's only accessible to hikers. The train passengers get great views, but otherwise, not even the dirt roads reach it, much less the highways."

"I have to speak to a conductor," I say. "Can you bring one here? I don't want to go back through all those cars filled with curious people—especially a bunch of folks I know. Not until I've nailed this down."

"Sure," he says, "although the two folks outside with us didn't seem that curious, so I'm not certain you're right about everyone possibly being so concerned when you tell them."

"How about you?" I say. "You don't think I made this up, do you?"

"Of course not," he says. "But what you observed could have lots of explanations. We were going fast, for one thing, so nothing's that clear. I'm still thinking it could have been a fisherman stretched out for a nap, or reaching for something. And if it is more drastic, how would you find them, anyway?"

"That's what the railroad personnel can tell us," I say.

Gus puts his arms around me in a quick bear hug, then stands up.

"Can I get you some water first?" he says. "Or anything else?"

"Thanks for understanding," I say, shaking my head no to the water.

"I won't be long," he says.

I lay my head back on the seat, take some deep breaths, and try to calm down while he's gone. But I have a really bad feeling about this. I just wish it hadn't happened so fast.

"Ruby, this is the conductor."

I've barely closed my eyes before Gus returns with an older man in uniform. He wears glasses and has a potbelly like something out of the movies—all that's missing is the watch and chain lying on his stomach.

"Miss, I'm Charles Strong. I understand you're reporting an accident you viewed as we were coming out of the tunnel?"

His matter-of-fact acceptance makes me feel better. Gus must have done a good job of giving him the details—such as they are. That makes me feel better about Gus, too. At least he didn't doubt me.

I tell Charles Strong what I saw and ask him what he can do about it.

"Sometimes we can check out these things," he says, "and sometimes not. It's hard to get back there in the wilderness, especially when we don't know where *there* is. 'Coming out of the tunnel' is not the same as having precise directions."

"But I do know where it is," I say. "It was right at milepost 128."

"You have the number?" he says. "Are you sure?"

"Yes, I've been photographing certain mileposts near scenes I want to keep track of, just in case I want to identify something later. I noticed that your guidebook lists mileposts, and I thought it would be a big help."

He writes down my information in his notebook.

"So can't you call this in now?" I say. "Certainly the police would want to know."

"I'll let them know," he says, "but don't assume they'll do anything about it right away—they have their priorities."

"But why can't the next train through here be on the lookout for the body, or whatever it was?" I say. "And certainly, if someone is wounded, we need to find him. Or her. When's the next train?"

"In a couple of hours," he says.

"Then follow your routine with the police report," I say, "but do me a favor—call the engineer of the next train and ask that he slow down at that milepost. Surely you can do that."

The conductor looks at Gus. "Your lady sure is strong-willed," he says.

"Well, she's not my lady, but I've seen firsthand that she's quite determined," Gus says. "If I were you, I'd give the next train a call. If you don't, it'll be too dark to do anything until tomorrow morning."

"And by then," I say, "an animal could disturb the scene, or do worse if the person is alive."

"I don't think you have any idea," the conductor says, "how difficult it is to get a railroad to go off schedule. It's not what they want to hear."

"Please," I say. "You can't tell me there aren't ways to cooperate between the lines here. Do you know the personnel on the next train?"

"As a matter of fact, I do," he says, "and that's the only reason I'm giving you any encouragement. I've been on this line for a long time now, and my buddy's operating the other train. We're meeting for dinner tonight."

"Could you call him for us off the record?" Gus says.

"All right, I'll call his cell phone," Mr. Strong says. "But we'll be well past Banff before he gets a chance to look.

You'll be off the train by then. You're with the big group that's getting off there, aren't you?"

"Yes, but that's okay," I say. "I just couldn't live with myself knowing nothing was being done. It could have been a camper having a medical problem, or who knows what else."

"We appreciate the heads-up," he says. "And we respect our passengers. Thank you both."

He starts down the aisle, when I stand up and touch his arm.

"Mr. Strong," I say, "could you please make the call now? I know how many distractions you can face once you go back through those cars."

Gus gets up, too, to my great relief.

"Why not have it behind you?" he says to Mr. Strong. "Then you won't have to look over your shoulder to find this lady following you. Or having you paged."

"You're a persuasive pair when you gang up on a fellow," he says, sitting down beside us. "But I do have a request of you both. Rumors multiply like flies inside the confined space of a train—especially if groups are traveling together. I'm asking you not to speak about this to anyone else until we verify something one way or another. It's a policy the railroad follows if at all possible. Have you spoken to anyone yet?"

"Well," I say, "those other two people were outside the last car with us when I first saw something, but they didn't seem very interested—I think they assumed I'd seen a person fishing. They went in shortly after, and Gus and I had no way of knowing who they were."

"Nothing we can do about that, then," Mr. Strong says. "But no one in your group has been told?"

"We're with people from different states here for a con-ference," Gus says, "and we haven't run into anyone—we've been busy reporting to you."

Mr. Strong seems satisfied, and makes the call to the next train. He asks his friend to watch out for a hiker or fisher-man down at milepost 128, and then hangs up.

"Will you do me a big favor and take my cell phone num-ber?" I say. "If you have any news of the hiker or whoever it is, will you give me a call? I just want to know the person's okay."

"I can do that," he says. He shakes our hands and leaves, tak-ing my number and the name of my hotel in Banff with him.

I put an arm around Gus and give him a quick half-hug.

"You're the man," I say. "Really, I couldn't be more appre-ciative. Without you, he might have thought I was just another hysterical woman. This conductor seemed to be a fair-minded person, but who knows what he would have done without your input? I was pretty excited."

"Ha." Gus laughs at me. "I don't believe for a minute that you couldn't have overwhelmed this guy on your own, Ruby. But I'm glad I'm appreciated, anyway."

"How about dinner when we get to Banff?" I say. "On me."

"I most definitely accept," he says. "We'll fight over the check later."

36

Gus and I find our separate seats for the rest of the trip to Banff. I want to relax, and Gus is meeting some friends in his part of the train. He invited me along, but I needed to calm down. I'm not in the mood to make conversation with strangers, and I can still look forward to seeing him for dinner tonight.

I slide into my window space, lean my head back, and close my eyes for a few minutes. At least, I think it's only a few minutes. The next thing I feel is Kevin punching my shoulder.

"Ouch. What are you doing?" I say.

"I'm nudging you awake," he says.

"That's not a nudge, Kevin, it's a hit. I'll probably have a bruise there. Haven't you heard of communicating with speech?"

"I tried that. You didn't wake up."

"I'm definitely awake now. What do you want?"

"Essie Sue sent me to find you and bring you to the club car—we're having a meeting there before we get off the train and go to the hotel. It's for that executive committee she set up."

Nobody told me I was on an executive committee, but that's no surprise. I don't bother protesting—she'll just come herself if Kevin doesn't fetch me. And I'd rather meet now than be disturbed later tonight when I'm having dinner.

"What's on tap for tonight?" I say.

"I have no idea," he says. "You know I'm always the last to find out stuff. Probably some sort of planning for the Choir-Fest tomorrow."

"Well, whatever it is tonight, I can't come."

Being Kevin, he's not curious, but that doesn't mean Essie Sue and the rest of them won't be. I'm wondering whether it'll be easier just to say I'm meeting Gus or be evasive. Straightforward is probably better with this crowd. If I'm cutesy about it, they'll be all over me. At least we're meeting in the club car, where they're serving drinks— maybe they'll be feeling no pain by the time I join them. And I can sure use a glass of wine or stronger.

Stronger it is—by the time I get back there, everyone's ordering whiskey sours—I haven't had one of those in years. The club car is filled with partiers, and the spirit is apparently infecting our little Eternal group meeting in one corner.

"Oh, you found her," Essie Sue says to Kevin by way of a greeting.

"Hello to you, too," I say. "I'll take one of those sours you're all having. Why *sours,* by the way?"

"Because they're made with Canadian whiskey," Essie Sue says. "We wanted to do as the natives do, and everyone started copying us."

I'm not sure the indigenous peoples would agree, but who am I to question such quaint practices, especially when backed by the expertise coming from our own natives of Eternal, Texas?

Bart and Irene have obviously had a few. It's always hard to tell what Essie Sue's been on, since she's so often high from her own narcissism. At any rate, maybe the meeting won't be so dull this way.

"Why didn't you find André?" Irene asks Kevin. "Weren't you supposed to?"

"André doesn't need finding," Essie Sue says, "he's much more responsible than Ruby. He'll find us rather than the other way around."

"Thanks for the backhanded compliment," I say.

"Oh, it wasn't a compliment, Ruby."

Imagine that.

"Maybe André's found a better way to spend the cocktail hour," I say. "Why don't we forget about the meeting and relax like everyone else?"

"No, we have to plan our strategy for the vocal contest taking place in two days," Essie Sue says. "My idea is to pass out flyers at the conference advertising how good our singers are. We should definitely put them in the restrooms—no one can miss them there. It's a unique approach to influencing the judges."

"Unique and classy—don't forget that," I remind her. "But only if the judges are having the travel trots, right?"

"Do you have a better idea, Ruby?" Irene asks.

"Not really. Let's vote on it and adjourn."

"I concur," Kevin says. "I have to meet Bitsy. She felt left out that you didn't invite her to the meeting."

"She's on a subcommittee," Essie Sue says. "She'll get her chance. Maybe she's with André."

Kevin obviously doesn't like that. If he were anyone else, I'd say his jaw just fell, but Kevin's jaw usually clenches in these situations. He gives me a helpless look.

"Why don't you go look for her?" I say. "I doubt she's with André. And this is a short meeting, isn't it, Essie Sue?"

"Well, since you all adopted my idea so readily, I suppose this part of the meeting is over," she says. "I'm assigning the task of producing the flyers to you, Irene. I'm sure you'll do a sterling job. Make them that popular color of chartreuse they're showing."

"That'll do worlds for the people in the bathrooms," I say. "If they're not nauseous when they come in, they will be before they come out. How about something more neutral?"

"Neutral is boring, Ruby. This premeeting is adjourned."

I don't mind at all being spurned, as long as I can get out of here.

"Ruby and Rabbi," Essie Sue says, "why are you leaving?"

"Because you said so," Kevin says.

"I only said this part was over," she says. "We're all joining the Eternal contingent in our regular car for a bus check. It's mandatory."

"Says who?" I say.

"All the groups are doing it," Essie Sue says. "We have announcements to make, room reservations to go over, ChoirFest schedule changes to hand out, and a question-and-answer session before we get on the buses. The planners decided it would be impossible to keep up with everyone once we arrive in Banff."

I can't argue with her—it does seem more practical. "But we're free once we get there, yes?" I ask.

"That's why we're having this meeting now," she says, "so we'll be finished. Unless you and I need to get together . . ."

"No way," I say. "I'm finished, too, for the evening. Don't wait up."

I jump up to lead the way back to our car before my last remark becomes provocative. It looks as if everyone has gotten the word, because a rambunctious bunch of Temple Rita congregants greet us. I'm sure they're all as restless as I am, despite the beauty of the train trip.

Essie Sue's in charge, of course, and I must say she's conducting the proceedings with dispatch. She makes the announcements and passes out the papers without the usual digressions.

"How about a closing prayer, Rabbi?" she says when her checklist is completed.

"Huh?" he says. "What's *closing* about this?"

"The end of the train trip."

"Can we have music first?" he says. The word *extemporaneous* is not part of Kevin's vocabulary, and he's angling for time.

"We can't," Irene says. "André's not here."

"He has to be," Essie Sue says. "We're doing a final count."

"Well, he isn't," Irene says.

"I already looked for him on the way here," Bart says to Essie Sue. "I gave his name to an attendant and they'll ask around for him."

"Well, we need him if we're having any music," she says. "He always leads. And we'll be pulling into Banff soon."

Kevin nudges me. "His backpack's on the floor under his seat," he says.

"Give it to me," I say. He kicks it along toward my seat and I put it with my own pack and my coat. I'm not quite sure yet why I want to keep this myself instead of letting someone else carry it, but I do. It's a miracle Kevin hasn't blurted this out, but I'm counting my blessings.

"Let's go to the bathroom," I say.

"I don't have to go," Kevin says. "And I have to make up a prayer."

"Just come for a minute and stay close to me," I say. "I'll keep this for André and I'll help you with the closing prayer, too."

"We're using the restroom while you're finding André," I tell Essie Sue as we get up. "We'll be back in a minute for the prayer."

"I'm canceling the prayer," she says. "We don't have a lot of time, and it won't be spiritual without the music. Everyone, get your things together."

Only Essie Sue and God can cancel prayers, I think, in that order. But whatever the sequence, Kevin seems relieved as we leave the car.

"You passed the bathroom back there," he says.

"I don't have to go," I say. "I wanted to save this for André without calling attention to it."

"Why?"

The train comes lurching to a stop before I have to answer, and since we're between cars, we're the first ones off. I see a couple of policemen at the station—maybe the conductor's called them.

I get Kevin to help me put all our stuff on the bus between our two seats. It's a short ride to the hotel, but it's dark and we can't really see the beautiful Banff I've heard about. Essie Sue gives André's name to the bus driver in case he appears. I'm very curious as to why he hasn't shown up—it's not that simple to get lost on a train, and I have an uneasy feeling about this. At least the bus and train people have his name.

"I've made all the announcements," Essie Sue says, "so our Temple Rita people should be totally caught up with what's going on. We're all accounted for except for one, and I'm sure he's probably on one of the other buses. And just to double-check again, has anyone seen André Korman this afternoon?"

I certainly hope I haven't.

37

Our hotel has a rustic flavor—beamed ceilings in the lobby and a huge fireplace. Kevin and I are standing in line to register, which gives me time to decide how I want to handle the matter of the extra backpack I'm carrying. No problem when André shows up—I can get points for keeping it safe for him. Our larger baggage is handled by the tour people— that'll be taken directly to our rooms. At the moment, though, I just don't want to unload his backpack in my own place if there's any chance my roommate might be there.

I decide that Kevin's room would be ideal—he's rooming with André, so it'll be perfectly natural if the backpack's there when André returns.

"Kevin, let's keep this in your room for André, okay? I'll take it up with you."

"Whatever you want to do, Ruby."

He's already lost interest, I can tell. We're next to register, and it doesn't take much time.

"There's Bitsy," I say, "standing in the last line on the right."

"Finally," he says. "I keep missing her. We have plans for dinner, and I need to talk to her."

"Give me your key," I say, "and I'll take this to your room while you go over there."

He hands me the key card. I separate it from my own and get on the elevator before the crowd. I don't see Essie Sue, which is a relief.

I open the door to Kevin's room and don't even bother to turn on the lamps. The curtain's open, and the lights from the hotel entrance below cast a glow back through the window. I'm suddenly tired, but before I do anything else, I put the backpack on the floor of the closet. Then I lay back on one of the double beds and stare at the dark sky outside.

When my cell phone rings, the sound seems to be drifting from another planet. It rings a few times before it hits me that I'm supposed to answer—my brain is foggy and I realize I've zonked out for who knows how long.

"Hello," I answer.

"Miss, this is Mr. Strong, the conductor you spoke to on the train. I'm about to go off duty, but I remembered you asked me to call."

"Yes, thanks so much for doing that. Did the other train pass the milepost before it got too dark to see anything?"

"It did. And I'm sorry to say that a body was seen at the place you indicated. It had likely fallen from a great height—either from the banks up by the train tracks or possibly from the train itself. That's all I know. But my supervisors had me give them the note you left with me—your phone number and the name of your hotel. Someone will be contacting you and your friend for more information, I'm sure."

I'm not groggy anymore, but what he's saying is not quite real, either.

"I have to go, miss," he says, "there's nothing else I know."

"Do you know if it was a man or a woman?" I ask.

"I believe it was a man."

Oh boy. I thank him for calling, fling myself back on the bed, and stare at the ceiling. I think of that man lying down there alone.

I know someone in authority will be calling any minute, and I have a sudden urge to call Paul before they do—he can get me to the right people and save a lot of time. Besides, I just need to hear his voice.

There's a knock on the door, and in my spaced-out state, I'm thinking they've already located me.

"Ruby, open up. It's Kevin."

I forgot that I'm not in my own room. I open the door and he comes in with his big duffel bag as well as his train case.

"I thought I'd bring my bag up before waiting for them to deliver it," he says. In my still-spaced-out state, I can't think of much to say, or that I should say, for that matter, so I ask to use his bathroom, which is fast becoming a necessity, anyway.

When I come out, Kevin's duffel has been put away in the closet, and he's sitting on one of the beds with André's back-pack open in his lap.

"Essie Sue asked me to look in this," he says. "André has all the notes and directions for our choir presentation tomorrow, and she can't wait until he shows up to get them. In fact, she's making preparations for Irene to take over, if necessary, and Irene needs his stuff now. I want to hurry so I can go out to dinner with Bitsy."

He dumps the contents of the center compartment onto the bed before I can stop him. And the truth is that I don't know what I could say *to* stop him without revealing a lot more than I want to at the moment. I've got to talk to Paul.

"Here's some stuff that looks musical," he says, pulling out a spiral notebook—it says *Choir*. "And here's a handwritten letter and some other stuff. Should I give her this, or the whole backpack?"

I can't answer, because I'm staring at a syringe that's rolling out on the bed—not musical but certainly private. Suddenly I know I have to do something before he goes any further.

"Kevin, André hasn't come to the room yet, and I think you should put these things back for when he does. We were just safeguarding it for him."

"No, Essie Sue said to look. And you know how she is when she needs something. He's not going to care, Ruby."

Yeah, I already thought of that.

I'm about to tell him to take the choir notebook so Essie Sue won't come to the room and search for herself, when he looks at the letter he found. I've never seen Kevin blush, believe it or not, but he's blushing now. He's a bit nearsighted, and he holds the paper close to his face while he concentrates. Frankly, I've never seen him focus all this much, either. I know I should stop him, but he's probably halfway through it already, and my natural curiosity's taking over. So I wait.

He's still reading, but he comes up for air.

"Wow," he says, and dives back in.

"So what's in it?" I say. I've never been too good at restraining myself. And I keep thinking that if I were the one who was reading this stuff, I might be doing something wrong, like tampering with evidence, knowing what I know. Or to be more accurate, guessing what I'm guessing.

The weird thing is that I can't really tell myself that the body I saw down at the river was André. I certainly don't know that yet, and there could be a thousand more explanations. Except, of course, that he hasn't turned up.

Kevin puts down the letter and takes off his glasses to wipe them.

"They're steamy," he says, suppressing a smile, which immediately turns into a frown. "André's gonna kill me. You won't tell him I read this, will you, Ruby?"

"Not if you give me a total description of it right this minute," I say, figuring the odds are good I won't be telling André.

"It's a passionate love letter he wrote," he says. "I heard this guy was hot with women, but this is amazing. If I could use some of this with my online dates, I'll bet they'd be flocking to me."

"Who's it written to?" I say.

"That's the peculiar part," he says. "I don't know why he has it—maybe he didn't send it, or he sent a copy of it."

"Or maybe he's getting ready to send it," I say.

"Well, if that's the case, then he's a little late," Kevin says. "The love letter is written to Serena Salit."

"So wait a minute," I say. "You're telling me there's a letter from André to Serena in André's backpack? She's been dead for a while now. Why would Serena have given it back to him, and why would he bring it to Canada with him?"

"I don't know, Ruby, and besides, I have to get back to Essie Sue—she said to meet her in the lobby with André's choir directions."

"I wish you hadn't told her we had his backpack," I say.

"You know how she sees right through me," he says. "But do you think I need to give her the other stuff I found?"

"Absolutely not, Kevin. Put it away in the backpack and leave it in the closet until I can speak to Paul."

We're on our way out of Kevin's room when his phone rings—so loud that it makes me jump.

"It's probably Essie Sue," he says, "wondering why I'm late. Tell her I'm on my way down."

"Oh, no," I say. "You get it. She doesn't need to know I'm anywhere near here."

He stays on the phone for a decidedly one-sided conversation that doesn't seem as if it will ever end. By the time he sits down on one of the beds to listen to the caller with a glazed look on his face, I'm convinced it's not Essie Sue.

"But why are you asking me?" he finally says. "Can you hold on for a minute?"

He covers the mouthpiece and I can see his hand trembling.

"Ruby, it's the Banff police calling. They have some identification on a body they found, and they want me to come down and confirm who it is. I can't quite believe this, but they think it's André Korman. Why are they calling me?"

He's not the only one who has to sit down. I grab for the other bed when I feel my knees buckling a bit.

"It's probably because you're clergy," I say. "Ask them."

He does and it is.

"Yeah," he says, "they say they heard I was with the group, and felt I'd be the appropriate person to come down, since they weren't sure if a next of kin was aboard. They're sending someone to the room now to escort me."

38

I'm glad I had the presence of mind to leave the room before Kevin could rouse himself and ask me to go along. I think we were both in shock, but I had more warning than he did. And I didn't want to have to explain to him just yet about my promise to the conductor not to say anything. I'm sure I'll be interviewed soon enough, and I want to talk to Paul first.

If I could just be sure Essie Sue's not in our room, I could go up and have the place to myself for a blessed few minutes. Double-locking the door will ensure she doesn't burst in on me while I'm on the phone. I know she was supposed to meet Kevin in the lobby, so I take the elevator from his floor up to mine, avoiding her altogether, I only hope. I'm feeling relieved, too, that Kevin's the one who opened André's backpack and not me. I'm sure he'll fill the cops in on all of it, and with the extra respect he's accorded, he'll be able to handle it if he doesn't panic.

Luckily, I don't run into Essie Sue, but I do see some of the choir members in the elevator.

"Did you hear about André Korman?" Cindy Eppsman asks. "He's missing. They looked all over the train and checked the buses, and they couldn't find him."

"Yeah," her husband says, "and he never checked into his hotel room. I even heard they looked into the airline database to see if he'd returned to Eternal without telling anyone, with no results. They were thinking maybe he got some emergency call from his wife back home."

I'm glad they get off at the floor before mine so that I can look surprised but don't have to answer. Gossip being what it is, I'm not shocked that the news has spread, but apparently no one knows anything worse yet. I'm wondering if our group will even stay at the ChoirFest if it turns out that the body I saw was conclusively André.

If they're verifying that André didn't go back to Eternal, they'll obviously call his wife first. I wonder if Paul will be brought in. Regardless, he'll be upset with me if I don't fill him in on everything soon.

I hold my breath as I open the door to the room, but as I expected, Essie Sue's not here. I lock the door, take off my shoes, fluff the pillows, and sit on my bed to relax for a minute, but not for long. The red light on the phone is flashing, and my curiosity outweighs my fatigue.

The message is from Gus, and he wants to meet me for dinner in an hour. That gives me practically no time to catch Paul before he leaves work, then shower and look halfway presentable for our—what? Is it a dinner date with Gus? A date at all? And do I want it to be?

Oy—since Gus knows about the events of the afternoon and was so supportive and helpful, I'm feeling I should at least call and alert him of the latest before I phone Paul. Why am I letting this simple decision turn into some sort of contest between the two of them?

If it is, then Paul wins, since I pick up my cell and dial his number. I'm not sure if I'm choosing him because I know how mad he'll be if I don't tell him fast, or because I'm afraid he'll call *me* when I'm out with Gus tonight.

One thing I do know—Gus can wait an hour to hear about André, and I need to contact Paul before the police interview me. We haven't phoned on this trip as much as I'd expected. Paul doesn't seem to be calling me all that often, and I'm not reaching for the telephone that much, either, so I guess we're both somewhat at fault.

"Ruby. It's good to hear from you. I was just about to go home. What's up there in Canada?"

I think I can safely assume he hasn't heard anything about André being missing—he wouldn't have started off that way.

"Good to hear your voice, too," I say. Of course, he didn't say it was good to hear my voice, just that it was good to hear from me—there's a difference. I mentally slap myself for being such a trivial idiot, and get to the point.

"I hardly know where to begin," I say, and then find a way to describe all the events of the afternoon while not saying much about the fact that Gus was experiencing the whole thing with me.

The most surprising thing is that I'm fighting back tears the whole time I'm talking to Paul.

"I'm sorry," I say. "I guess the day was more stressful and emotional than I've been willing to admit. If I'd given in to it earlier, I'm not certain I would have been able to get through everything."

"You mean seeing a body and then learning it was someone you knew? I'd say that would throw anyone, Ruby. None of this has filtered back down here to Eternal—or at least not to the police. But surely someone will notify Sara Korman of her husband's death as soon as the rabbi identifies the body. Is there a chance it's not André?"

"I doubt it—they said there was identification on him. Do you think he threw himself off the train, or could he have fallen while he was taking pictures or something? I don't see him as being the suicidal type—not that it's that easy to tell."

"There's a third alternative, Ruby. André could have been pushed."

39

Paul wants me back right away—no surprise there. And after I tell him that a love letter to Serena was found in André's backpack along with a syringe, he's even more adamant.

"Serena's death was caused by an injection, Ruby. A murderer could have been loose on that train. I want you out of there."

"If you're talking murderers, Paul, maybe André killed Serena. The syringe was found in his own backpack, remember—if its presence doesn't have some more innocent explanation. We're not in the enclosed space of a train right now, so I can't see that my safety's compromised. Not any more than that of the other choir members. I'm thinking that if André was as in love with Serena as that letter indicated, and then was driven by some unknown circumstance to kill her, suicide's looking a lot more probable, right?"

"It'd be great if you'd leave the speculation to the police," he says, "not that you've ever done that before. Which reminds me—they won't have much chance of seeing the whole picture if you don't turn in that backpack to them right away."

"I figured they'd search his hotel room as soon as Kevin identifies the body," I say. "I think it's better if I stay out of it."

"If they don't search the room by the end of the evening, then either you or the rabbi should tell them it's there," Paul says. "One more time, though—did you see anyone or anything suspicious on the train this afternoon?"

I tell him about the fleeting glance I had earlier of the face in the baseball cap, but I can't think of anything else. And since that happened so fast it was almost ethereal, it's not too helpful. The only thing I can compare it to is something you see in a dream, but that's lost as soon as you awake.

"Someone's knocking on my door, Paul," I say, not mentioning that it's probably Gus. "Can I call you back later tonight or tomorrow morning? I'm sure I'll know lots more when Kevin gets back."

I'm glad the conversation didn't have a chance to get personal. Although Paul knows I haven't wanted an exclusive relationship yet—and I'm not sure he wants it, either—I still feel uncomfortable keeping things from him. On the other hand, why tell him about a date with Gus, or having drinks with Bart in Vancouver, or anything else that could get magnified at this great distance? He has no reason to think I'm restricting my socializing to the women at the conference.

As I answer the knock on the door of my room, I realize

I'm now calling this a date and not just a dinner out together, so I guess it is one. I wonder if Gus thinks the same.

We never get the chance to find out, because as we're about to hail a cab outside the hotel, Kevin pulls up in a taxi of his own.

"Ruby—where are you going?" he says from the back-seat.

He won't let me explain that we're headed out for dinner together.

"No, no, don't go. I have too much to tell you."

Gus and I look at each other. As much as we want to grab our own cab, we're both sufficiently curious to hear what Kevin has to say.

We get into the cab with him, which surprises him as much as us.

"Come to dinner with us, then," I say. "We're not wasting our time in Banff eating at the hotel. You can leave us after dinner, okay?"

"But Bitsy's supposed to meet me later, Ruby. At least let me get out of the cab to go find her."

"Nothing doing," I say, "it's now or never."

"You can have a drink while we're eating," Gus says. "Unless you want to talk to us late tonight instead."

"You seem to be in a hurry to talk," I say to Kevin. Then I'm suddenly sorry for hassling him when he's no doubt had a rough time of it at the morgue.

"Sorry," I tell him. "You must be in bad shape from earlier."

"Yeah," he says, "let's just go." He eases back into his seat.

We direct the taxi to a Chinese place we've been told about, and we all go upstairs to the seating area for drinks and dinner.

"It was André," Kevin blurts out as soon as we're shown to our table with a view of the mountains. "I think I need a scotch.

"His face was pretty messed up, but I had no trouble recognizing him," he continues. "It made me sick, so they didn't keep me in the room long. This is the first time I've ever had to do that as clergy—I still don't know why they chose me. Everyone here knew him as well as I did."

"Maybe they want to keep it quiet," Gus says, "and they didn't think you'd spread it around."

Oh, yeah, they really have the right person for secrecy. I don't think it matters, though—things like this have a tendency to get out one way or another.

"They questioned me for a while after I left the room and had some water," Kevin says.

"What did they ask you?" I say.

"How I thought it happened, which of course I had no idea about. I told them they were talking to the wrong person—that you were the one who saw the body, and that you also thought of smuggling André's backpack off the train so no one would take it by accident."

"*Smuggling?*" I say. "Could you have thought of a word that's any more incriminating? They probably think I pushed him overboard myself."

Gus smiles. "Don't worry about it, Ruby—I'll vouch for you. Although now that I think of it, maybe we were lucky that we hopped into the rabbi's cab before the police were at your door. I'll bet you're in for an interrogation later tonight when they find you."

He's right, and I'm not looking forward to it. Unfortunately, my conversation with Paul didn't make me feel any more ready for confrontations with the police, either. Paul's a lot more paranoid about this situation than I am. Maybe I can just refer them to him.

"You must have seen André's body right after he fell from the train," Kevin says.

"He had to have jumped from the very front cars," I say, "or have been thrown or whatever. When I saw him from the last car a minute or so later, he was facedown by the river bend. My guess is that if he took a leap from the train, he waited until it had just emerged from one of the Spiral Tunnels—otherwise, he would have been in total blackness."

"And if someone pushed him," Gus says, "they waited, too, until that instant when daylight flashed through the windows again. It's always a disorienting moment."

"This was carefully planned," I say, "no matter who caused it."

The three of us are gradually realizing that the alcohol is the only thing on our table that's disappearing. Kevin's had two scotches, and Gus and I are three-quarters through our bottle of wine, but none of us has touched the food.

"Do you want this boxed up?" the waiter finally asks, and we all shake our heads no.

"What a waste," I say, and the others look at me, not sure whether I'm talking about the food or the meaningless death we just witnessed today.

I guess I mean both.

40

Today our Temple Rita bus is taking a short sightseeing trip to Lake Louise, thirty minutes or so from Banff. I've always wanted to visit this place, and I'm glad I didn't heed Paul's advice to hop the next plane home. Although I feel as bad as everyone else about André's death, I can't say that my emotional ties are any stronger than those of the other congregants here. Besides, the police are assuming that we'll be in the area for the remainder of the ChoirFest if they need us—although, so far, they haven't contacted me specifically. I hear that their questioning has been quite methodical, and I have no doubt they'll get around to me soon.

Last night, of course, with the news so fresh, was a bummer from beginning to end. By the time Gus and I worked our way through the Chinese dinner that wasn't, we were no more in the mood to enjoy the evening than Kevin was. So much for the date I was keeping from Paul. Kevin didn't leave us early, and instead, we all took the same taxi back to the hotel. I fell into bed, no doubt helped along by the three glasses of wine, and didn't even hear Essie Sue when she unlocked the door to our room. I did hear the TV she turned on later, but I was so out of it that it was easy to ignore the noise. No way would I have been ready for a discussion with her about the events of the day, not that she didn't try to rouse me several times.

The windows of our bus are open, and the mountain air is beyond invigorating—it's making me feel alive again after a groggy morning. Even the thermos of coffee the hotel made for me is perfect, and helps to mute the incessant chatter all around me. I can't stand a lot of noise before about eleven o'clock—my ears just won't take it. I don't even like the radio in the morning, and I'm certainly not ready to interact with our group just now.

Lake Louise, a mile high in the Rockies near the Continental Divide, is filled with exquisite emerald green water. The guide tells us that the glaciers above Lake Louise grind the minerals from the streams into the lake waters, and that the sunlight reflected off the mineral sediment is what makes the water color so vivid. The lake is encircled by mountains, and later today we're taking a sightseeing lift halfway up the Lake Louise ski area, so we can look down at the lake and the peaks surrounding it. I can't wait.

First, though, we're invited to get off the bus and walk Lakeshore Trail, which follows the north shore to the far border of the lake. You don't even need to be a hiker to enjoy this walk—it's a stroll, really, through a wooded area by the water.

Lake Louise is an international tourist attraction, and like the Grand Canyon, it's easy to pick up several languages coming from those marveling at the views. I see a Scandinavian group ambling in front of me, and following them presents me with a perfect opportunity to ensure a few more minutes of solitude, where I'm not in reach of Essie Sue and company.

It's easy to daydream while I'm walking along, and I'm mesmerized by the few small boats bobbing in the water—I'd love to know where I could rent one. I can't stop the visions of both Paul and Gus running through my mind, although I'd rather imagine myself floating on that gentle green expanse out there. Who knows how cold it is, though—we *are* in Canada, after all, not like Barton Springs in Austin, where the water temperature is in the midsixties winter and summer.

I stay a few paces behind the group, happily detached from the chatter in what sounds like Swedish. I'm amazed at how tiny the lake is—like a jewel. When I first saw the "Mona Lisa" in person, I was surprised at how small that was, too—in both cases, celebrity seems to magnify reality.

My eyes can't focus on the faces of the group in front of me except for an occasional profile when one turns to another in conversation. That's why I'm surprised when I glimpse a face that seems familiar, looking back at me from those walking farthest ahead. Again, a hat shadowing the face—this time a brown, broad-brimmed Alpine mountaineer's fedora. I think it's a man, but it could be a woman, too—the figure is wearing khaki pants, a zippered jacket, and hiking boots. Whatever hair there is must be tucked under the hat and not visible. Not much *is* visible, since the group so far ahead of us is setting the pace for everyone else, and they're moving fast.

I hurry to catch up with them, weaving easily in and out of the crowd, since aside from the familiar figure, no one is paying the least bit of attention to me. I'm contrasting this with our own group from Eternal, where a stranger couldn't be a part of the crowd for thirty seconds without someone asking who, what, and why, and then reporting back to everyone else.

It's annoying not to be able to place the person who looked back at me, but it's obvious that this is the same face I saw for an instant on the train. This is a good time to satisfy my curiosity—I'm not meeting the others for a half hour. I've promised Kevin I'll go on the lift with him up the mountain, and in return, he's promised to pick up fresh batteries for my digital camera.

I'm jogging by the time I work my way to the front of the crowd—these people are making good time. First, I try to find the person on my own, but everyone looks alike. Most have on baseball caps or wool ski hats with parkas—there's not anything you could call a real hat in the bunch. Maybe I was hallucinating about the hat, so I examine the faces around me. Not a familiar puss in the lot.

When I don't see what I'm looking for, I interrupt a couple of conversations around me with questions in English that are obviously routinely understood, but which produce no good answers. A woman does remember briefly seeing someone with that hat, so I'm not crazy, but she shrugs when I ask which direction. So I guess this is another dead end, unless I stop in my tracks, turn around to face the upcoming hikers, and scrutinize the crowd.

Even this doesn't help, so I have no choice but to keep walking against the current of the crowd and back toward my starting point.

The lift isn't far from the lake, and Kevin's already there and pacing when I arrive.

"Look, Ruby, I made a mistake," he says. "I couldn't find the backup batteries you wanted, but I'm also not going up with you. I'll stay here at the bottom, where it's safe."

"Safe?" I say. "All this is safe, Kevin. They've put thousands of tourists on these chairlifts, and I've never heard of one falling off yet. It's supposed to be gorgeous up there at Whitehorn Lodge. Why miss it?"

"Okay, but only if you'll take one of the enclosed chairs."

I hadn't noticed, but Kevin's obviously already checked out the lifts and learned that there are two kinds—the open chairs that look like double garden swings, and the boxes with shaded plastic windows. Those hold four people, not two. But they're shielded from the wind and, in my opinion, from the best views. For anyone with a fear of heights, though, the box is the way to go.

"That's fine," I say. "I can always take the other kind after you and I make the ride if I want to try the open route."

We wait for the attendant to tell us when to jump onto the enclosed box as the mechanical pulley brings it around to where we're standing.

"It's rocking," Kevin says, and I have to give him a gentle push to get him inside before the lift continues up the mountainside without us.

"I'm right behind you," I say, and he slides into a seat. No one else has joined us, which is probably a good thing for Kevin, who's sitting stiffly at the edge of his chair.

"Relax and enjoy it," I say. "Look, you can almost reach out and touch the treetops. I'll bet that you can actually touch them in one of the open cars."

I can tell that the air's thinner as we ascend, and as advertised, the view is spectacular. Kevin's enjoying it in spite of himself.

"I'm glad I came," he says. "The lake looks like a postage stamp down there."

"You deserve some fun," I say. "Yesterday was rough."

"I guess I'll have to do the funeral," he says. "I've only done one suicide, and it was awful."

I hadn't even thought that far ahead, but he's probably right that the funeral will be in Eternal. I'm wondering how long they'll hold André's body here before his wife can claim it.

"Let's don't talk about it right now," I suggest. "We're about to jump off at the exit gate, so get ready."

Our getaway is perfectly satisfactory, except for the fact that once we hop out, we're met by Essie Sue and her cousin Belle.

"Let's have tea and low-fat muffins," Essie Sue says, "and we can talk about poor André."

"I'll pass," I say. "I was just telling Kevin that I want to save that conversation for down below."

"I don't want to talk, either," Kevin says.

"Well, can I at least tell you what gossip I've heard?" Essie Sue says.

"Can we stop you?" I say.

"The police took André's luggage this morning, and I heard they found some clues to his death," she says.

"They didn't take it while I was in the room," Kevin says. "It must have been later, after I'd gone. I wonder if they looked through my duffel, too. Some of my socks have holes in them."

"I'm sure they're not interested in your hole-y clothes," Belle says. "*Holy* clothes—get it?"

When her joke gets the reception it deserves, Belle loses interest, but Essie Sue's not deterred.

"Rabbi, I want you, in your clerical role, to see what other information you can dig up. No one was able to tell me exactly what those clues were."

"No thanks," Kevin says. "I've had all the talks with the police I want to have—I already told Ruby about it."

"And thanks to you, Ruby, I know next to nothing," Essie Sue says. "You were asleep last night when I came in, and sleeping when I got up this morning. What good are you as a roommate? I envisioned us as having a much better time than this."

Well, I didn't, but thanks to my artful dodging, I've managed to hold the damage to a minimum, and I'm pretty proud of myself. This rooming situation could have been a lot worse, although as I'm well aware, it's not over yet.

41

We end up having tea and muffins with Essie Sue and Belle after all, but I quickly realize that, as Essie Sue said, she really knows nothing more about the police investigation. One sure way to get rid of these two is to suggest a long walk—they're not big hikers—so I push Kevin to go with me.

"I'm not really a great walker, either, Ruby," he says to me. This is not exactly news, but I give him time to absorb the fact that if he turns me down, he's stuck with Essie Sue and Belle.

"Well, okay, I guess," he says. "Can we stop a lot?"

"Sure, Kevin," I say as soon as we're alone. "I just wanted an excuse to get away, and I'm more interested in taking photos than racking up the miles."

I wouldn't miss this photo op for the world—the vista before us is spectacular, and the light today is shimmering and perfect. The lake looks almost lost among the snow-capped peaks, but my lens has no problem picking up that luminescent green.

Kevin's patient as I take advantage of the good light, and at lunchtime we slip away to a café that's adjacent to the larger restaurant, where I'm sure Essie Sue will be holding court.

"I could stay up here all day," I say when we're finished with lunch, "but I'm antsy about that police interrogation. I'm also curious to hear people's reactions now that the news is public. I'm wondering if some of them will be going home early—Irene, for instance; she was close to André, and maybe she'll want to be with his wife."

"How about Dr. Goldman?" Kevin says. "The whole quartet was tight."

"It's possible. Kevin, would you be disappointed if we went down the mountain now instead of waiting for the others?"

"Are you kidding?" he says. "I'm ready for a nap—yesterday did me in."

"Good. It'll give me time to poke around the lobby and see what's going on."

It's early afternoon, and the tourists are swarming all over the place. I thought the lifts might be less busy now, but people are hopping on and off as fast as the cars can handle them. I see a few enclosed cabins, but most of the lifts are open ones.

"Let's do it, Kevin," I say. "Who knows when we'll ever be back here?"

"You're not suggesting we take one of the open lifts?"

"We can link arms," I say. "Once you're on there, you're going to love it. The view out the plastic windows of the other car doesn't compare with these. And they're much more frequent."

"I don't know, Ruby. Maybe. I'll think about it."

"Fair enough," I say. "I don't want to push you, and we can go separately if you want. But you're going to have to make a fast decision once we're on the launching platform. If you don't jump, you miss it and it goes on by."

The lifts are moving quickly, so although we're waiting in a glut of humanity, the process of getting all those people down the mountain is quite efficient.

"If you do it," I say while we're standing there, "I want to get a snapshot of you once you've jumped aboard. You'll never believe you did it once you get home."

"It'll be proof," he says. "But that's not your camera in your hand—what is that thing?"

"My camera's out of juice," I say. "I used up the battery taking all those photos of the views. This is my PDA—personal digital assistant. It has a camera, voice recorder, extra memory, and everything else I could cram into it. It's like a backup."

"Whatever."

We're standing side by side, and Kevin straightens his shoulders. I think he's getting up the nerve to do it. I take his hand.

"Are we set for this, then?" I say.

"Yep," he says, tightening his grip.

When the lift finally glides right in front of us, I go first. Then so many things happen at once that my brain can't put them in sequence.

For openers, Kevin lets go of my hand, and I figure he

must feel more secure grabbing the pole attached to the lift. At the same time, I hear an odd little nervous hum that seems vaguely familiar. I leap on board and turn around to aim my camera in Kevin's direction, so I can get a photo of him jumping on.

The weight of his body shakes the floor of the lift, but I can still get a shot if I hurry. The lift keeps moving and leaves the platform behind us. I look in the viewfinder and take my picture just in time. There's only one problem. The person I see through the camera lens isn't Kevin.

It's Rose.

42

I'm absolutely sure I'm hallucinating. I already know my good friend Rose Baker didn't make the trip to Canada—she stayed home in Eternal because she'd traveled to Ohio earlier this year to see Serena's sister. Rose didn't want to leave her family again so soon, so she passed up the choir trip.

I give my head a shake to straighten out my brain, and flop down on the hard bench. This makes the car lurch, and this woman who can't be Rose suddenly lands on the seat beside me.

"Where's Kevin?" I say. "Did he lose his nerve?" A stupid remark, but I'm not following this at all.

The passenger just stares at me, humming that odd little tune that comes out of Rose when she's stressed.

"Rose?" I say.

Fedora and all, it's Rose—there's no mistaking her face now, but I needed to hear the hum again to put it all together.

As if to assure me, she takes her hat off and throws it down at our feet.

"Don't tell me you weren't expecting me," she says.

"I'm dumbfounded," I say, and then I figure it out and have to smile. "Wait a minute—did you and Kevin get together on this? He stepped back and let you on here as a surprise? I didn't even think he could keep a secret, frankly. Did you decide to fly up at the last minute?"

"I've been here awhile," she says, "as you well know." She's not smiling back.

"Look," I say, "I don't know anything. I need a minute to work this out—I'm totally confused. That was you on the train? And by the lake?"

"You saw me on the train before it even happened," she says. "And then after, by the lake."

"I saw someone familiar," I say, "but certainly not you. I never remotely believed it was you—why would I? So why the elaborate hide-and-seek, babe? You wasted two days when we could have hung out together—I certainly could have used you with all that was going on. Do you know about what's happened?"

"You're saying you didn't recognize me?" she says.

"Not until now."

Rose visibly slumps in her seat.

"I don't believe it," she says. "You know, Ruby, you wouldn't be a part of this at all if you hadn't caught sight of me on the train. I'd been so good at staying away from all of you. Why did you have to be in that part of the train when the entire Temple Rita choir had seats somewhere else?"

I'm getting frustrated now, and my voice shows it. "What in the world are you talking about, Rose? Quit playing around."

"You're right," she says, moving closer to me. "I have very little time to do what I have to do. This is only a fifteen-minute ride, and we've thrown away five already. I've timed this lift twice, and we'll be passing over the ravine in another five."

She's coming close, almost as if to give me an affectionate hug despite her demeanor. But instead of sensing her arm circling my waist, I feel a prickly jab in my ribs, like a pin-prick through my sweater, only a bit sharper.

"Ouch," I say, moving over, "your bracelet or something's sticking me. Rose, are you upset about André—is that why you're so agitated? You did hear he was—"

"Killed. Yes, obviously I know. You saw me only a short while before I killed him."

I feel myself slipping into some alternate universe—this is too much to absorb at one time. Not only don't I believe I'm hearing what I just heard, but I'm pretty sure I'm losing my senses. I'd chalk it all up to some sort of mental break-down if I wasn't suddenly much more concerned with the sharp pain in my side.

"Yes, it's a bone-handled knife I bought at a gift shop in Banff," Rose says. "And you do know I grew up with knives. You learn a lot when your father's a lox cutter in a New York deli. He taught me a lot about biology, too—I know exactly where the heart lies under the ribs."

Her grip is firm, and I don't think I can safely move, or yell, either—not that anyone would hear me; the lifts aren't that close together, and it's windy up here. But my head is clear now—danger can do that. I stop trying to understand it all, and focus on the more immediate peril. I need to distract her.

"Why do you need to kill me, too?" I say.

"I told you," she says. "If you hadn't seen me, I would have flown home from Banff right away, and I'd be back in Eternal by now, paying a condolence call on Sara. But I couldn't take that chance. When I saw you speak to the conductor, and caught sight of the police at the train station, I knew you had recognized me. I kept tabs on you at the lake, and followed you up the mountain."

"But I didn't recognize you," I say. "I had no idea who that was."

"I couldn't take the risk," she says. "The connection could have come to you at any time, even if you hadn't put it all together yet."

"You're here, and I still haven't put it all together," I say, moving slightly away from her. "Not you."

"Whoa," she says, and I feel the point of the knife again.

Rose manages to take quick glimpses of the mountainside as we go down. I don't want to remember that she's looking for the ravine she talked about.

I need to keep her talking. "Why did you do it?" I ask. "And why here?"

"The gossip in Eternal," she says. "I heard they'd discovered Serena's poisoning, and Joellyn confirmed it, so I had to see André right away. I wanted him to know I'd done it for us—I'd been hoping he'd never find out she didn't die of a heart attack."

"You and André? I thought Serena and André . . ."

"It was all her, not him—she took him from me. I discovered a letter from him in Serena's car one day when we were riding somewhere. I didn't tell either of them that I had it.

Once I got rid of her, though, I knew he'd come back to me. And when it was known Serena had been murdered, he'd be a prime suspect—he used to give her B_{12} shots, for God's sake. I thought we could stay in Canada, or abroad, and be safe. But when I told him why we should run away, he said he was horrified. Repelled. I took all the risks, and he's repelled? He's going to turn me in? No way."

My head might be clear now, but more like frozen clear. I'm still feeling paralyzed—the knife's too close to take chances.

"What do you want?" I finally say.

"Easy. You're going to jump when we're over the ravine, or be killed instantly now. I'm good at this, Ruby—make no mistake. I've killed two people—a third won't make any difference at all."

"There'll be questions—you won't get away with it. Kevin must have seen you, too."

"I doubt it—he hesitated and moved away, decided not to jump on here with you. I merely stepped in front of him— he only saw my back. Besides, I have two chances. If I get away unnoticed when the lift reaches the bottom of the mountain, that'll be the best I can hope for, and I'll head for the airport. If someone down there does stop me, I'll deal with it. No one suspects me of anything. I'll be as shocked over your terrible accidental fall as everyone else."

"Your husband and daughter will know you left Eternal," I say. "Are you going to trust Ray and Jackie not to tell, when even André wouldn't go along with you?"

"I've taken care of that," Rose says. "I was depressed over my father's death two years ago and then Serena's, and Ray agreed to have me go away for treatment in Ohio. Discreetly and quietly. If I'm recognized, and I won't be, then I left the

treatment facility to join the choir here. A messier explanation, but what evidence would they have that I made you
fall? Besides, it's not going to happen."

"But maybe—"

"Shut up, Ruby—it's not important to you. Nothing
will be."

She's right about that—I'd better deal with priorities
first, since it's obvious I'm not going to talk her out of this.
She's planned her nasty surprise too well. My only hope is to
wrestle the knife away from her right now or to jump before
I'm directly over the ravine.

And if I do come away from this alive, I have a surprise of
my own for Rose.

43

Rose Baker may have been my friend for years, but I've never had to size her up as if she were a middleweight coming at me in the ring—never mind one who hits below the belt. I'd say we weigh the same, but she has about four inches on me. My core body strength probably beats hers, which would mean more if she wasn't already holding a knife so close to my pounding heart.

Her arms are much longer than mine, too—I know that because of the way she's able to wrap one of them around me from behind while keeping her weapon steady with the other.

"Don't even think about it, Ruby," she says, as if reading my mind. "You can't begin to grab hold of me while I've got this blade pointing through your clothes—I can stick you before you'd have the opportunity to wrest away. You'll have a better chance of jumping clean than wounded."

She's offering me a good reason for leaping down into a ravine? Give me a break, Rose. You just want to make absolutely sure that I'm not found with a knife wound—it wouldn't look good on the accident report. But the choice she's presenting represents a certain weakness on her part—I'm thinking she'll do a lot to keep from stabbing me as I fall over the rail between me and oblivion.

One thing's certain—I have seconds to make my move. We're passing over a thick stand of tall cedars, not my idea of a safe fall, but better than the wide-open vista ahead of us. If I thought I could take her, I would, but I don't think I have the leverage to throw her off the lift without having that knife go into me first. And I just don't relish the idea of a wrestling match all the way down—I think I'd come out the loser. A fanatical killer is an opponent I totally respect.

She has the knife in her right hand, so I push her left hand away as hard as I can, twisting her body away from me while I unlatch the rail holding me in. But the movement also coils her right arm closer around me, and I feel the point of the blade ripping into my stomach—her aim has slipped a few inches in the melee. Reflexively, I push the knife away as I jump, and I'm pretty sure it goes into some part of her— not that I can afford to worry about that right now.

I'm counting on my two arms to hang on to one of those very tall cedar trees, but I can't calculate how flimsy a tree-top can be when a human body comes whirling into it. The trees are growing out of the side of the mountain very close to me, but I have no idea what the fall will be like if I miss. The surface slamming up to meet me will be a slanting one, and might only intensify the impact of my plunge.

Even though the wind has died down as we've descended, the slender treetop bends with me on it, and I can't stay on, even with both my legs wrapped around the branches. I feel myself falling to the ground—a crooked or straight landing, I don't know. But the tree has broken my dive, at least, and a part of my pant leg is hooked on one of the thick lower branches.

I'm down, I'm relatively alive, and I'm conscious enough to scream for the time it takes for the next open lift to pass by.

44

I awake with Essie Sue peering over my bed, so I know I'm not dreaming—this is not the person I'd waste a drug-induced hallucination on.

"You're in a hospital in Banff," she says, "and you're not supposed to be disturbed."

"So why are you disturbing me?" I ask, and immediately regret it because even moving my lips makes my head ache.

I whisper, which isn't as painful, so she leans farther over me. "How badly am I hurt?" I say.

"Not much," she says. "Only a broken ankle and a stab wound."

Oh, good. I'd like to know what her definition of *much* is. I close my eyes and decide to get my bad news from someone less anxious to deliver it.

I can feel the buzzer that's been wrapped loosely around my left wrist, so I press it for the nurse.

"Can I see a doctor?" I whisper when an orderly arrives. "And may I please have some privacy for a few minutes?"

"Go away," Essie Sue tells the orderly, "this woman needs her privacy to recuperate."

I point as well as I can manage at Essie Sue, and fortunately, the orderly gets it.

"But I'm her caretaker," I hear Essie Sue say, and I shake my head as vigorously as possible without taking the top of my skull off.

"You'll have to come back later," the man says to her.

"Her clergyman's here," Essie Sue says, apparently hoping to hear secondhand what she can't witness for herself. On her way out the door she gestures to Kevin.

"It's okay," I say. "He can come in."

"Ruby, I feel awful," he says. "Can you make me feel any better about this?"

This is what I most love about Kevin and Essie Sue— they're never self-absorbed.

"Don't expect too much of me," I say. "I'm learning I have a few problems of my own. Can we deal with yours later?"

"But if I hadn't finked out, you wouldn't be in the hospital. I lost my nerve about jumping on that open lift, and before I knew it, someone had taken my place. The police told us later that it was Rose Baker, of all people."

"They found her? How long have I been here?" I ask.

"All afternoon. It's past dinnertime now. Rose collapsed after the sightseeing lift came down from the mountain by Lake Louise. She got off and was trying to walk away when she passed out in a pool of blood."

"Where is she? Do they know she tried to kill me? And that she killed André and Serena?"

"Huh? How do you know that? I'm not sure what they've discovered. They found you right after she came down the mountain, and I know they took her in an ambulance—to this hospital, I think. And it's all my fault."

"Why were the police even involved with her?" I say.

"Because when they picked you up, you kept yelling that Rose had pushed you off the lift and knifed you. I guess someone in authority put it all together. The knife had come down with you—caught in your clothes, I think."

"I'm glad, at least, that she didn't get rid of it herself," I say. "But we need to post a guard outside this room. Can you take care of that? I'm scared she'll come in here to finish the job—she was possessed."

"I'll tell Essie Sue to do it," he says. "I'm too upset."

"No Essie Sue," I say. "Look, Kevin, do me just one favor. Do you know where my cell phone is?"

"I don't know where your stuff is—maybe it's lost. You can have my cell, but it's not set for international calls."

"Don't worry about it," I say. "They'll just charge you extra if I can get to an operator. I'll pay you back."

I grab his cell and make sure he stays to give the operator his identification—then I ask him to leave and stand by the door, just in case.

Thank heavens I find Paul at work.

"Ruby, what happened? I just heard you were in surgery, and I was trying to get in touch with the doctors. I'm coming up there."

"I'm okay," I say. "But, Paul, I need you to help now, and if you're flying here, you'll be out of reach. I'm worried that the doctors will give me something that'll knock me out, or that they'll take my phone away. You've got to stand in for me."

I persuade him to stay there and help me by phone or fax or whatever, and I try to remember the whole sequence of events this afternoon—everything Rose said and did. I'm petrified she could get away with this.

"How are you going to do it all?" I say. "And what are you going to do first?"

"Calm down, honey," he says. "I do this for a living. I'm calling the police to get a guard for your room from hospital security, and I'll check on Rose's condition. Then I'll do everything else."

"But I don't even know where my clothes are," I say. "They must have cut them off of me. I have to get my cell phone—I hid it in my jacket pocket."

"That's the least of your worries," he says. "I'll call your hospital room."

"First, they might not let me take calls," I say. "But that's not the problem. I need the cell for other reasons."

"Later, Ruby. Let me get started."

"No, Paul, you have to know this. My phone has a camera and a voice recorder. Since I was set up to photograph Kevin as he jumped onto the lift, I got a shot of Rose instead, and I recorded everything she said."

45

"People have flown home with worse injuries than a broken ankle," I tell my partner Milt Aboud as he passes a warm poppy-seed bagel across the quilt where I'm propped up on my favorite down pillows. Oy Vey and Chutzpah want to share the cream cheese with me, but nothing doing—they'll have to be satisfied with being the center of attention at this impromptu brunch taking place on the queen-size bed in my house on Watermelon Lane.

Milt has brewed a strong Italian roast to make sure I overcome my painkillers enough to describe every detail of what is undoubtedly the hottest topic ever to make the rounds in Eternal, Texas. This occasion was supposed to be coffee and bagels with just me and Milt, but when he left The Hot Bagel to come over here, Essie Sue and Kevin somehow got the word, picked up Bitsy, and joined us.

"I still think you came home too early, Ruby," Essie Sue says. "It's just like you to defy your doctor's advice. And after I offered to nurse you back to health, too. If I'd had the chance, I would have asked them to do a little liposuction while they were sewing up your stomach wound."

Milt snorts—he still hasn't learned to hold it in when he's around Essie Sue. "So that's why you left the hospital so soon," he says to me, "to ditch the personalized nursing care."

"I wanted my own cozy bed," I say, "before Essie Sue's care turned into coronary care. And I was uneasy with Rose being just down the hall, even if she was unconscious for a while. I answered every question the authorities could throw at me, and by then I was itching to get out of there."

"I heard when she woke up she accused *you* of attacking *her* with the knife," Kevin says.

"She did," I say, "but that didn't hold up when the gift shop clerk in Banff identified her as the person who bought a souvenir knife from them the day before she used it on me. And after she heard her words recorded on my organizer, she opted for a deal."

"You were going to take my picture when I jumped on board, weren't you?" Kevin says. "I remember talking to you about using your electronic organizer as a backup camera."

"Yep, and it's a voice recorder, also. I had it turned on along with the camera, and I left it that way. Rose was so intent on taking me by surprise and hiding her knife under her sleeve that I doubt she even noticed the camera when she jumped on—I was so shocked that I almost dropped it myself. We had other things to think about, and I just let it fall into my big jacket pocket. I thought about it midway, though, when she was telling me about killing André and Serena."

"Rose, a killer?" Essie Sue repeats for the umpteenth time. "Never in a million years would I have suspected. I'm speechless."

Not quite, but close—this is the first time I've seen her willing to take a backseat in any conversation.

"What did these women see in that guy André?" Bitsy says. "He gave me the creeps, and he wasn't even sexy."

I never imagined Bitsy and I would have anything in common, but I must admit she's echoing my thoughts exactly. Not that it's very charitable of her to be knocking one of the victims. André Korman didn't kill Serena—his biggest crime was his cheatin' heart, I guess, along with the chutz-pah and greed to think he could franchise Jewish philosophy.

"It's Rose who has me bewildered, too—she was my friend," I tell Milt, trying to pretend the others aren't hovering. "We've only been home from Canada for two days, and everyone seems to think I have more information here than I had in Banff. The truth is that the whole Canadian experi-ence now seems fuzzy to me—I think I'm still in shock from the afternoon on the lift. Paul says he's protecting me from information overload, but he should know better. The police haven't even told me about Rose's status in Canada, since she killed one victim there and the other here in Eternal.

"What have you all learned?" I ask. My pain might have prevented me from being my terrier-doggish self, but I doubt Essie Sue's been as passive. She'd be surprised to know I'm hoping to discover as much from her as she is from me.

"I've found out some of the gossip from this end," she says, brushing away little Chutzpah, who responds by digging his claws into her cashmere cardigan. He's not so easy to get rid of, though she doesn't know it yet. I try to retrieve him before he tears any threads—he doesn't know who he's dealing with, either.

"So give," I tell Essie Sue by way of diversion, "who did you talk to?"

"That's a secret," she says, "but suffice it to say that Rose was a busy little bee. I have it on good authority from a hairdresser who shall remain anonymous that she had an affair with André right under his wife's nose before he fell in love with Serena Salit."

"In love?" Bitsy says. "Maybe in lust."

"In lust with Rose, maybe," Essie Sue says, "but he definitely fell for Serena emotionally as well as physically. Apparently, Rose couldn't take it and decided to get rid of her rival. She put a fast-acting poison in the same type of syringe André had been using to give B_{12} shots to some of the choir members, including Serena. He gave them all the time to his health food store customers. Since Serena was always nervous when she had to solo, Rose suggested to her that day at the temple latke party that she have André give her a shot just for a boost."

"It's not a tranquilizer," Milt says.

"No, but people were always convinced the shots made them feel good," Essie Sue says, "and André was glad to oblige. I heard the poison might have been nicotine sulfate—it works within minutes and stops heart action. That's just gossip, though."

"As if gossip would stop you," Milt says. "But it is amazing that André gave Serena the shot that killed her."

"Yes," Essie Sue says, ignoring his little dig. "And when Rose confronted André on the train that day with how she'd set him up, she expected him to take her back—especially with the threat of exposure hanging over his head. The police would never believe he hadn't known he was inject-ing poison—and no one would have suspected Rose."

"I gather from what Rose told me," I say, "that André was more of a mensch—"

"That means a real man," Essie Sue tells Milt, who answers that he already knew.

"—more of a mensch than Rose thought he'd be," I con-tinue. "He told Rose he was horrified at what she had done, and that he had not only loved Serena, but was hoping to leave his wife for her.

"Rose thought she had no choice but to get rid of André before he told the police. My guess is that she revealed her-self to him when he was alone and coming out of the bath-room near the space between the engine and the next car, where he took all his photos—it was outside and away from the reflection from the windows. When he reacted badly, she knew she had to get rid of him fast. She was also able to take advantage of the fact that the train was in and out of those tunnels—passengers on the train were distracted by the alter-nate light and darkness. I doubt she planned that, but it helped. When I took pictures from the last car of the train, I saw the body that Rose had pushed from the forward car min-utes before. It was André."

"And she left that syringe we found in his backpack," Kevin says.

"Plus the letter to Serena," I say. "She found it in Serena's car one day and kept it. Rose must have wanted to empha-size the connection between André and Serena for the police's benefit when he went missing, so she made sure it was in his backpack. Then, when André didn't show up or wasn't discovered, people would think he committed suicide or ran away."

"So do you think she told André and prepared for a possible rejection at the same time?" Milt says.

"There's no doubt she was cunning," I say. "I think she truly believed André would have no choice but to go away with her, but she knew what she'd do if he didn't. She planned everything."

46

Email to: Ruby
From: Nan
Subject: RE: The latest about Rose

I'm still reeling from the news—don't
forget, babe, I want every detail as you
hear it. Thanks for the calls and email
updates.

I'll bet Rose couldn't wait to go to
Ohio when she heard that Serena's sister,
Joellyn, had the laptop—and, of course,
the information on it only confirmed what
Rose already knew about the affair. Plus,
the exposure of Serena's fears about
André's little Kabbalah cult helped cre-

ate other possible reasons for her murder—Rose must have been thrilled at those
discoveries. Did Rose trick Joellyn into
helping arrange for her alibi, too—Rose's
supposed treatment at the mental health
facility in Ohio? That was a great cover
story for her flight to Canada.

Email to: Nan
From: Ruby
Subject: Answers

Yeah, Joellyn was more than happy to help
arrange the stay at the clinic for Rose;
she didn't suspect a thing—not that any of
us did. Rose never showed up, of course,
and flew to Canada instead. Since she'd told
Joellyn she wouldn't hear from her for a
while, the plan went perfectly. Joellyn
kept the visit to the mental health clinic
a secret—it was logical that Rose wouldn't
have wanted her friends in Eternal to know
about her problems.

The authorities aren't sure yet how she
obtained the poison, although at one time
she had access to Serena's keys, and there
was always a key to Dr. Bart's clinic on
them. Rose's husband, Ray, is a printer,
too, and uses many chemicals. It's possible she knew a supplier through him. The
police have probably found out plenty
during questioning that they haven't
released yet.

It also makes sense to me now why Rose avoided me for so long after her visit to Ohio—she knew I'd ask a lot of questions.

Changing the subject—which I'm desperately trying to do around here so I can recover faster—I'm forwarding you a cheery email Gus wrote. He says he misses me. He also sent me some flowers—nice, huh?

Email to: Ruby
From: Nan
Subject: Avoidance

Gus's email was indeed *nice,* but what's up with he who has no name? Has Paul fallen into a well or something? You haven't mentioned him since you returned home, and I certainly hope you're not expecting me to forget he exists.

Email to: Nan
From: Ruby
Subject: When did you ever forget *anything*?

I *was* avoiding this subject, because it's like cotton candy—I can't bite into it without having it evaporate. Paul learned from reading the Canadian police reports that Gus was with me when I told the con-

ductor about seeing the body, and that
we'd spent time together during the trip.
You know how jealous he was over Ed
Levinger, and I simply didn't want another
scene over someone I'd just met, so I
hadn't mentioned it.

Bottom line is that we're in an awk-
ward place right now. I want to remind
him that we're not in an exclusive relationship, but whenever I bring it up, I
feel I'm going to hurt him. So I keep
quiet. He, on the other hand, doesn't
really want to get into anything with me
while I'm still recovering. We're both
futzing around and feeling distant.

Email to: Ruby
From: Nan
Subject: I get it

I didn't mean to put you on the spot, but
I'm glad I asked. Maybe you should follow the rabbi's lead and stir up a little trouble online. What I'm reading into
this is that you honestly don't want to
settle down just now. Am I right? If so,
I'll respect that, and I'll quit hound-
ing you about it. So do you want me to have
Paul? Just kidding.

```
Email to: Nan
From: Ruby
Subject: Your query

Well, I wouldn't go that far. You might
want to meet Gus sometime, though—he
lives a lot closer to you.
    Funny you should mention our rabbi and
his online pursuits. I'll definitely send
you updates on the latest. Kevin just
called here in a panic—one of his virtual
cuties just showed up on his doorstep!
```

Ruby's Chanukah Latkes

6 large potatoes
½ small onion
2 eggs
¼ cup Matzo meal
Salt and pepper

Serves 4 to 6

Peel and grate 6 large potatoes and half small onion. Soak mixture in water, then drain until dry. Add 2 eggs, one quarter cup Matzo meal, salt and pepper to taste.

Heat one cup oil and drop medium spoonfuls into hot oil for thin and crispy pancakes. Fry until brown and golden. From frying pan, place latkes on paper towels to absorb extra oil.

Serve with applesauce and sour cream.

Enjoy!

Acknowledgments

To Ruby's greatest cheering section—the family I love: David Weizenbaum, Suzanne Weizenbaum, Jon Weizenbaum and Nancy Nussbaum, Emma and Camille Weizenbaum.

To my friends Sue and Ned Bloomfield, Lindsy Van Gelder, Kathi Stein, Olga Wise, and the Shoal Creek Writers—Nancy Bell, Judith Austin Mills, Eileen Joyce, Dena Garcia, and Linda Foss—for their love and support.

My thanks to Helen Rees of the Helen Rees Agency, for her enthusiasm and down-to-earth advice, and to Sarah Knight, my editor at Scribner, for her invaluable contributions to the book.

My appreciation to Angella Baker, Meg Carstens, and Erica Gelbard of Scribner, Joan Mazmanian of the Helen Rees Agency, Charlene Crilley for Ruby's website, www.sharonkahn.com, and all those at Scribner who helped guide the book along its way.

My very special thanks to Susanne Kirk, dear friend and editor, whose belief in the Ruby series launched a new chapter in my life. I'll always be grateful for your constant help and encouragement.

About the Author

Sharon Kahn has worked as an arbitrator, attorney, and freelance writer. She is a graduate of Vassar College and the University of Arizona Law School. The mother of three, and the former wife of a rabbi, she lives in Austin, Texas. *Fax Me a Bagel,* a Ruby, the Rabbi's Wife novel and her mystery debut, appeared in 1998 and was nominated for an Agatha Award. Visit her website at www.sharonkahn.com.